Middle School 3-1

중간고사 완벽대비

적중 100

영어 기출 문제집

중3

시사 | 송미정

Best Collection

구성과 특징

교과서의 주요 학습 내용을 중심으로 학습 영역별 특성에 맞춰 단계별로 다양한 학습 기회를 제공하여
단원별 학습능력 평가는 물론 중간 및 기말고사 시험 등에 완벽하게 대비할 수 있도록 내용을 구성

Words & Expressions

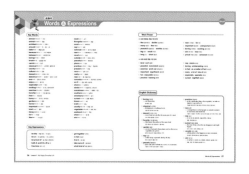

Step1	Key Words 단원별 핵심 단어 설명 및 풀이
	Key Expression 단원별 핵심 숙어 및 관용어 설명
	Word Power 반대 또는 비슷한 뜻 단어 배우기
	English Dictionary 영어로 배우는 영어 단어
Step2	실력평가 단원별 수시평가 대비 주관식, 객관식 문제풀이
Step3	서술형 대비 학업성취도 및 수행능력평가 대비 서술형 문제풀이

Conversation

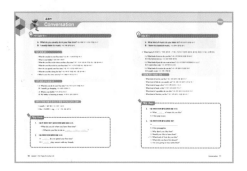

Step1	핵심 의사소통 소통에 필요한 주요 표현 방법 요약
	핵심 Check 기본적인 표현 방법 및 활용능력 확인
Step2	대화문 익히기 교과서 대화문 심층 분석 및 확인
Step3	교과서 확인학습 빈칸 채우기를 통한 문장 완성 능력 확인
Step4	기본평가 시험대비 기초 학습 능력 평가
Step5	실력평가 단원별 수시평가 대비 주관식, 객관식 문제풀이
Step6	서술형 대비 학업성취도 및 수행능력평가 대비 서술형 문제풀이

Grammar

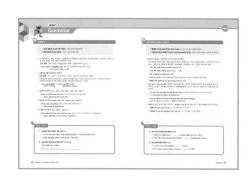

Step1	주요 문법 단원별 주요 문법 사항과 예문을 알기 쉽게 설명
	핵심 Check 기본 문법사항에 대한 이해 여부 확인
Step2	기본평가 시험대비 기초 학습 능력 평가
Step3	실력평가 단원별 수시평가 대비 주관식, 객관식 문제풀이
Step4	서술형 대비 학업성취도 및 수행능력평가 대비 서술형 문제풀이

Reading

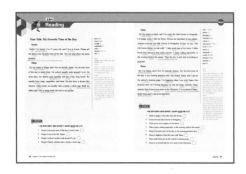

Step1	구문 분석 단원별로 제시된 문장에 대한 구문별 분석과 내용 설명
	확인문제 문장에 대한 기본적인 이해와 인지능력 확인
Step2	확인학습A 빈칸 채우기를 통한 문장 완성 능력 확인
Step3	확인학습B 제시된 우리말을 영어로 완성하여 작문 능력 키우기
Step4	실력평가 단원별 수시평가 대비 주관식, 객관식 문제풀이
Step5	서술형 대비 학업성취도 및 수행능력평가 대비 서술형 문제풀이
	교과서 구석구석 교과서에 나오는 기타 문장까지 완벽 학습

Composition

|영역별 핵심문제|
단어 및 어휘, 대화문, 문법, 독해 등 각 영역별 기출문제의 출제 유형을 분석하여 실전에 대비하고 연습할 수 있도록 문제를 배열

|단원별 예상문제|
기출문제를 분석한 후 새로운 시험 출제 경향을 더하여 새롭게 출제될 수 있는 문제를 포함하여 시험에 완벽하게 대비할 수 있도록 준비

|서술형 실전 및 창의사고력 문제|
학교 시험에서 점차 늘어나는 서술형 시험에 집중 대비하고 고득점을 취득하는데 만전을 기하기 위한 학습 코너

|단원별 모의고사|
영역별, 단계별 학습을 모두 마친 후 실전 연습을 위한 모의고사

INSIGHT on the textbook

교과서 파헤치기

- **단어Test1~3** 영어 단어 우리말 쓰기, 우리말을 영어 단어로 쓰기, 영영풀이에 해당하는 단어와 우리말 쓰기
- **대화문Test1~2** 대화문 빈칸 완성 및 전체 대화문 쓰기
- **본문Test1~5** 빈칸 완성, 우리말 쓰기, 문장 배열연습, 영어 작문하기 복습 등 단계별 반복 학습을 통해 교과서 지문에 대한 완벽한 습득
- **구석구석지문Test1~2** 지문 빈칸 완성 및 전문 영어로 쓰기

Contents

Lesson 1

Passion for Life

🎙 의사소통 기능

- 정보 묻고 답하기

  A: How was he able to become a famous reporter?

  B: He practiced speaking with people in public.

- 알고 있는지 묻기

  A: Have you heard of Mia, the guitar player?

  B: Yes, I have. I heard that she taught herself to play.

🎙 언어 형식

- too ... to부정사

  You knew that you were **too** far behind **to** win a medal.

- to부정사의 부정형

  For me and my country, it was important **not to** give up.

Words & Expressions

Key Words

- □ **accept** [æksépt] 동 받다
- □ **accident** [ǽksidənt] 명 사고
- □ **admire** [ædmáiər] 동 존중하다
- □ **athlete** [ǽθliːt] 명 운동선수
- □ **author** [ɔ́ːθər] 명 작가
- □ **cartoon** [kɑːrtúːn] 명 만화
- □ **celebrate** [séləbrèit] 동 축하하다, 기념하다
- □ **celebration** [sèləbréiʃən] 명 축하
- □ **ceremony** [sérəmòuni] 명 식, 의식
- □ **cheer** [tʃiər] 동 환호성을 지르다, 환호하다
- □ **competition** [kàmpətíʃən] 명 시합
- □ **congratulate** [kəngrǽtʃulèit] 동 축하하다
- □ **contest** [kántest] 명 경연
- □ **decide** [disáid] 동 결정하다
- □ **developer** [divéləpər] 명 개발자
- □ **draw** [drɔː] 동 그리다
- □ **enter** [éntər] 동 들어가다
- □ **especially** [ispéʃəli] 부 특별히
- □ **experiment** [ikspérəmənt] 동 실험하다
- □ **famous** [féiməs] 형 유명한
- □ **finish line** 결승선
- □ **happen** [hǽpən] 동 일어나다
- □ **hurt** [həːrt] 동 다치다
- □ **injure** [índʒər] 동 부상을 입히다
- □ **injury** [índʒəri] 명 부상
- □ **invent** [invént] 동 발명하다
- □ **knock** [nɑk] 동 두드리다
- □ **leave** [liːv] 동 떠나다

- □ **lie** [lai] 명 거짓말
- □ **marathon** [mǽrəθɑ̀n] 명 마라톤
- □ **movie** [múːvi] 명 영화
- □ **nearby** [nìərbái] 형 부근의 부 부근에
- □ **official** [əfíʃəl] 명 관료, 공무원, 경기 임원
- □ **passion** [pǽʃən] 명 열정
- □ **photographer** [fətágrəfər] 명 사진사
- □ **plan** [plæn] 동 계획을 세우다
- □ **practice** [prǽktis] 명 연습
- □ **preparation** [prèpəréiʃən] 명 준비
- □ **prepare** [pripɛ́ər] 동 준비하다
- □ **proud** [praud] 형 자랑스러운
- □ **public** [pʌ́blik] 명 대중
- □ **realize** [ríːəlàiz] 동 깨닫다
- □ **remove** [rimúːv] 동 제거하다
- □ **reporter** [ripɔ́ːrtər] 명 기자, 리포터
- □ **represent** [rèprizént] 동 대표하다
- □ **respect** [rispékt] 동 존경하다
- □ **shout** [ʃaut] 동 외치다
- □ **stadium** [stéidiəm] 명 경기장
- □ **suddenly** [sʌ́dnli] 부 갑자기
- □ **toward** [tɔːrd] 전 ~ 쪽으로, ~을 향하여
- □ **training** [tréiniŋ] 명 훈련
- □ **try** [trai] 명 시도
- □ **volunteer** [vɑləntíər] 명 자원봉사자
- □ **whenever** [hwenévər] 접 ~할 때마다
- □ **winner** [wínər] 명 우승자, 수상자

Key Expressions

- □ **as a result** 결과적으로
- □ **at war** 전쟁 중인
- □ **be done with** ~을 끝내다
- □ **be good at** ~을 잘하다
- □ **be into** ~에 관심이 많다
- □ **be proud of** ~을 자랑스러워하다
- □ **come up to** ~에 다가가다
- □ **fall to the ground** 땅에 넘어지다
- □ **far behind** 멀리 뒤쳐신

- □ **give up** 포기하다
- □ **in public** 공개적으로, 사람들이 있는 데서
- □ **keep -ing** 계속 ~하다
- □ **more than** ~ 이상
- □ **stand for** ~을 나타내다, 상징하다
- □ **take a picture** 사진을 찍다
- □ **teach oneself** 독학하다
- □ **that's why** 그것이 ~하는 이유다, 그런 이유로 ~
- □ **Why not?** 왜 아니겠어?

Word Power

※ 서로 비슷한 뜻을 가진 어휘

- □ **admire** 존경하다 : **respect** 존경하다
- □ **cheer** 환호하다 : **encourage** 격려하다
- □ **happen** 일어나다 : **take place** 발생하다
- □ **passion** 열정 : **enthusiasm** 열정
- □ **remove** 제거하다 : **eliminate** 제거하다

- □ **author** 작가 : **writer** 작가
- □ **competition** 시합 : **contest** 경연
- □ **leave** 떠나다 : **depart** 떠나다
- □ **realize** 깨닫다 : **understand** 이해하다

※ 서로 반대되는 뜻을 가진 어휘

- □ **accept** 받다 ↔ **refuse** 거절하다
- □ **famous** 유명한 ↔ **infamous** 악명이 높은
- □ **public** 대중적인 ↔ **private** 사적인

- □ **praise** 칭찬하다 ↔ **blame** 비난하다
- □ **far** 먼 ↔ **near** 가까운
- □ **suddenly** 갑자기 ↔ **expectedly** 예상대로

※ 동사+-ation = 명사

- □ **prepare** 준비하다 – **preparation** 준비
- □ **invite** 초대하다 – **invitation** 초대
- □ **recommend** 추천하다 – **recommendation** 추천
- □ **organize** 조직하다 – **organization** 조직
- □ **celebrate** 축하하다 – **celebration** 축하
- □ **experiment** 실험하다 – **experimentation** 실험

- □ **inform** 알리다, 정보를 주다 – **information** 정보
- □ **transport** 수송하다 – **transportation** 수송
- □ **found** 설립하다 – **foundation** 설립
- □ **admire** 존중하다 – **admiration** 존중
- □ **congratulate** 축하하다 – **congratulation** 축하
- □ **realize** 깨닫다 – **realization** 깨달음

English Dictionary

- □ **accept** 받다
  → to take something that someone offers
  어떤 사람이 제안하는 것을 받아들이다
- □ **athlete** 운동선수
  → a person who plays sports well 운동을 잘하는 사람
- □ **author** 작가
  → the writer of a book 책의 저자
- □ **congratulate** 축하하다
  → to tell someone that you are happy when something pleasant has happened to them
  어떤 좋은 일이 일어난 사람에게 기쁘다고 말하다
- □ **far** 먼
  → used to talk about a great distance
  매우 먼 거리에 관하여 말할 때 사용되는
- □ **give up** 포기하다
  → to stop doing something that you have tried hard to do 열심히 애쓰던 일을 중단하다
- □ **injury** 부상

  → harm or damage to a person's or an animal's body
  사람이나 동물의 신체에 가해지는 손상
- □ **marathon** 마라톤
  → a race where people run a distance of 42.195 kilometers 42.195킬로미터 거리를 달리는 시합
- □ **passion** 열정
  → a strong emotion or feeling 강렬한 정서나 감정
- □ **realize** 깨닫다
  → to become aware of something 어떤 것을 인식하게 되다
- □ **remove** 없애다
  → to take something away 무엇인가를 치우다
- □ **represent** 대표하다
  → to officially speak or take action for people in a group
  집단에 속한 사람들을 위하여 공식적으로 대신 말하거나 행동을 취하다
- □ **toward** ~을 향해서
  → in the direction of someone or something
  어떤 사람 또는 사물이 있는 방향으로

서답형

01 〈보기〉와 같은 관계가 되도록 빈칸에 알맞은 말을 쓰시오.

┌─ 보기 ─┐
invite : invitation
└─────┘

(1) _____ : celebration
(2) _____ : information

02 다음 빈칸에 들어가기에 적절한 단어를 써서 문장을 완성했을 때 자연스러운 것은?

The last runner finished the race more than an hour before. "There will be no more runners coming," the _____ decided.

① Kelly represented our _____ at the quiz show.
② Running a _____ is challenging.
③ This area is only for the _____.
④ Harry prepares _____ every Sunday for his family.
⑤ The student was proud of himself when he got a good _____ on the math exam.

03 다음 중 밑줄 친 부분의 뜻풀이가 바르지 <u>않은</u> 것은?

① Finally, the <u>athlete</u> was able to take part in the Olympic games. (운동선수)
② Eric's passing the exam called for a big <u>celebration</u>. (축하)
③ They <u>cheered</u> when the soccer player scored the first goal. (환호했다)
④ My sister is busy preparing for her wedding <u>ceremony</u>. (의식, 기념식)
⑤ I <u>gave up</u> trying to solve the problem because it was difficult. (나누어주었다)

04 다음 중 〈보기〉에 있는 단어를 사용하여 자연스러운 문장을 만들 수 <u>없는</u> 것은?

┌─ 보기 ─┐
cheered marathon remove ceremony
└─────┘

① There will be a graduation _____ in the auditorium.
② My classmates _____ for me and shouted my name.
③ Kee-chung Sohn was a _____ runner who won a gold medal at the 1936 Berlin Olympics.
④ The players are _____ for the final match.
⑤ I boiled the meat to _____ the fat.

05 다음 밑줄 친 부분과 의미가 가장 가까운 것을 고르시오.

He became an <u>author</u> late in life.

① competitor   ② athlete
③ creator   ④ writer
⑤ developer

06 다음 빈칸에 공통으로 들어가기에 알맞은 것은?

• She must be very proud _____ herself.
• How was Hyeon Chung able to be one _____ the final four players in the tennis competition?

① to   ② of   ③ in
④ on   ⑤ with

01 주어진 단어를 이용해 빈칸을 완성하시오.

Careful _____ for the exam is essential.

➡ _____ (prepare)

02 다음 짝지어진 단어의 관계가 같도록 빈칸에 알맞은 말을 쓰시오.

congratulate : congratulation
= experiment : _____

[03~04] 빈칸에 공통으로 들어갈 단어를 쓰시오.

03
- She shut her eyes and wished for him to _____ better.
- Left alone, the problem could _____ worse.

04
- There is no bus service. That's _____ I usually take a taxi.
- "Let's eat out." "_____ not?"

05 밑줄 친 부분과 의미가 가장 가까운 단어를 주어진 철자로 시작하여 쓰시오.

His father noticed his passion for football.

➡ e_____

06 빈칸에 알맞은 단어를 〈보기〉에서 골라 쓰시오.

┌ 보기 ┐
up   done   good   result

(1) Skiing is not easy. Not many people are _____ at skiing.
(2) When I'm _____ with the pencil case, I'm planning to make my own desk.
(3) Reporters came _____ to Wasiqi and started asking him questions.
(4) Finally I won a marathon in Germany. As a _____, I was able to come to Atlanta.

07 다음 우리말에 맞게 빈칸에 알맞은 말을 쓰시오.

(1) 네가 만화 클럽에 가입했다고 들었어. 만화 그리기에 관심 있니?
➡ I heard that you joined the cartoon club. Are you _____ in drawing cartoons?

(2) 경기 중에 제 상처는 점점 더 심각해졌지만, 저는 포기할 수 없었습니다.
➡ The injury got worse during the race, but I couldn't _____ up.

(3) 그는 대중 앞에서 사람들과 말하는 것을 연습했다.
➡ He practiced speaking with people in _____.

(4) 그러나 그는 계속 결승선을 향해 움직였다.
➡ Still, he kept going _____ the finish line.

Conversation

① 정보 묻고 답하기

> **A** How was he able to become a famous reporter? 그가 어떻게 유명한 기자가 될 수 있었지?
>
> **B** He practiced speaking with people in public.
> 그는 대중 앞에서 사람들과 말하는 것을 연습했어.

■ 상대에게 방법 등의 정보를 요청할 때는 "How 동사+주어 ~?"(어떻게 ~?)로 물어볼 수 있다. "How was she/he able to ~?" 또는 "How were you able to ~?"는 "어떻게 ~할 수 있게 되었는가?"라는 뜻으로 어떻게 된 일인지에 대하여 묻는 말이다. 자신이 원하는 정보에 따라 시간, 장소, 이유, 방법 등 적절한 의문사로 물을 수 있다. 각각의 의문사는 when(언제), where(어디서), who(누가), what(무엇을), how(어떻게), why(왜)의 의미를 가진다.

■ 의문사를 사용하지 않고 원하는 정보를 묻고자 할 때 사용하는 표현으로는 "Can/Could you tell me ~?", "Would/Will you please tell me ~?" 등이 있다. 동사 know를 사용하여 "Do you know ~?", "Do you know 의문사절?", "Do you happen to know 의문사 ~?" 등도 상대에게 정보를 요청하는 표현이고, "Would you like to show me ~?"(~에 대해서 알려주시겠습니까?)와 같은 표현으로도 상대에게 정보를 요청할 수 있다.

■ 상대에게 정보를 요청하는 표현은 평서문의 형태로 "I wonder/am wondering ~."(나는 ~가 궁금하다)처럼 말할 수도 있다. wonder를 사용할 때 어순은 「I wonder+의문사+주어+동사~.」, 「I wonder+if/whether+주어+동사 ~.」이다. 또한 궁금한 내용을 "I want to know ~.", "I don't know why ~."로 표현할 수 있다.

정보 묻고 답하기

• How was she/he able to ~?	그녀가/그가 어떻게 ~할 수 있게 되었니?
• Could/Can you tell me ~?	~에 대해 말해 줄 수 있니?
• Can I ask you + 의문사절?	~에 대하여 물어봐도 되니?
• Do you know ~?	~을 알고 있니?
• I want to know 명사구/명사절.	~을 알고 싶다.
• I'm wondering + if/whether 주어+동사/의문사절.	~인지 궁금하다.

핵심 Check

1. 다음 우리말에 해당하는 영어 문장을 주어진 단어를 포함하여 완성하시오.

B: _____? (able / so well)

(어떻게 그녀가 영어를 그렇게 잘 말할 수 있게 되었지?)

G: She learned English by watching many Hollywood movies.

② 알고 있는지 묻기

A Have you heard of Mia, the guitar player? 미아라는 기타 연주자에 대하여 들어 본 적이 있니?

B Yes, I have. I heard that she taught herself to play.
응. 들어 봤어. 그녀가 연주를 독학으로 배웠다고 들었어.

■ "Have you heard of/about ~?"는 "~대하여 들어 본 적이 있니?"라는 의미로 상대방이 지금 이야기하는 것에 대해 알고 있는지의 여부를 물어보는 말이다. 접속사 that을 사용하여 "Have you heard that 주어+동사 ~?" 형태로 말할 수도 있다.

■ 어떤 사실을 상대방이 알고 있는지 물어보는 말은 know를 사용하여 "Do you know about ~?"(~을 아십니까?) 또는 "You know about ~, don't you?", "Did you know that ~?", "Do you know (about) ~?"라고 물어볼 수도 있다. "You know ~, don't you?"는 "너는 ~을 알고 있지?"라는 뜻으로 상대방이 이미 알고 있을 법한 소재의 이야기를 꺼낼 때 사용한다. hear를 사용하여 "Have you (ever) heard about ~?"(~을 들어본 적이 있니?) 또는 "Did you hear about ~?"라고 하면 know를 사용하여 직접적으로 물어보는 것보다는 완화된 느낌을 준다.

■ "Have you heard ~?"는 현재완료를 사용하여 어떤 일에 대하여 과거에 들어 본 적이 있어서 현재에 그것을 알고 있는지 물어보는 것으로, 현재완료의 용법 중에서 '경험'에 해당한다. "Have you heard ~?"에 대한 대답은 "Yes, I have.", "No, I haven't."라고 하여야 하지만 경우에 따라서는 "Have you heard ~?"로 질문하는 경우에 그 의도가 새로운 정보를 전달하는 것일 때도 있기 때문에 "Really?" "I didn't know that." 등으로 대답하기도 한다.

알고 있는지 묻기

- Have you (ever) heard (about) ~? (한번이라도) ~을(에 대해서) 들어 본 적이 있습니까?
- Have you been told about ~? ~에 대하여 들어 본 적이 있지?
- You know that ~, don't you? 너 ~을 알지, 그렇지 않니?   • Do you know about/that ~? ~을 아십니까?
- Are you aware of/that ~? ~을 알고 있니?   • Do you realize that ~? ~을 알고 있니?

핵심 Check

2. 다음 밑줄 친 말 대신 쓰기에 적절한 것은?

B: <u>Have you heard of</u> the winner of the singing contest?

G: No, I haven't. Who won?

B: The winner is Vintop, who wrote all of his own songs.

① Why did you know
② Have you been told about
③ What have you told
④ Have you talked about
⑤ How did you realize

Real-Life Zone

G: ❶Have you heard of Eui Hyun Sin, the skier?

B: No. Who is he?

G: He's a Paralympian skier. He won the first gold medal for Korea in the 2018 Winter Paralympics.

B: Wow! That's great.

G: ❷He was in a car accident in his early twenties and hurt his legs.

B: How was he able to become a skier?

G: After his accident, he tried several different sports to get better. Then he became especially interested in skiing.

B: Skiing is not easy. Not many people are good at skiing.

G: ❸That's why he's so respected.

G: 신의현이라는 스키 선수에 대해 들어 본 적 있니?

B: 아니, 그가 누구야?

G: 그는 페럴림픽의 스키 선수야. 그는 2018 동계 페럴림픽에서 한국의 첫 금메달을 땄어.

B: 와! 훌륭하다.

G: 그는 20대 초반에 차 사고를 당하고 다리를 다쳤어.

B: 어떻게 그가 스키 선수가 될 수 있었니?

G: 사고 후에 그는 회복하기 위해 여러 가지 운동들을 시도했어. 그때 그는 특히 스키 타는 것에 관심을 가지게 됐어.

B: 스키를 타는 것은 쉽지 않잖아. 스키를 잘 타는 사람들은 많지 않아.

G: 그것이 그가 그렇게 존경받는 이유야.

❶ "Have you heard of ~?"는 "~에 대하여 들어 본 적이 있니?"라고 상대에게 알고 있는지를 묻는 질문이다.

❷ "in his early twenties"는 "이십대 초반에"라는 뜻으로 "~십대"는 "~ties"라고 한다.

❸ "That's why"는 "그런 이유로 ~하다/그것이 ~한 이유이다"의 뜻으로 관계부사의 선행사 the reason이 생략된 표현이다.

Check(√) True or False

(1) Eui Hyun Sin won the first gold medal for Korea in the 2018 Winter Paralympics.   T ☐ F ☐

(2) He was in a car accident in his early thirties and hurt his legs.   T ☐ F ☐

(3) After his accident, he tried several different sports to get better.   T ☐ F ☐

Wrap Up

B: Sora, ❶have you heard about the fire last night?

G: Yes, I heard that there was a big fire in a building nearby. Was anybody hurt?

B: No, one man saved ten people ❷who were in the building.

G: Oh, really? How was he able to save so many people?

B: He knocked on every door to tell people to leave the building.

G: Wow, that's amazing!

B: 소라야, 지난밤 화재에 대해 들었니?

G: 응, 이 근처 건물에서 큰 화재가 있었다고 들었어. 다친 사람이 있어?

B: 아니, 한 남자가 건물 안에 있던 열 명의 사람들을 구했어.

G: 오, 진짜? 어떻게 그는 그 많은 사람들을 구할 수 있었니?

B: 그는 사람들에게 건물을 떠나라고 말하기 위해서 모든 문을 두드렸어.

G: 와, 정말 놀랍구나!

❶ "last night"은 명사 "the fire"를 수식한다. last night이 동사를 수식할 때는 현재완료를 쓸 수 없다.

❷ who는 주격 관계대명사로 ten people을 선행사로 하고 있다.

Check(√) True or False

(4) Sora didn't hear about the fire last night.   T ☐ F ☐

(5) One man knocked on every door to tell people to leave the building.   T ☐ F ☐

Listen & Speak 1 Listen

1. B: How was she able to become a great runner?
   G: She ran 3 kilometers every day.
2. G: How was he able to become a basketball player?
   B: He was short, but he ❶practiced shooting three-point shots a lot.
3. B: How was she able to speak English so well?
   G: She learned English ❷by watching many Hollywood movies.
4. G: How was he able to become a famous reporter?
   B: He practiced speaking with people in public.

❶ practiced의 목적어로 동명사 shooting이 사용되었다.
❷ 전치사 by의 목적어로 동명사가 쓰였다.

 Listen & Speak 1 A-1

B: How was Thomas Edison able to invent so many things?
G: Many people think that he invented things on his first try, but that's not true.
B: Oh, really?
G: Yes. Whenever he invented something, he experimented many times.
B: Maybe ❶that's why so many people admire him.

❶ "that's why ～."는 "that's the reason why ～"에서 선행사 the reason을 생략한 형태로 "그런 이유로 ～하다."로 해석한다.

 Listen & Speak 1 A-2

G: How was Hyeon Chung able to be one of the final four players in the tennis competition?
B: He could do it only after years of hard training.
G: I see. ❶When did he start playing tennis?
B: He started to play tennis when he was seven.

❶ "When ～?"은 시점을 묻는 말이므로 현재완료와는 같이 쓰지 않는다.

 Listen & Speak 2 Listen

1. B: Have you heard of the winner of the singing contest?
   G: No, I haven't. Who won?
   B: The winner is Vintop, ❶who wrote all of his own songs.
2. G: Have you heard of Mia, the guitar player?
   B: Yes, I have. ❷I heard that she taught herself to play.
3. B: Have you heard about BTG, the world famous dance group?
   G: Yes, I have. I have watched their video many times on the Internet.
4. G: Have you heard of Jiho, the photographer?
   B: No, I haven't. What kind of pictures does he take?
   G: He usually takes pictures of street artists.

❶ who는 계속 용법으로 쓰인 주격 관계대명사이다.
❷ "teach oneself to ～"는 "～을 독학하다"의 뜻이다.

 Listen & Speak 2 A-1

B: Have you heard about the cartoon club, Edutoon?
G: Yes, I have. ❶Are you interested in drawing cartoons?
B: Yes, I want to be a famous cartoon writer, so I want to join that club.
G: Oh, I didn't know ❷that you're interested in drawing cartoons.

❶ "be interested in"은 "～에 관심을 가지다"의 뜻이다.
❷ that은 접속사로 사용되어 know의 목적어가 되는 명사절을 유도한다.

 Listen & Speak 2 A-2

G: Have you heard of D.I.Y.?
B: No, what is D.I.Y.?
G: D.I.Y. ❶stands for 'do-it-yourself.' I'm really into it. Right now, I'm making a pencil case.
B: What are you going to make after you finish that?
G: ❷When I'm done with the pencil case, I'm planning to make my own desk.

❶ "stand for ～"는 "～을 나타내다, 상징하다"의 뜻이다.
❷ "be done with ～"는 "～을 끝내다"라는 뜻이다.

● 다음 우리말과 일치하도록 빈칸에 알맞은 말을 쓰시오.

Listen & Speak 1 Listen

1. **B:** _____ was she _____ to become a great _____?
   G: She _____ 3 kilometers _____ day.

2. **G:** How was he _____ to become a _____ player?
   B: He was _____, but he _____ shooting three-point shots a lot.

3. **B:** _____ was she _____ to _____ English so _____?
   G: She _____ English by _____ many Hollywood movies.

4. **G:** _____ was he able to _____ a famous _____?
   B: He _____ speaking with people in _____.

Listen & Speak 1-A

1. **B:** _____ was Thomas Edison _____ to invent so many things?
   G: Many people _____ that he _____ things on his _____ try, but that's not _____.
   B: Oh, _____?
   G: Yes. _____ he invented something, he _____ many times.
   B: Maybe that's _____ so many people _____ him.

2. **G:** _____ was Hyeon Chung able to be one of the _____ four _____ in the tennis competition?
   B: He _____ do it _____ _____ years of hard training.
   G: I see. When did he start _____ _____?
   B: He _____ to play tennis when he was _____.

Listen & Speak 2 Listen

1. **B:** _____ you heard of the _____ of the singing _____?
   G: No, I _____. Who won?
   B: The _____ is Vintop, who wrote all of his _____ songs.

2. **G:** Have you _____ of Mia, the _____ _____?
   B: Yes, I have. I heard that she _____ herself to play.

3. **B:** Have you _____ about BTG, the world famous _____ group?
   G: Yes, I have. I have _____ their video many _____ on the Internet.

4. **G:** Have you _____ of Jiho, the _____?
   B: No, I _____. What kind of _____ does he _____?
   G: He usually _____ pictures of _____ artists.

해석

1. B: 어떻게 그녀는 훌륭한 달리기 선수가 될 수 있었니?
   G: 그녀는 매일 3킬로미터를 달렸어.
2. G: 어떻게 그는 농구 선수가 될 수 있었니?
   B: 그는 작았지만 3점 슛을 많이 연습했어.
3. B: 어떻게 그녀는 영어를 잘할 수 있었니?
   G: 그는 많은 할리우드 영화를 보면서 영어를 배웠어.
4. G: 어떻게 그는 유명한 기자가 될 수 있었니?
   B: 그는 대중 앞에서 사람들과 말하는 것을 연습했어.

1. B: 어떻게 토머스 에디슨을 그렇게 많은 것들을 발명할 수 있었을까?
   G: 많은 사람들은 그가 그것들을 첫 시도에 발명했다고 생각하지만 그것은 사실이 아니야.
   B: 오, 진짜?
   G: 응. 그는 무언가를 발명할 때마다 여러 번 실험했어.
   B: 아마 그것이 그렇게 많은 사람들이 그를 존경하는 이유일 거야.
2. G: 정현이 어떻게 테니스 경기에서 마지막 네 선수 중 한 명이 될 수 있었을까?
   B: 그는 혹독한 훈련을 몇 년 거친 뒤에야 그것을 할 수 있었어.
   G: 그렇구나. 그는 언제 테니스 치는 것을 시작했니?
   B: 그는 일곱 살 때 테니스 치는 것을 시작했어.

1. B: 노래 대회 우승자에 대해 들어 본 적 있니?
   G: 아니, 못 들어 봤어. 누가 이겼어?
   B: 우승자는 빈탑인데, 그는 자신의 모든 노래를 작곡했어.
2. G: 미아라는 기타 연주자에 대해 들어 본 적 있니?
   B: 응, 들어 봤어. 나는 그녀가 연주를 독학했다고 들었어.
3. B: BTG라는 세계적으로 유명한 댄스 그룹에 대해 들어 본 적 있니?
   G: 응, 들어 봤어. 나는 인터넷에서 그들의 영상을 여러 번 본 적이 있어.
4. G: 지호라는 사진작가에 대해 들어 본 적 있니?
   B: 아니, 못 들어 봤어. 그는 어떤 종류의 사진을 찍니?
   G: 그는 보통 거리 예술가들의 사진을 찍어.

Listen & Speak 2-A

1. **B:** _____ you _____ about the _____ club, Edutoon?

   G: Yes, I have. Are you _____ in _____ _____?

   B: Yes, I _____ _____ _____ a famous cartoon writer, so I want to _____ that club.

   G: Oh, I didn't _____ that you're _____ in _____ cartoons.

2. **G:** Have you _____ of D.I.Y.?

   B: No, _____ is D.I.Y.?

   G: D.I.Y. _____ for 'do-it-yourself.' I'm really _____ it. Right now, I'm _____ a pencil _____.

   B: _____ are you going to make _____ you _____ that?

   G: When I'm _____ with the _____ case, I'm _____ to make my own _____.

Real-Life Zone

G: _____ you heard of Eui Hyun Sin, the _____?

B: No. _____ is _____?

G: He's a Paralympian _____. He won the first gold _____ for Korea in the 2018 Winter Paralympics.

B: Wow! That's _____.

G: He _____ in a car _____ in his early _____ and hurt his legs.

B: How was he able to _____ a skier?

G: After his _____, he tried _____ different sports to _____ better. Then he became _____ interested in _____.

B: _____ is not easy. Not many people _____ _____ at skiing.

G: That's _____ he's so _____.

Wrap Up

B: Sora, have you _____ about the _____ last night?

G: Yes, I _____ that there _____ a big fire in a building _____. Was anybody _____?

B: No, _____ man _____ ten people who _____ in the building.

G: Oh, really? _____ was he able to _____ so many people?

B: He _____ on every door to _____ people to _____ the building.

G: Wow, that's _____!

해석

1. **B:** 에듀툰이라는 만화 동아리에 대해 들어 본 적 있니?
   G: 응, 있어. 만화 그리는 것에 관심이 있니?
   B: 나는 유명한 만화 작가가 되고 싶어서 그 동아리에 가입하고 싶어.
   G: 오, 나는 네가 만화 그리기에 관심이 있는 줄 몰랐어.

2. **G:** D.I.Y에 대해 들어 본 적 있니?
   B: 아니, D.I.Y가 뭐야?
   G: D.I.Y는 '너 스스로 해라'를 의미해. 나는 그것에 푹 빠졌어. 지금 나는 필통을 만들고 있어.
   B: 그것을 완성하고 나면 무엇을 만들 거니?
   G: 필통을 완성하면, 나는 내 책상을 만들 계획이야.

G: 신의현이라는 스키 선수에 대해 들어 본 적 있니?
B: 아니, 그가 누구야?
G: 그는 페럴림픽의 스키 선수야. 그는 2018 동계 페럴림픽에서 한국의 첫 금메달을 땄어.
B: 와! 훌륭하다.
G: 그는 20대 초반에 차 사고를 당하고 다리를 다쳤어.
B: 어떻게 그가 스키 선수가 될 수 있었니?
G: 사고 후에 그는 회복하기 위해 여러 가지 운동들을 시도했어. 그때 그는 특히 스키 타는 것에 관심을 가지게 됐어.
B: 스키를 타는 것은 쉽지 않잖아. 스키를 잘 타는 사람들은 많지 않아.
G: 그것이 그가 그렇게 존경받는 이유야.

B: 소라야, 지난밤 화재에 대해 들었니?
G: 응, 이 근처 건물에서 큰 화재가 있었다고 들었어. 다친 사람이 있어?
B: 아니, 한 남자가 건물 안에 있던 열 명의 사람들을 구했어.
G: 오, 진짜? 어떻게 그는 그 많은 사람들을 구할 수 있었니?
B: 그는 사람들에게 건물을 떠나라고 말하기 위해서 모든 문을 두드렸어.
G: 와, 정말 놀랍구나!

[01~02] 다음 대화의 빈칸에 들어갈 말로 알맞은 것은?

01

G: ___(A)___ was Hyeon Chung able to be one of the final four players in the tennis competition?
B: He could do it only after years of hard training.
G: I see. ___(B)___ did he start playing tennis?
B: He started to play tennis when he was seven.

① How – When   ② Where – When   ③ Why – How
④ What – How   ⑤ When – How

02

G: _____
B: No, what is D.I.Y.?
G: D.I.Y. stands for 'do-it-yourself.' I'm really into it. Right now, I'm making a pencil case.
B: What are you going to make after you finish that?
G: When I'm done with the pencil case, I'm planning to make my own desk.

① How about hearing D.I.Y.?   ② Where did you hear of it?
③ What did you hear of?   ④ Have you heard of D.I.Y.?
⑤ Have you done with D.I.Y.?

03 대화에 이어지기에 적절하게 배열된 순서를 고르시오.

B: Sora, have you heard about the fire last night?
G: Yes, I heard that there was a big fire in a building nearby. Was anybody hurt?
(A) He knocked on every door to tell people to leave the building.
(B) No, one man saved ten people who were in the building.
(C) Oh, really? How was he able to save so many people?
G: Wow, that's amazing!

① (A) – (C) – (B)   ② (B) – (A) – (C)   ③ (B) – (C) – (A)
④ (C) – (A) – (B)   ⑤ (C) – (B) – (A)

01 다음 대화의 빈칸에 적절한 것은?

> B: How was she able to become a great runner?
>
> G: _____

① She practiced speaking in public.
② She ran 3 kilometers every day.
③ She didn't skip any meals of the day.
④ She learned English by watching many Hollywood movies.
⑤ She practiced shooting shots a lot.

[02~03] 다음 대화를 읽고 물음에 답하시오.

> B: How was Thomas Edison able to invent so many things?
>
> G: Many people think that he invented things on his first try, but that's not true.
>
> B: Oh, really?
>
> G: Yes. _____ he invented something, he experimented many times.
>
> B: Maybe that's why so many people admire him.

02 위 대화의 빈칸에 들어가기에 적절한 것은?

① Whenever   ② However
③ Wherever   ④ Whoever
⑤ Whatever

03 위 대화의 내용과 일치하지 <u>않는</u> 것은?

① Thomas Edison invented many things.
② The boy didn't know about Edison.
③ Edison experimented many times when he invented something.
④ Edison didn't usually invent something on his first try.
⑤ Many people admire Edison.

[04~05] 다음 대화를 읽고 물음에 답하시오.

> B: (A)<u>Have you heard about the cartoon club, Edutoon?</u>
>
> G: Yes, I have. Are you interested in drawing cartoons?
>
> B: Yes, I want to be a famous cartoon writer, so I want to join that club.
>
> G: Oh, I didn't know that you're interested in drawing cartoons.

04 위 대화의 밑줄 친 (A)가 의도하는 것은?

① 소개하기   ② 정보 교환하기
③ 알고 있는지 묻기   ④ 광고하기
⑤ 충고하기

05 위 대화의 내용과 일치하지 <u>않는</u> 것은?

① The boy asks the girl if she knows about the cartoon club.
② The girl has heard about the cartoon club.
③ The girl wants to be a cartoon writer.
④ The boy will join the cartoon club.
⑤ The boy is interested in drawing cartoons.

06 다음 대화의 빈칸에 적절한 것은?

> B: Have you heard of the winner of the singing contest?
>
> G: No, I haven't. _____
>
> B: The winner is Vintop, who wrote all of his own songs.

① Who won?   ② What's that?
③ I know that.   ④ She is the winner.
⑤ Are you busy?

[07~09] 다음 대화를 읽고 물음에 답하시오.

G: Have you heard of Eui Hyun Sin, the skier?

B: No. __(가)__ is he? (A)

G: He's a Paralympian skier. He won the first gold medal for Korea in the 2018 Winter Paralympics. (B)

B: Wow! That's great.

G: He was in a car accident in his early twenties and hurt his legs. (C)

B: __(나)__ was he able to become a skier?

G: After his accident, he tried several different sports to get better. (D)

B: Skiing is not easy. Not many people are good at skiing. (E)

G: That's why he's so respected.

07 대화의 내용으로 보아, 빈칸 (가), (나)에 들어가기에 가장 적절한 것은?

① When – Who
② Who – Why
③ Who – How
④ How – Why
⑤ What – When

08 (A)~(E) 중에서 다음 문장이 들어가기에 가장 적절한 곳은?

> Then he became especially interested in skiing.

① (A) ② (B) ③ (C) ④ (D) ⑤ (E)

09 위 대화를 읽고 대답할 수 <u>없는</u> 것은?

① Does the boy know about Eui Hyun Sin?
② When did Eui Hyun Sin win the gold medal?
③ Why did Eui Hyun Sin become a skier?
④ Who told Eui Hyun Sin to be a skier?
⑤ Why do people respect Eui Hyun Sin?

[10~11] 다음 대화를 읽고 물음에 답하시오.

B: Sora, _____(A)_____ the fire last night?

G: Yes, I heard that there was a big fire in a building nearby. Was anybody hurt?

B: No, one man saved ten people __(B)__ were in the building.

G: Oh, really? How was he able to save so many people?

B: He knocked on every door to tell people to leave the building.

G: Wow, that's amazing!

10 빈칸 (A)에 들어가기에 적절한 것은?

① have you been to
② have you seen
③ have you saved
④ have you gone to
⑤ have you heard about

11 다음 중 (B)에 들어갈 말과 같은 말이 들어갈 수 있는 것은?

① I read the book _____ he had written.
② This is the house _____ he designed.
③ Do you know the man _____ helped her?
④ Would you tell me _____ you were late for class?
⑤ I know _____ he lives.

[01~03] 다음 대화를 읽고 물음에 답하시오.

B: _____ (A) _____ to invent so many things? (어떻게 Thomas Edison은 그렇게 많은 것을 발명할 수 있었니?)

G: ⓐMany people think that ⓑhe invented things on his first try, but ⓒthat's true.

B: Oh, really?

G: Yes. Whenever ⓓhe invented something, he experimented many times.

B: Maybe that's ____ (B) ____ so many people ⓔadmire him.

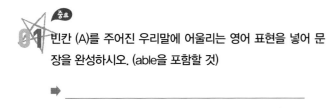

01 빈칸 (A)를 주어진 우리말에 어울리는 영어 표현을 넣어 문장을 완성하시오. (able을 포함할 것)

➡ _____

02 빈칸 (B)에 알맞은 단어를 쓰시오.

➡ (B) _____

03 ⓐ~ⓔ 중에서 대화의 흐름상 어색한 것을 찾아 쓰고 적절한 것으로 바꾸어 쓰시오.

어색한 것의 기호 → 적절한 표현

_____ ➡ _____

04 밑줄 친 (가)의 우리말을 영어로 옮기시오. (주어진 단어를 포함하고, 필요한 단어를 추가할 것)

> G: Have you heard of Mia, the guitar player?
> B: Yes, I have. (가)나는 그녀가 독학으로 연주하는 것을 배웠다고 들었어. (herself) (8 words)

➡ _____

[05~06] 다음 대화를 읽고 물음에 답하시오.

G: Have you heard of D.I.Y.?

B: No, what is D.I.Y.?

G: D.I.Y. stands for 'do-it-yourself.' (가)나는 그것에 정말로 관심이 많아.(into) Right now, I'm making a pencil case.

B: What are you going to make after you finish that?

G: When ____ (나) ____ with the pencil case, I'm planning to make my own desk.

05 밑줄 친 (가)의 우리말을 영작하시오. (주어진 단어를 포함할 것)

➡ _____

06 내용상 (B)에 들어가기에 적절한 두 단어를 쓰시오. (축약형은 한 단어 취급)

➡ _____

07 다음 대화의 내용에 어울리도록 아래 빈칸에 적절한 말을 쓰시오.

> B: Sora, have you heard about the fire last night?
> G: Yes, I heard that there was a big fire in a building nearby. Was anybody hurt?
> B: No, one man saved ten people who were in the building.
> G: Oh, really? How was he able to save so many people?
> B: He knocked on every door to tell people to leave the building.
> G: Wow, that's amazing!

> There was a big fire last night. But no one was hurt because a man (A)_____ on every door to tell people to (B)_____ the building.

Grammar

1 too ... to부정사

- You knew that you were **too** far behind **to** win a medal.
  당신은 메달을 따기에 너무도 멀리 뒤떨어져 있었다는 것을 알고 있었잖아요.
- It was **too** hot **to** go out. 날씨가 너무 더워서 밖에 나갈 수가 없었다.

■ 'too ~ to부정사'는 '너무 ~해서 …할 수 없다[…하기에는 너무 ~하다]'라는 의미이다.
- I was **too** nervous **to eat**. 나는 너무 불안해서 먹을 수가 없었다.
- It's **too** late **to save** her now. 이제 그녀를 구하기에는 너무 늦다.

■ 'too … to부정사'는 'so … that + 주어 + can't[couldn't] + 동사원형'으로 바꾸어 쓸 수 있다.
- She was **too** weak **to stand**. 그녀는 너무 힘이 없어서 서 있을 수가 없었다.
  = She was **so** weak **that** she couldn't stand.
- He's **too** young **to go** on his own. 그는 혼자 가기에는 너무 어리다.
  = He's **so** young **that** he can't go on his own.

■ 'enough + to부정사'는 '~하기에 충분한'이라는 의미를 나타내며, 'so … that + 주어 + can[could] + 동사원형'으로 바꾸어 쓸 수 있다.
- I was stupid **enough to** believe him. 내가 그를 믿을 만큼 어리석었다.
  = I was **so** stupid **that** I could believe him.
- It's warm **enough to** eat outside. 밖에서 식사를 해도 될 정도로 날이 따뜻하다.
  = It's **so** warm **that** we[I] can eat outside.

핵심 Check

1. 다음 괄호 안에서 알맞은 말을 고르시오.
(1) Is it (so / too) late to cancel my order?
(2) He is (so / too) strong that he can bend almost any metal.
(3) He's (old enough / enough old) to take care of himself.

② to부정사의 부정형

- For me and my country, it was important **not to give** up.
  저와 제 조국을 위해서는, 포기하지 않는 것이 중요했어요.
- Try **not to get** your shoes wet. 네 신발이 젖지 않도록 해라.

■ to부정사의 부정은 to부정사 바로 앞에 'not'이나 'never'를 쓴다. 보통, 'never'는 부정의 의미를 더 강조하고 싶을 때 사용한다.
  - She decided **not to go** through with the operation. 그녀는 그 수술을 받지 않기로 했다.
  - He makes it a rule **never to borrow** money. 그는 절대 돈을 빌리지 않는 것을 원칙으로 삼고 있다.

■ to부정사 부정의 의미

to부정사의 내용과 반대되는 말을 할 때

to부정사의 해석	to부정사 부정의 해석
~하는 것 (명사적 용법)	~하지 않는 것 (명사적 용법)
~하는 (형용사적 용법)	~하지 않는 (형용사적 용법)
~하기 위해서 (부사적 용법)	~하기 않기 위해서 (부사적 용법)

  - He decided **not to go** there. 그는 그곳에 안 가기로 결정했다.
  - You are **not to leave** your station without permission. 허락 없이 자기 위치를 떠나서는 안 된다.
  - Be careful **not to cross** the line. 선을 넘어가지 않도록 조심하라.

■ to부정사 부정의 형태

to부정사 바로 앞에 'not'이나 'never'를 쓴다.
  - It was an opportunity **not[never] to be** missed. 그것은 놓쳐서는 안 될 기회였다.

핵심 Check

2. 다음 괄호 안에서 알맞은 말을 고르시오.
  (1) Try (to not / not to) wake the baby up.
  (2) He pretended (not to / to never) notice that she was there.
  (3) I tried hard (don't to / never to) laugh.

Grammar 시험대비 기본평가

01 다음 중 어법상 바르지 <u>않은</u> 것은?

① This light is too dim to read by.
② The joke is too rude to repeat.
③ The computer in the classroom is too slow to use.
④ Is it so late to cancel my order?
⑤ He was so tired that he could not walk straight.

02 다음 중 어법상 바른 것을 <u>두 개</u> 고르시오.

① Be careful to not wake the baby.
② She begged him not to go.
③ To not smile was hard.
④ I was resolved to see not him.
⑤ He warned me not to be late.

03 다음 주어진 단어를 어법에 맞게 빈칸에 쓰시오.

(1) The gloves were too small _____. (wear)
(2) We were all too polite _____. (object)
(3) I'm so busy that I can't _____ to the meeting. (come)

04 괄호 안에 주어진 어휘를 이용하여 우리말을 영어로 옮기시오.

(1) 그녀는 뽑히지 못해서 실망했다.
   (disappointed, chosen, 7 단어)
   ➡ _____

(2) 너무 오래전이라 기억할 수 없어요.
   (it, long, ago, so, 9 단어)
   ➡ _____

(3) 그녀는 항상 너무 바빠 들어 줄 시간이 없었다.
   (busy, listen, to, 7 단어)
   ➡ _____

(4) 그녀가 친절하게도 우리에게 밥을 사 주었다.
   (buy, kind, a meal, to, 9 단어)
   ➡ _____

01 다음 대화의 빈칸에 들어갈 말로 가장 적절한 것은?

> A: Let's go swimming.
> B: Sorry, but I can't. I am _____ to go swimming.

① busy
② really busy
③ very busy
④ so busy
⑤ too busy

02 다음 중 어법상 자연스러운 것은?

① Anne asked me not waited for her.
② She studied hard to fail not the math exam.
③ The teacher warned us not use our cell phone in class.
④ A lot of young people in the country choose not to marry.
⑤ The doctor told me not smoking.

03 주어진 문장과 같은 의미의 문장은?

> She was so lucky that she could be chosen for the team.

① She was too lucky to be chosen for the team.
② She was too lucky for being chosen for the team.
③ She was lucky enough to be chosen for the team.
④ She was lucky and she was chosen for the team.
⑤ She was very lucky being chosen for the team.

서답형

04 다음 괄호 안에서 알맞은 말을 고르시오.

(1) Eddie was too sick (to go / going) to school yesterday.
(2) The desk was (too / so) heavy for me to move alone.
(3) Micky begged his mom (not to / to not) punish him.
(4) Can you promise (never to / to never) repeat that?

05 다음 우리말을 영어로 바르게 옮긴 것을 모두 고르시오.

> 그 아이들은 콘서트 내내 앉아 있기에는 너무 어리다.

① The children are too young to sit through a concert.
② The children are so young that they can't sit through a concert.
③ The children are so young that they can sit through a concert.
④ The children are too young that they can't sit through a concert.
⑤ The children are young enough to sit through a concert.

06 다음 중 'not'이 들어갈 위치로 알맞은 것은?

> In the library, ① we ② need ③ to be careful ④ to make ⑤ any noise.

①   ②   ③   ④   ⑤

서답형

07 다음 문장에서 어법상 어색한 부분을 바르게 고치시오.

(1) It was too rough for us to sailing that night.

_____ ➡ _____

(2) I was too excited that I couldn't even eat my dinner.

_____ ➡ _____

(3) I was foolish enough believe what Jeff told me.

_____ ➡ _____

(4) I told him to never be late for meetings again.

_____ ➡ _____

(5) We have decided to pursue not the matter.

_____ ➡ _____

서답형

08 다음 문장과 같은 의미의 문장을 쓰시오.

I am too shy to sing in front of many people.

➡ _____

_____

09 다음 우리말을 영어로 바르게 옮긴 것을 고르시오.

Brian은 버스를 놓치지 않기 위해서 빠르게 달렸다.

① Brian ran fast to miss the bus.

② Brian ran fast to not miss the bus.

③ Brian ran fast not to miss the bus.

④ Brian didn't run fast to miss the bus.

⑤ Brian didn't run fast not to miss the bus.

10 다음 빈칸에 들어갈 말로 가장 적절한 것은?

My brother was too young _____ that horror movie.

① seeing
② to see
③ to seeing
④ that he could see
⑤ that he couldn't see

중요

11 다음 두 문장이 같은 의미가 되도록 빈칸에 들어갈 말로 알맞은 것은?

The man is holding the umbrella not to get wet.
= The man is holding the umbrella _____ get wet.

① enough not to
② too to not
③ so not to
④ as to not
⑤ so as not to

서답형

12 다음 문장을 같은 의미의 문장으로 바꿔 쓰시오.

(1) The cellphone was too expensive for me to buy.

➡ _____

_____

(2) The ice is too thin to bear your weight.

➡ _____

_____

(3) The rope was long enough to reach the ground.

➡ _____

_____

(4) She is healthy enough to travel.

➡ _____

_____

13 다음 빈칸에 알맞은 것을 고르시오.

> We talked quietly so as _____ wake the baby.

① not to ② to not
③ to ④ not
⑤ at

14 다음 중 빈칸에 들어갈 말이 바르게 짝지어진 것은?

> • You knew that you were _____ far behind to win a medal.
> • From now on, _____ let it happen again, I will always check what day it is.

① enough – to not
② too – not to
③ so – to
④ too – not to
⑤ enough – to not

15 그림을 보고 주어진 문장의 빈칸을 괄호 안의 어휘를 이용하여 알맞게 채우시오.

(1) He drove _____ with the car coming toward him. (fast, avoid, collide, to)

(2) When driving, be careful _____ a car accident. (cause)

16 다음 문장의 빈칸에 들어갈 말로 어법상 올바른 것을 고르시오.

> I told him a big secret and asked _____.

① him not tell anybody
② him telling not anybody
③ him not telling anybody
④ him to not tell anybody
⑤ him not to tell anybody

17 다음 우리말을 10 단어의 영어로 옮길 때, 4 번째와 7 번째로 오는 단어를 바르게 묶은 것은?

> 내 동생은 너무 어려서 음식을 스스로 먹을 수 없다.

① too – to ② too – eat
③ enough – to ④ enough – eat
⑤ enough – food

18 다음 밑줄 친 부분을 부정하여 문장을 다시 쓰시오.

> My sister went to Japan to open a restaurant, to study Japanese.

➡ _____

19 다음 빈칸에 알맞은 말을 고르시오.

> The text is too long for me to read.
> = The text is _____ _____ _____ _____ _____ read it.

① too long that I can't
② too long that I can
③ so long that I can't
④ so long that I can
⑤ such long that I can

01 다음 문장을 that을 이용하여 바꿔 쓰시오.

(1) This computer is too slow to surf the web.
➡ _____

_____

(2) Boris was too nervous to give a speech.
➡ _____

_____

(3) The woman was kind enough to help the old lady.
➡ _____

_____

(4) The cable is long enough to reach the socket.
➡ _____

_____

(5) Your computer is too slow to use.
➡ _____

_____

02 괄호 안에 주어진 어휘를 이용하여 우리말을 영어로 옮기시오.

(1) 이 TV는 너무 커서 나 혼자서는 들 수 없다.
(big, carry, this TV, on my own, to)
➡ _____

_____

(2) Susie는 너무 느려서 Mike를 따라잡을 수 없었다. (slow, catch up with, to)
➡ _____

_____

(3) 그 가방은 너무 작아서 그 책들을 담을 수 없다. (small, the bag, put, so, in)
➡ _____

_____

03 다음 두 문장을 해석하고 그 차이를 서술하시오.

(1) I didn't tell him to go.
(2) I told him not to go.

➡ 해석: (1) _____
(2) _____

차이: _____

_____

04 다음 우리말을, (a) to를 이용하여 (b) that을 이용하여 영작하시오.

(1) 그 닭튀김은 너무 매워서 먹을 수가 없다. (eat, the fried chicken, spicy)
(a) _____
(b) _____

(2) 그 질문들은 답하기에 너무 어렵다. (answer, the questions, difficult)
(a) _____
(b) _____

(3) 그는 자동차 한 대도 충분히 들어올릴 정도로 힘이 세요. (a car, strong, lift)
(a) _____
(b) _____

(4) 인쇄물이 충분히 선명해서 읽을 수 있었어. (read, the print, clear)
(a) _____
(b) _____

05 빈칸을 채워 다음 표지판이 의미하는 바를 완성하시오.

We ask you _____ your mobile phone here.

➡ _____

---

06 to부정사를 이용하여 주어진 두 문장을 한 문장으로 연결하시오.

(1) • I run very slowly.
 • I can't finish the race within the limited amount of time given.

 ➡ _____
 _____

(2) • This coat is too big.
 • So it can't fit you.

 ➡ _____

(3) • I can't read the text.
 • It's because the text is so long.

 ➡ _____

(4) • The man is very strong.
 • So he can move the rock.

 ➡ _____

(5) • She can make a good decision.
 • It's because she is very wise.

 ➡ _____

(6) • The dress is so beautiful.
 • You can wear it at the party.

 ➡ _____
 _____

---

07 다음 두 문장이 같은 뜻을 갖도록 빈칸을 알맞게 채우시오.

(1) She said to me, "Please don't make a noise."
 = She asked me _____.

(2) The officer told us, "Do not run."
 = The officer ordered us _____.

---

08 주어진 형용사와 to부정사를 활용하여 빈칸을 알맞게 채우시오.

smart / young / weak / good

(1) The girl is _____ ride a roller coaster.

(2) I think you are _____ carry those bags at a time.

(3) Don is not _____ be our leader.

(4) Consumers are _____ to know that.

---

09 다음 문장과 같은 의미의 문장을 쓰시오.

(1) Henry was too busy to answer the phone.
 ➡ _____
 _____

(2) The car is too old for me to drive.
 ➡ _____
 _____

(3) A boy under 15 is too young to watch the movie.
 ➡ _____
 _____

(4) The film was interesting enough for me to watch again.
 ➡ _____
 _____

Reading

The Last Runner

The last runner finished the race more than an hour before. "There
will be no more runners coming," the officials decided. They removed
the tape at the finish line and started to prepare for the closing
ceremony for the 1996 Atlanta Summer Olympics in the United States.

Someone shouted, "Look! There comes another runner!" A runner
was just entering the stadium, but there was something wrong with
his legs. Still, he kept going toward the finish line. The band and
the volunteers stopped their preparations for the closing ceremony.

All eyes were on the runner.

Suddenly, the band started playing celebration music, and the
volunteers cheered. "Go! Go! Go for it!" Two volunteers ran to the
finish line with a tape. Finally, the runner ran through the tape and then
fell to the ground. His name was Abdul Baser Wasiqi. He was from
Afghanistan.

official 관료, 공무원, 경기 임원
remove 제거하다
prepare 준비하다
ceremony 식, 의식
stadium 경기장
toward ~ 쪽으로, ~을 향하여
celebration 축하
cheer 환호성을 지르다, 환호하다

확인문제

● 다음 문장이 본문의 내용과 일치하면 T, 일치하지 않으면 F를 쓰시오.

1   People thought the last runner finished the race over an hour before. ☐

2   The officials started to prepare for the opening ceremony for the 1996 Atlanta
    Summer Olympics in the United States. ☐

3   A runner was just entering the stadium, but there was something wrong with his
    legs. ☐

4   The band and the volunteers kept preparing for the closing ceremony. ☐

5   Two volunteers ran to the finish line with a tape. ☐

6   The runner fell to the ground, so he couldn't run through the tape. ☐

Reporters came up to Wasiqi and started asking him questions.
= approached

Reporter: What happened to you?
happen to ~ ((일·사건 등이) 일어나다, 생기다)

Wasiqi: I injured my leg during a practice run. The injury got worse
(사고로) 부상을 입히다(타동사)　　　　　　　　　get/become/grow+비교급: 더 ~해지다
during the race, but I couldn't give up.
= abandon: 포기하다

Reporter: Why not? You knew that you were too far behind to win a
too ... to부정사: 너무 …해서 ~할 수 없다
medal.

Wasiqi: I am the only athlete here representing Afghanistan. There was
현재분사: 대표하는
no way I could give up.

Reporter: Afghanistan is still at war, isn't it?
= That's the reason that

Wasiqi: Yes, we have been at war for 16 years. That's why we were not
현재완료 계속적 용법　That's why: 그래서 ~하게 된 것이다, why 뒤에는 어떤 행동의 결과가 되는 내용이 옴.
able to send athletes to the Barcelona Olympics four years ago.
I was sad for my country back then when I could see no Afghan
athletes in the opening ceremony.

Reporter: Were you running marathons then?
과거진행형 시제: 과거 특정 시점에 진행되고 있던 일을 묻고 있음.

Wasiqi: No. I started running after Barcelona. I ran in lots of races.
Finally I won a marathon in Germany. As a result, I was able to
win: ~에서 이기다(타동사), 전치사 없이 바로 목적어를 취한다.　　그 결과
come to Atlanta.

Reporter: How do you feel now?

Wasiqi: I am proud of myself and proud to be from Afghanistan. For me
to부정사의 부사적 용법(감정의 원인)
and my country, it was important not to give up. I didn't come
to부정사의 부정은 to 앞에 not을 쓴다.
here to win. For me, it was enough to be here and to finish the
to부정사의 부사적 용법(목적)
race.

reporter 기자, 리포터
injure 부상을 입히다
athlete 운동선수
represent 대표하다
give up 포기하다
at war 전쟁 중인
marathon 마라톤
be proud of ~을 자랑스러워하다

확인문제

● 다음 문장이 본문의 내용과 일치하면 T, 일치하지 않으면 F를 쓰시오.

1 Wasiqi injured his leg during a practice run. ☐

2 Wasiqi didn't know that he was too far behind to win a medal. ☐

3 Wasiqi was the only athlete there representing Afghanistan. ☐

4 Afghanistan was not able to send athletes to the Atlanta Olympics. ☐

5 Wasiqi won a marathon in Germany. ☐

6 For Wasiqi and his country, winning was very important. ☐

● 우리말을 참고하여 빈칸에 알맞은 말을 쓰시오.

1 The _____ Runner

2 The last runner finished the race _____ _____ an hour before.

3 "There will be _____ _____ runners _____," the officials decided.

4 They removed the tape at the finish line and started to _____ _____ the _____ _____ for the 1996 Atlanta Summer Olympics in the United States.

5 Someone shouted, "Look! _____ _____ _____ runner!"

6 A runner was just entering the stadium, but there was _____ _____ with his legs.

7 _____, he _____ _____ toward the finish line.

8 The band and the volunteers _____ _____ _____ for the closing ceremony.

9 _____ _____ _____ the runner.

10 Suddenly, the band started playing _____ _____, and the volunteers _____.

11 "Go! Go! _____ _____ _____!"

12 Two volunteers ran to the finish line _____ _____ _____.

13 _____, the runner _____ _____ the tape and then _____ _____ the ground.

14 _____ _____ was Abdul Baser Wasiqi.

15 He _____ _____ Afghanistan.

16 Reporters _____ _____ _____ Wasiqi and started asking him questions.

17 **Reporter:** What _____ _____ you?

18 **Wasiqi:** I injured my leg _____ _____ _____ _____.

1	마지막 주자
2	마지막 주자가 한 시간도 더 전에 경주를 끝냈다.
3	"더 들어오는 선수는 없을 겁니다."라고 경기 임원들은 결론을 내렸다.
4	그들은 결승선에서 테이프를 걷어내고 1996년 미국 애틀랜타 하계 올림픽의 폐막식을 준비하기 시작했다.
5	누군가가 외쳤다. "봐! 저기 또 다른 선수가 온다!"
6	한 선수가 경기장으로 막 들어오고 있었는데, 그의 다리에 이상이 있었다.
7	그러나 그는 계속 결승선을 향해 움직였다.
8	밴드와 자원봉사자들이 폐막식을 위한 준비를 멈추었다.
9	모든 눈들이 그 선수에게 머물렀다.
10	갑자기 밴드가 축하 음악을 연주하기 시작했고, 자원봉사자들이 환호했다.
11	"달려! 달려! 잘해라!"
12	두 명의 자원봉사자가 테이프를 가지고 결승선으로 달려갔다.
13	결국, 그 주자는 테이프를 통과해 달렸고, 바닥에 쓰러졌다.
14	그의 이름은 압둘 베사르 와시키였다.
15	그는 아프가니스탄 출신이었다.
16	기자들은 와시키에게 가서 그에게 질문을 하기 시작했다.
17	리포터: 당신에게 무슨 일이 있었나요?
18	와시키: 저는 연습 경기를 하던 중 다리를 다쳤습니다.

19 The injury _____ _____ during the race, but I couldn't give up.

20 **Reporter:** _____ _____ ?

21 You knew that you were too _____ _____ to win a medal.

22 **Wasiqi:** I am the only athlete here _____ _____ .

23 There was _____ _____ I could give up.

24 **Reporter:** Afghanistan is still _____ _____ , _____ _____ ?

25 **Wasiqi:** Yes, we _____ _____ at war for 16 years.

26 _____ _____ we were not able to send athletes to the Barcelona Olympics four years ago.

27 I _____ _____ _____ my country _____ _____ when I could see no Afghan athletes in the opening ceremony.

28 **Reporter:** _____ you _____ marathons then?

29 **Wasiqi:** No. I _____ _____ after Barcelona.

30 I ran in _____ _____ races.

31 Finally I _____ _____ _____ in Germany.

32 _____ _____ _____ , I was able to come to Atlanta.

33 **Reporter:** _____ do you feel now?

34 **Wasiqi:** I am proud of _____ and proud _____ _____ _____ Afghanistan.

35 For me and my country, it was important _____ _____ _____ _____ .

36 I didn't come here _____ _____ .

37 For me, _____ _____ _____ to be here and to finish the race.

19 경기 중에 제 상처는 점점 더 심각해졌지만, 저는 포기할 수 없었습니다.

20 리포터: 왜 포기할 수 없었죠?

21 당신은 메달을 얻기에 너무도 크게 뒤떨어져 있었다는 것을 알고 있었잖아요.

22 와시키: 저는 아프가니스탄을 대표하는 유일한 선수입니다.

23 제가 포기할 수 있는 방법은 없었습니다.

24 리포터: 아프가니스탄은 여전히 전쟁 중입니다, 맞나요?

25 와시키: 네, 우리나라는 16년째 전쟁 중입니다.

26 그것이 우리가 4년 전 바르셀로나 올림픽에 선수들을 보낼 수 없었던 이유입니다.

27 저는 개회식에서 아프가니스탄 선수를 볼 수 없었던 그 당시, 제 나라에 대해 매우 슬펐습니다.

28 리포터: 그 당시 마라톤을 뛰고 있었나요?

29 와시키: 아니요. 저는 바르셀로나 올림픽 이후에 달리기를 시작했습니다.

30 저는 많은 경주에서 뛰었어요.

31 마침내 독일 마라톤에서 우승했지요.

32 그 결과 애틀랜타에 올 수 있었어요.

33 리포터: 지금은 기분이 어떠신가요?

34 와시키: 저는 제 자신이, 그리고 제가 아프가니스탄 출신인 것이 자랑스러워요.

35 저와 제 조국을 위해서는, 포기하지 않는 것이 중요했어요.

36 저는 이곳에 이기러 온 것이 아닙니다.

37 제가 여기에 있고 경주를 끝마친 것으로 충분합니다.

● 우리말을 참고하여 본문을 영작하시오.

1 마지막 주자
➡ _____

2 마지막 주자가 한 시간도 더 전에 경주를 끝냈다.
➡ _____

3 "더 들어오는 선수는 없을 겁니다."라고 경기 임원들은 결론을 내렸다.
➡ _____

4 그들은 결승선에서 테이프를 걷어내고 1996년 미국 애틀랜타 하계 올림픽의 폐막식을 준비하기 시작했다.
➡ _____

5 누군가가 외쳤다. "봐! 저기 또 다른 선수가 온다!"
➡ _____

6 한 선수가 경기장으로 막 들어오고 있었는데, 그의 다리에 이상이 있었다.
➡ _____

7 그러나 그는 계속 결승선을 향해 움직였다.
➡ _____

8 밴드와 자원봉사자들이 폐막식을 위한 준비를 멈추었다.
➡ _____

9 모든 눈들이 그 선수에게 머물렀다.
➡ _____

10 갑자기 밴드가 축하 음악을 연주하기 시작했고, 자원봉사자들이 환호했다.
➡ _____

11 "달려! 달려! 잘해라!"
➡ _____

12 두 명의 자원봉사자가 테이프를 가지고 결승선으로 달려갔다.
➡ _____

13 결국, 그 주자는 테이프를 통과해 달렸고, 바닥에 쓰러졌다.
➡ _____

14 그의 이름은 압둘 베사르 와시키였다.
➡ _____

15 그는 아프가니스탄 출신이었다.
➡ _____

16 기자들은 와시키에게 가서 그에게 질문을 하기 시작했다.
➡ _____

17 리포터: 당신에게 무슨 일이 있었나요?
➡ _____

18 와시키: 저는 연습 경기를 하던 중 다리를 다쳤습니다.
➡ _____

19 경기 중에 제 상처는 점점 더 심각해졌지만, 저는 포기할 수 없었습니다.

➡ _____

20 리포터: 왜 포기할 수 없었죠?

➡ _____

21 당신은 메달을 얻기에 너무도 크게 뒤떨어져 있었다는 것을 알고 있었잖아요.

➡ _____

22 와시키: 저는 아프가니스탄을 대표하는 유일한 선수입니다.

➡ _____

23 제가 포기할 수 있는 방법은 없었습니다.

➡ _____

24 리포터: 아프가니스탄은 여전히 전쟁 중입니다, 맞나요?

➡ _____

25 와시키: 네, 우리나라는 16년째 전쟁 중입니다.

➡ _____

26 그것이 우리가 4년 전 바르셀로나 올림픽에 선수들을 보낼 수 없었던 이유입니다.

➡ _____

27 저는 개회식에서 아프가니스탄 선수를 볼 수 없었던 그 당시, 제 나라에 대해 매우 슬펐습니다.

➡ _____

28 리포터: 그 당시 마라톤을 뛰고 있었나요?

➡ _____

29 와시키: 아니요. 저는 바르셀로나 올림픽 이후에 달리기를 시작했습니다.

➡ _____

30 저는 많은 경주에서 뛰었어요.

➡ _____

31 마침내 독일 마라톤에서 우승했지요.

➡ _____

32 그 결과 애틀랜타에 올 수 있었어요.

➡ _____

33 리포터: 지금은 기분이 어떠신가요?

➡ _____

34 와시키: 저는 제 자신이, 그리고 제가 아프가니스탄 출신인 것이 자랑스러워요.

➡ _____

35 저와 제 조국을 위해서는, 포기하지 않는 것이 중요했어요.

➡ _____

36 저는 이곳에 이기러 온 것이 아닙니다.

➡ _____

37 제가 여기에 있고 경주를 끝마친 것으로 충분합니다.

➡ _____

[01~03] 다음 글을 읽고 물음에 답하시오.

The last runner finished the race more than an hour before. "(A)There will be no more runners coming," the officials decided. They removed the tape at the finish line and started to prepare ___ⓐ___ the closing ceremony ___ⓑ___ the 1996 Atlanta Summer Olympics in the United States.

01 위 글의 빈칸 ⓐ와 ⓑ에 공통으로 들어갈 전치사를 고르시오.

① to ② at
③ with ④ for
⑤ on

서답형

02 위 글의 밑줄 친 문장 (A)에서 coming 앞에 생략된 두 단어를 쓰시오.

➡ _____

서답형

03 Why did the officials decide that there would be no more runners coming? Answer in English beginning with "Because".

➡ _____

_____

[04~06] 다음 글을 읽고 물음에 답하시오.

Reporters came up to Wasiqi and started asking him questions.
Reporter: What ⓐhappened to you?
Wasiqi: I injured my leg during a practice run. The injury got worse during the race, but I couldn't give up.
Reporter: Why not? You knew that you were too far behind to win a medal.

Wasiqi: I am the only athlete here representing Afghanistan. There was no way I could give up.
Reporter: Afghanistan is still at war, isn't it?
Wasiqi: Yes, we have been at war for 16 years. ⓑThat's because we were not able to send athletes to the Barcelona Olympics four years ago. I was sad for my country back then when I could see no Afghan athletes in the opening ceremony.

04 위 글의 밑줄 친 ⓐhappened to와 같은 의미로 쓰인 것을 모두 고르시오.

① She happened to be out when we called.
② Something must have happened to him.
③ I happened to see him on the street.
④ He happened to hear it.
⑤ Yesterday something strange happened to her.

서답형

05 위 글의 밑줄 친 ⓑ에서 어법상 틀린 부분을 찾아 고치시오.

_____ ➡ _____

서답형

06 다음 문장에서 위 글의 내용과 다른 부분을 찾아서 고치시오.

Wasiqi injured his leg during the race.

_____ ➡ _____ 또는

_____ ➡ _____

[07~09] 다음 글을 읽고 물음에 답하시오.

Someone shouted, "Look! There comes another runner!" A runner was just entering the stadium, but there was something wrong with his legs. Still, he kept going toward the finish line. The band and the volunteers stopped their preparations for the closing ceremony. All eyes were on the runner.

ⓐSuddenly, the band started playing celebration music, and the volunteers cheered. "Go! Go! Go for it!" Two volunteers ran to the finish line with a tape. Finally, the runner ran through the tape and then fell to the ground. His name was Abdul Baser Wasiqi. He was from Afghanistan.

07 다음 중 위 글의 분위기로 가장 알맞은 것을 <u>모두</u> 고르시오.

① shameful   ② touching
③ moving   ④ embarrassing
⑤ disappointing

서답형

08 위 글의 밑줄 친 ⓐSuddenly와 바꿔 쓸 수 있는 말을 쓰시오.

➡ _____

09 According to the passage, which is NOT true?

① There was something wrong with Wasiqi's legs.
② The band and the volunteers stopped preparing for the closing ceremony.
③ All the people in the stadium watched Wasiqi.
④ Wasiqi ran toward the finish line but fell to the ground before it.
⑤ Abdul Baser Wasiqi was from Afghanistan.

[10~13] 다음 글을 읽고 물음에 답하시오.

Finally, the runner ran through the tape and then fell to the ground. His name was Abdul Baser Wasiqi. He was from Afghanistan.

Reporters came up to Wasiqi and (A)<u>started asking him questions</u>.

Reporter: What happened to you?

Wasiqi: I injured my leg during a practice run. The injury got worse during the race, but I couldn't give up.

Reporter: Why not? You knew that you were too far behind to win a medal.

Wasiqi: I am the only athlete here ___ⓐ___ Afghanistan. There was no way I could give up.

Reporter: Afghanistan is still at war, isn't it?

Wasiqi: Yes, we (B)<u>have been</u> at war for 16 years. That's why we were not able to send athletes to the Barcelona Olympics four years ago. I was sad for my country back then when I could see no Afghan athletes in the opening ceremony.

서답형

10 위 글의 빈칸 ⓐ에 represent를 알맞은 형태로 쓰시오.

서답형 ➡ _____

11 위 글의 밑줄 친 (A)와 같은 뜻이 되도록 빈칸을 채우시오.

➡ started asking questions _____ him

12 위 글의 밑줄 친 (B)have been과 현재완료의 용법이 같은 것을 <u>모두</u> 고르시오.

① Have you ever <u>been</u> to Japan?
② She <u>has been</u> sick since last Friday.
③ I <u>have been</u> to the station to see my friend off.
④ I <u>have been</u> to Jeju Island three times.
⑤ He <u>has been</u> in his room for hours.

서답형

13 본문을 참조하여 다음 빈칸 (A)와 (B)에 알맞은 단어를 쓰시오. 단, (A)에는 interview를 알맞은 형태로 쓰시오.

> The reporters are having an interview with an (A)_____. He was Wasiqi, a marathon runner from Afghanistan. It can be said that he showed the spirit of Olympics by finishing the race without (B)_____ _____ in spite of the severe injury.

[14~15] 다음 글을 읽고 물음에 답하시오.

> **Reporter:** How do you feel now?
> **Wasiqi:** I am proud of myself and proud to be from Afghanistan. For me and my country, ⓐ포기하지 않는 것이 중요했어요. I didn't come here to win. For me, it was enough ⓑto be here and to finish the race.

서답형

14 위 글의 밑줄 친 ⓐ의 우리말에 맞게 가주어를 사용하여 7 단어로 영작하시오.

➡ _____

15 아래 〈보기〉에서 위 글의 밑줄 친 ⓑto be와 to부정사의 용법이 같은 것의 개수를 고르시오.

> ┌─── 보기 ───┐
> ① It is warm enough to be outside.
> ② It was good enough to be present at the party.
> ③ He was wise enough to be satisfied with the present.
> ④ It is strong enough to be used here.
> ⑤ I practiced hard enough to be far ahead of others.

① 1개 ② 2개 ③ 3개 ④ 4개 ⑤ 5개

[16~18] 다음 글을 읽고 물음에 답하시오.

> Someone shouted, "Look! There comes another runner!" A runner was just entering the stadium, but there was something wrong with his legs. ⓐStill, he kept going toward the finish line. The band and the volunteers stopped their preparations for the closing ceremony. All eyes were on the runner.
> Suddenly, the band started playing celebration music, and the volunteers cheered. "Go! Go! Go for it!" Two volunteers ran to the finish line with a tape. Finally, the runner ran through the tape and then fell to the ground. His name was Abdul Baser Wasiqi. He was from Afghanistan.

16 위 글의 밑줄 친 ⓐStill과 같은 의미로 쓰인 것을 고르시오.

① Do you still live at the same address?
② The next day was still warmer.
③ Keep still while I brush your hair.
④ The weather was cold and wet. Still, we had a great time.
⑤ I wrote to them last month and I'm still waiting for a reply.

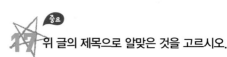

17 위 글의 제목으로 알맞은 것을 고르시오.

① The Last but the Most Impressive Runner
② Preparations for the Closing Ceremony
③ The Consideration of the Volunteers
④ The Band Playing Celebration Music
⑤ Alas! The Runner Fell to the Ground

18 Which question CANNOT be answered after reading the passage?

① What was wrong with Wasiqi when he was entering the stadium?

② Did the band and the volunteers keep preparing for the closing ceremony after Wasiqi entered the stadium?

③ What did the band and the volunteers do when they were watching Wasiqi?

④ What happened right after Wasiqi ran through the tape at the finish line?

⑤ How long did Wasiqi run?

[19~20] 다음 글을 읽고 물음에 답하시오.

Reporter: Were you running marathons then?

Wasiqi: No. I started running after Barcelona. I ran in lots of races. Finally I won a marathon in Germany. ___ⓐ___, I was able to come to Atlanta.

Reporter: How do you feel now?

Wasiqi: I am proud of myself and proud to be from Afghanistan. For me and my country, it was important not to give up. I didn't come here to win. For me, it was enough to be here and to finish the race.

19 위 글의 빈칸 ⓐ에 들어갈 알맞은 말을 고르시오.

① As a result ② However

③ Still ④ Whereas

⑤ For example

20 Which question CANNOT be answered after reading the passage?

① When did Wasiqi start running?

② How many races did Wasiqi participate in before he won a marathon in Germany?

③ How did Wasiqi feel at the time of the interview?

④ What was important for Wasiqi and his country?

⑤ Did Wasiqi come to Atlanta to win?

[21~23] 다음 글을 읽고 물음에 답하시오.

Someone shouted, "Look! (A)There comes the other runner!" A runner was just entering the stadium, but there was something wrong with his legs. Still, he kept going toward the finish line. The band and the volunteers stopped their preparations ___ⓐ___ the closing ceremony. (B)모든 눈들이 그 선수에게 머물렀다.

Suddenly, the band started playing celebration music, and the volunteers cheered. "Go! Go! Go for it!" Two volunteers ran to the finish line with a tape. Finally, the runner ran ___ⓑ___ the tape and then fell to the ground. His name was Abdul Baser Wasiqi. He was from Afghanistan.

21 위 글의 빈칸 ⓐ와 ⓑ에 들어갈 전치사가 바르게 짝지어진 것은?

ⓐ ⓑ ⓐ ⓑ

① for – from ② at – through

③ for – through ④ at – to

⑤ on – to

서답형

22 위 글의 밑줄 친 (A)에서 어법상 틀린 부분을 찾아 고치시오.

_____ ➡ _____

서답형

23 위 글의 밑줄 친 (B)의 우리말에 맞게 주어진 어휘를 이용하여 6 단어로 영작하시오.

all eyes

➡ _____

Reading **37**

[01~03] 다음 글을 읽고 물음에 답하시오.

The (A)[last / latest] runner finished the race ⓐmore than an hour before. "ⓑ더 들어오는 선수는 없을 겁니다," the officials decided. They (B)[installed / removed] the tape at the finish line and started to prepare for the (C)[closing / opening] ceremony for the 1996 Atlanta Summer Olympics in the United States.

01 위 글의 괄호 (A)~(C)에서 문맥상 알맞은 낱말을 골라 쓰시오.

➡ (A) _____ (B) _____ (C) _____

02 위 글의 밑줄 친 ⓐmore than과 바꿔 쓸 수 있는 한 단어를 쓰시오.

➡ _____

03 위 글의 밑줄 친 ⓑ의 우리말에 맞게 주어진 어휘를 이용하여 7 단어로 영작하시오.

there, no, coming

➡ _____

[04~06] 다음 글을 읽고 물음에 답하시오.

Someone shouted, "Look! There comes another runner!" A runner was just entering the stadium, but there was something wrong with his legs. Still, he kept ___ⓐ___ toward the finish line. The band and the volunteers stopped their preparations for the closing ceremony. All eyes were on the runner.

Suddenly, the band started playing celebration music, and the volunteers cheered. "Go! Go! _____ⓑ_____!" Two volunteers ran to the finish line with a tape. Finally, the runner

ran through the tape and then fell to the ground. His name was Abdul Baser Wasiqi. He was from Afghanistan.

04 위 글의 빈칸 ⓐ에 go를 알맞은 형태로 쓰시오.

➡ _____

05 위 글의 빈칸 ⓑ에 go를 포함하는 격려와 응원의 구호를 쓰시오. (세 단어)

➡ _____

06 다음 문장에서 위 글의 내용과 다른 부분을 찾아서 고치시오.

When Wasiqi entered the stadium, the band and the volunteers stopped to prepare for the closing ceremony.

_____ ➡ _____

[07~10] 다음 글을 읽고 물음에 답하시오.

Reporters came up to Wasiqi and started asking him questions.

Reporter: What happened to you?

Wasiqi: I injured my leg during a practice run. The injury got worse during the race, but I couldn't give up.

Reporter: Why not? You knew that (A)you were too far behind to win a medal.

Wasiqi: I am the only athlete here representing Afghanistan. There was no way I could give up.

Reporter: Afghanistan is still at war, ___ⓐ___?

Wasiqi: Yes, we have been at war for 16 years. That's why we were not able to send athletes to the Barcelona Olympics four years ago. I was sad for my country back then when I could see no Afghan athletes in the opening ceremony.

07 위 글의 빈칸 ⓐ에 들어갈 알맞은 부가의문문을 쓰시오.

➡ _____ _____

08 위 글의 밑줄 친 (A)를 복문으로 고치시오.

➡ _____

_____

09 Why couldn't Afghanistan send athletes to the Barcelona Olympics? Fill in the blanks with suitable words.

> Because Afghanistan had been _____ _____ for 12 years at that time.

10 본문의 내용과 일치하도록 다음 빈칸 (A)와 (B)에 알맞은 단어를 쓰시오.

> Even though Wasiqi knew it was impossible for him to win a medal, he couldn't (A)_____ _____ because he was the only athlete there (B)_____ _____.

[11~14] 다음 글을 읽고 물음에 답하시오.

Reporter: Were you running marathons then?
Wasiqi: No. I started running after Barcelona. I ran in lots of races. ⓐFinally I won a marathon in Germany. As a result, I was able to come to Atlanta.

Reporter: How do you feel now?
Wasiqi: ⓑI am proud of myself and proud to be from Afghanistan. For me and my country, it was important not to give up. I didn't come here to win. For me, it was enough to be here and to finish the race.

11 위 글의 밑줄 친 ⓐFinally와 바꿔 쓸 수 있는 말을 쓰시오.

➡ _____

12 위 글의 밑줄 친 ⓑ를 다음과 같이 바꿔 쓸 때 빈칸에 공통으로 들어갈 알맞은 단어를 쓰시오.

> ➡ I take _____ in myself and _____ in being from Afghanistan.

13 How was Wasiqi able to come to Atlanta? Fill in the blanks (A) and (B) with suitable words.

> After Wasiqi started running, he ran in (A)_____ races and finally won a marathon in (B)_____, which led him to come to Atlanta.

14 본문의 내용과 일치하도록 다음 빈칸 (A)와 (B)에 알맞은 단어를 쓰시오.

> Wasiqi was proud of himself and proud to be an Afghan athlete. For him and his country, not (A)_____ _____ was important. He didn't come to Atlanta (B)_____ _____, and it was sufficient for him to take part in the Atlanta Olympics and finish the race.

Communication Task

A: Have you heard of Jain Kim?
"~에 대하여 들어 본 적이 있니?"(경험을 나타내는 현재완료)

B: Yes, I have. She's a famous rock climber.
현재완료에 대한 대답은 have/has를 사용하여 대답한다.

A: How was she able to become a famous rock climber?

B: She trained hard for five hours every day.
시간을 포함하는 일반적인 기간은 전치사 for를 사용한다.

구문해설 • **rock climber:** 암벽 등반가 • **train:** 훈련하다

해석

A: 너는 김자인에 대하여 들어본 적이 있니?

B: 그래. 그녀는 유명한 암벽 등반가야.

A: 어떻게 그녀가 유명한 암벽 등반가가 될 수 있었지?

B: 그녀는 5년 동안 매일 열심히 훈련했어.

Language in Use B

Last night, I set my clock for 8 o'clock not to be late for school today.
to부정사의 부정

Because it is a long way to my school, it is important not to miss the bus.
비인칭주어   가주어   to부정사의 부정

Without having breakfast, I quickly left the house and went to the bus stop.
전치사 다음에 나온 동명사

Surprisingly, there was nobody. Then, I remembered that today was Saturday.
nobody가 주어이므로 단수 동사   명사절을 이끄는 접속사

From now on, not to let it happen again, I will always check what day it is.
to부정사의 부정 사역동사 let의 목적격보어(동사원형)   간접의문문

구문해설 • **set:** (시계를) 맞추다 • **surprisingly:** 놀랄 정도로, 놀랍게도, 의외로

어젯밤에 나는 오늘 학교에 늦지 않으려고 시계를 8시에 맞춰 놓았다. 학교까지는 길이 멀기 때문에, 버스를 놓치지 않는 것이 중요하다. 아침도 먹지 않고 나는 빠르게 집을 떠나 버스 정거장으로 갔다. 놀랍게도 아무도 없었다. 그때, 나는 오늘이 토요일임을 기억했다. 이제부터 그런 일이 다시 일어나지 않도록, 나는 항상 무슨 요일인지 확인하겠다.

Writing Workshop Step 3

I Have a Goal to Win the Singing Contest

I want to win the school singing contest. I love singing, and I think I
winning(×)   = to sing

have a good voice. However, I am too shy to sing in front of many people.
= I am so shy that I can't sing in front of many people

Not to be nervous during the contest, I will practice singing in front of my
= In order that I may not be nervous   to sing(×)

class first.

구문해설 • **goal:** 목표 • **singing contest:** 노래 대회 • **shy:** 수줍어[부끄러워]하는
• **nervous:** 불안해[초조해/두려워] 하는 • **practice:** 연습하다

나는 노래 대회에서 이기려는 목표를 가지고 있다

나는 학교 노래 대회에서 이기고 싶다. 나는 노래 부르는 것을 좋아하고 목소리가 좋다고 생각한다. 그러나, 나는 너무 수줍어서 많은 사람들 앞에서 노래를 부를 수 없다. 대회 도중에 불안해하지 않기 위해서 먼저 학급 친구들 앞에서 노래 부르기를 연습할 것이다.

Words & Expressions

01 다음 두 문장에 공통으로 알맞은 것을 고르시오.

> • Come _____ to the front when I call your names.
> • He chose not to give _____ hope.

① at   ② on   ③ up
④ by   ⑤ in

02 다음 빈칸에 들어가기에 적절한 단어의 형태를 고르시오.

> All the _____ will be done soon.

① prepare   ② prepared
③ prepares   ④ to prepare
⑤ preparation

03 다음 영영풀이에 해당하는 단어를 고르시오.

> a person who plays sports well

① athlete   ② driver
③ trainer   ④ developer
⑤ scientist

04 다음 밑줄 친 부분의 우리말 뜻이 알맞지 <u>않은</u> 것은?

① Why did the woman <u>injure</u> her knee? (부상을 입다)
② This must not <u>happen</u> again. (일어나다)
③ Will you <u>join</u> us? (보호하다)
④ I will <u>invent</u> a robot. (발명하다)
⑤ Don't <u>knock</u> the door. (두드리다)

Conversation

[05~06] 다음 우리말과 일치하도록 빈칸에 알맞은 말을 쓰시오.

05
> B: _____ (노래 대회 우승자에 대해 들어 본 적 있니?) (hear of, singing contest, 10 words)
> G: No, I haven't. Who won?
> B: The winner is Vintop, who wrote all of his own songs.

➡ _____

06
> B: _____ (어떻게 그녀가 영어를 잘할 수 있었니?) (able, speak, so, 9 words)
> G: She learned English by watching many Hollywood movies.

➡ _____

07 다음 대화의 빈칸 (가)에 들어가기에 적절한 것은?

> B: How was Thomas Edison able to invent so many things?
> G: Many people think that he invented things on his first try, but that's not true.
> B: Oh, really?
> G: Yes. Whenever he invented something, he experimented many times.
> B: Maybe _____ (가) _____ so many people admire him.

① that's the way   ② this is the place
③ that's why   ④ that's where
⑤ this is because

[08~10] 다음 대화를 읽고 물음에 답하시오.

G: Have you heard of Eui Hyun Sin, the skier?

B: No. Who is he?

G: He's a Paralympian skier. He won the first gold medal for Korea in the 2018 Winter Paralympics.

B: Wow! That's great.

G: (A)그는 20대 초반에 차 사고를 당하고 다리를 다쳤어.

B: How was he able to become a skier?

G: After his accident, he tried several different sports to get better. Then he became especially ___(B)___ in skiing.

B: Skiing is not easy. Many people are good at skiing.

G: That's why he's so respected.

08 (A)의 우리말에 해당하는 영어 문장으로 적절한 것은?

① He hurt his legs in his early twenties and in a car accident.

② He was and hurt his legs in a car accident in his early twenties.

③ He was his legs and hurt in a car accident in his early twenties

④ He in a car accident was in his early twenties hurt and his legs.

⑤ He was in a car accident in his early twenties and hurt his legs.

09 빈칸 (B)에 들어가기에 적절한 것은?

① surprised ② frightened

③ interested ④ amazed

⑤ increased

10 위 대화에서 내용상 어색한 부분이 있는 문장을 찾아 자연스러운 문장으로 고쳐 쓰시오.

_____ ➡

_____

[11~13] 다음 대화를 읽고 물음에 답하시오.

B: Sora, (A)have you heard about the fire last night?

G: Yes, I heard that there was a big fire in a building nearby. Was anybody hurt?

B: No, one man saved ten people who were in the building.

G: Oh, really? How was he able to save so many people?

B: He ___(B)___ on every door to tell people to leave the building.

G: Wow, that's amazing!

11 (A)와 같은 의미의 문장으로 적절하지 않은 것은? (2개)

① have you told about the fire last night?

② have you been told about the fire last night?

③ do you know about the fire last night?

④ are you aware of the fire last night?

⑤ are you heard about the fire last night?

12 빈칸 (B)에 들어가기에 적절한 것은?

① painted ② fixed

③ locked ④ drew

⑤ knocked

13 위 대화를 통해서 알 수 있는 것이 아닌 것은?

① There was a big fire last night.

② The boy has heard about the big fire.

③ The girl didn't know how many people were saved.

④ The man told people to leave the building.

⑤ One fireman saved ten people.

Grammar

14 다음 중 나머지 넷과 의미가 <u>다른</u> 문장은?

① I was too slow to win the race.

② I was so slow but I could win the race.

③ I was so slow that I couldn't win the race.

④ I couldn't win the race because I was so slow.

⑤ I was very slow, so I couldn't win the race.

15 다음 중 어법상 옳은 문장은?

① Some people told her to become not a professional.

② I read the newspaper every morning in not order to get behind the times.

③ The teacher asked us to not make any sound during the class.

④ I hurried not so as to be late for the meeting.

⑤ The weather is getting colder, so you need to be careful not to catch a cold.

16 주어진 단어를 활용하여 다음 우리말을 영어로 쓰시오.

> 나는 나의 학급 친구들을 방해하지 않기 위해 조용히 책을 읽었다. (quietly, disturb, 10 words)

➡ _____

17 다음 중 <u>어색한</u> 것을 고르시오.

① The smartphone was cheap enough to buy.

→ The smartphone was very cheap, so I could buy it.

② The puppy was very small, so she could hold it in one hand.

→ The puppy was so small that she could hold it in one hand.

③ The box was too heavy for me to carry.

→ The box was so heavy that I couldn't carry.

④ Jim is so rich that he can buy the luxurious car.

→ Jim is rich enough to buy the luxurious car.

⑤ Mike is very poor. He can't buy the ring for his wife.

→ Mike is too poor to buy the ring for his wife.

18 다음 밑줄 친 부분을 부정하여 문장을 다시 쓰시오.

> They tried hard so as <u>to fail</u> the entrance exam.

➡ _____

_____

19 다음 문장의 빈칸에 들어갈 알맞은 것은?

> It's too hot to take a long walk.
> = It's _____ we can't take a long walk.

① very hot that　　② hot enough that

③ so hot that　　④ not hot enough to

⑤ too hot that

20 다음 두 문장을 지시에 맞게 하나의 문장으로 쓰시오.

> • We were very late.
> • We couldn't catch the last train.

(1) to부정사를 활용하여

➡ _____

(2) that을 활용하여

➡ _____

21 다음 문장의 빈칸에 들어갈 올바른 것을 고르시오.

> Linda got a terrible cold, so she asked her husband _____.

① not opening the window
② not to opening the window
③ to not open the window
④ never to open the window
⑤ never opening the window

22 주어진 단어를 활용하여 다음 우리말을 영어로 쓰시오.

> 그 남자는 너무 피곤해서 테니스를 칠 수 없었다.
> (tired, play tennis, so)

➡ _____

23 다음 우리말에 맞게 괄호 안의 단어를 배열할 때, 6번째 올 어휘를 고르시오.

> 학생들은 다시는 소란을 피우지 않겠다고 약속했다. (not, any, the, make, noise, to, again, students, promised)

① promised   ② not   ③ noise
④ make   ⑤ to

24 to부정사를 이용하여 주어진 두 문장을 한 문장으로 연결하시오.

(1) • I can't focus on the test.
    • It's because I was very tired.

➡ _____

(2) • The presenter was really nervous.
    • So, he couldn't eat dinner.

➡ _____

(3) • The evidence is detailed.
    • So, it can support his argument.

➡ _____

25 주어진 문장을 that을 이용하여 바꿔 쓰시오.

> The cellphone was too expensive for me to buy.

➡ _____

_____

Reading

[26~27] 다음 글을 읽고 물음에 답하시오.

Reporters came up to Wasiqi and started asking him questions.

Reporter: What happened to you?

Wasiqi: I injured my leg during a practice run. The injury got worse during the race, but I couldn't give up.

Reporter: Why not? You knew that you were too far behind to win a medal.

Wasiqi: I am the only athlete here representing Afghanistan. There was no way I could give up.

Reporter: ⓐ아프가니스탄은 여전히 전쟁 중입니다, isn't it?

Wasiqi: Yes, we have been at war for 16 years. That's why we were not able to send athletes to the Barcelona Olympics four years ago. I was sad for my country back then when I could see no Afghan athletes in the opening ceremony.

26 위 글의 밑줄 친 ⓐ의 우리말에 맞게 5 단어로 영작하시오.

➡ _____

27 According to the passage, which is NOT true?

① Wasiqi injured his leg during a practice run.
② Wasiqi's injury got worse during the race.
③ Wasiqi was too far behind to win a medal.
④ Wasiqi couldn't give up because he was the only athlete there representing Afghanistan.
⑤ Wasiqi was sad when he was the only Afghan athlete in the opening ceremony.

[28~29] 다음 글을 읽고 물음에 답하시오.

A Little Big Hero from Afghanistan

There was a marathon race at the end of the 1996 Atlanta Summer Olympics. When most runners finished ___ⓐ___, and the officials started to prepare for the closing ceremony, a runner entered the stadium. The runner finally ran through the tape and then fell to the ground. His name was Abdul Baser Wasiqi, and he was the only athlete representing Afghanistan. He did not give up running the race for his country.

28 위 글의 빈칸 ⓐ에 race를 알맞은 형태로 쓰시오.

➡ _____

29 위 글의 종류로 알맞은 것을 고르시오.

① diary   ② article
③ biography   ④ book report
⑤ review

[30~32] 다음 글을 읽고 물음에 답하시오.

I Have a Goal to Win the Singing Contest

I want to win the school singing contest. I love singing, and I think I have a good voice. ___ⓐ___, ⓑI am too shy to sing in front of many people. Not to be nervous during the contest, I will practice singing in front of my class first.

30 위 글의 빈칸 ⓐ에 들어갈 알맞은 말을 고르시오.

① For example   ② Therefore
③ However   ④ That is
⑤ Moreover

31 위 글의 밑줄 친 ⓑ를 복문으로 고치시오.

➡ _____
_____

32 위 글을 읽고 글쓴이의 목표를 달성하는 데에 있어 (1) 강점과 약점 (2) 약점 때문에 하기 어려운 것 (3) 이를 극복하기 위한 계획을 우리말로 쓰시오.

➡ (1) 강점: _____
   약점: _____
   (2) _____
   (3) _____
   _____

출제율 95%

01 짝지어진 단어의 관계가 같도록 빈칸에 알맞은 말을 쓰시오.

> author : writer = a_____ : respect

출제율 90%

02 다음 빈칸에 들어갈 말로 적절한 것은?

> What does this picture _____?

① represent   ② reduce

③ take   ④ save

⑤ realize

출제율 95%

03 다음 빈칸에 들어갈 말이 바르게 짝지어진 것은?

> • She must be very _____ of herself.
> • I'm not very _____ at tennis.

① proud – aware   ② aware – poor

③ poor – aware   ④ proud – good

⑤ careful – proud

출제율 100%

04 다음 제시된 단어로 자연스러운 문장을 만들 수 없는 것은?

> ┌─ 보기 ─┐
> public   removed   officials   preparation

① I think _____ for the party started early.

② They _____ the tape at the finish line.

③ He was educated at a _____ school when he was a child.

④ Someday, she will be _____ for her acting.

⑤ The ship was boarded by customs _____.

[05~07] 다음 대화를 읽고 물음에 답하시오.

> G: Have you ___(A)___ of Eui Hyun Sin, the skier?
> B: No. Who is he?
> G: He's a Paralympian skier. He won the first gold medal for Korea in the 2018 Winter Paralympics.
> B: Wow! That's great.
> G: He was in a car accident in his early twenties and hurt his legs.
> B: (가)How was he able to become a skier?
> G: After his accident, he tried several different sports to ___(B)___ better. Then he became especially interested in skiing.
> B: Skiing is not easy. Not many people are good at skiing.
> G: That's why he's so respected.

출제율 90%

05 밑줄 친 (가) 대신 쓰기에 적절한 것은?

① Do you know he was a skier?

② Do you know why he was able to become a skier?

③ Could you tell me how he was able to become a skier?

④ Did you realize how to become a skier?

⑤ Do you know that he was a skier?

출제율 95%

06 빈칸 (A)와 (B)에 들어가기에 알맞은 것으로 짝지어진 것은?

	(A)	(B)
①	taken	stay
②	made	look
③	heard	take
④	heard	get
⑤	taken	make

07 Which one of the following is NOT true according to the text above?

① Eui Hyun Sin is a Paralympian skier.

② The boy didn't hear of Eui Hyun Sin.

③ The skier hurt his legs in a car accident.

④ Eui Hyun Sin won the first gold medal for Korea in the 2018 Winter Paralympics.

⑤ The boy tried several different kinds of sports.

[08~10] 다음 대화를 읽고 물음에 답하시오.

> **G:** ①Have you heard of D.I.Y.?
> **B:** No, what is D.I.Y.?
> **G:** ②D.I.Y. stands for 'do-it-yourself.' (A)I'm really into it. ③Right now, I'm buying a pencil case.
> **B:** ④What are you going to make after you finish that?
> **G:** When I'm done with the pencil case, ⑤I'm planning to make my own desk.

08 밑줄 친 (A)에 대신 쓸 수 있는 것은?

① I'm running for it.

② I'm doing it myself.

③ I have talked about it.

④ I'm really interested in it.

⑤ I really don't like it.

09 위 대화의 흐름상 어색한 문장은?

① ② ③ ④ ⑤

10 Which one CANNOT be answered from the dialogue above?

① Does the girl know about D.I.Y.?

② What does D.I.Y. stand for?

③ What is the girl interested in?

④ Where did the girl hear about D.I.Y.?

⑤ What will the girl make after she finishes a pencil case?

11 다음 빈칸에 들어갈 말로 가장 적절한 것은?

> No one is too old to learn.
> = No one is _____.

① very old to learn

② old enough to learn

③ very old that he can learn

④ so old that he can't learn

⑤ so old that he can learn

12 괄호 안의 어휘를 이용하여 다음 우리말을 영어로 옮길 때 8번째로 오는 단어는?

> 그 노인은 화를 내지 않기 위해 심호흡을 했다.
> (a deep breath, took, upset)

① took ② breath ③ not

④ upset ⑤ deep

13 다음 중 어법상 바르지 않은 것은?

① The noodles were so delicious that I can't help overeating.

② He was so poor that he couldn't buy bread.

③ He was simple enough to believe that.

④ I was too short to reach the top shelf.

⑤ I'm so hungry that I can eat anything.

14 출제율 95%

다음 중 어법상 적절한 것은?

① To not be nervous during the contest, I will practice singing in front of my class first.

② Because it is a long way to my school, it is important not to miss the bus.

③ The player practiced hard to be proud of himself, not win a gold medal.

④ I was taught from the cradle never cry.

⑤ For me and my country, it was important not to giving up.

15 출제율 90%

다음 문장을 that을 이용하여 바꿔 쓰시오.

(1) I'm too sick to go out to eat.

➡ _____

(2) She is old enough to do what she wants.

➡ _____

[16~17] 다음 글을 읽고 물음에 답하시오.

Someone shouted, "Look! There comes another runner!" A runner was just entering the stadium, but there was something wrong ___ⓐ___ his legs. Still, he kept going toward the finish line. The band and the volunteers stopped their preparations for the closing ceremony. All eyes were ___ⓑ___ the runner.

Suddenly, the band started playing celebration music, and the volunteers cheered. "Go! Go! Go for it!" Two volunteers ran to the finish line with a tape. Finally, the runner ran through the tape and then fell to the ground. His name was Abdul Baser Wasiqi. He was from Afghanistan.

16 출제율 95%

위 글의 빈칸 ⓐ와 ⓑ에 들어갈 전치사가 바르게 짝지어진 것은?

	ⓐ	ⓑ		ⓐ	ⓑ
①	with	on	②	about	by
③	about	to	④	with	by
⑤	to	on			

17 출제율 100%

위 글에서 알 수 있는 Wasiqi의 성격으로 가장 알맞은 것을 고르시오.

① generous   ② outgoing

③ passive   ④ strong-willed

⑤ aggressive

[18~20] 다음 글을 읽고 물음에 답하시오.

Reporters came up to Wasiqi and started asking him questions.

Reporter: What happened to you?

Wasiqi: I injured my leg during a practice run. The injury got worse during the race, but I couldn't give up.

Reporter: ⓐWhy not? You knew that you were too far behind to win a medal.

Wasiqi: I am the only athlete here representing Afghanistan. There was no way I could give up.

Reporter: Afghanistan is still at war, isn't it?

Wasiqi: Yes, we have been at war for 16 years. ⓑ그것이 우리가 4년 전 바르셀로나 올림픽에 선수들을 보낼 수 없었던 이유입니다. I was sad for my country back then when I could see no Afghan athletes in the opening ceremony.

18 위 글의 밑줄 친 ⓐWhy not?에 생략된 말을 넣어 문장을 다시 쓰시오.

➡ _____

19 위 글의 밑줄 친 ⓑ의 우리말에 맞게 한 단어를 보충하여, 주어진 어휘를 알맞게 배열하시오.

> were not able to / four years / to / we / ago / athletes / that's / the Barcelona Olympics / send

➡ _____

_____

20 위 글의 제목으로 알맞은 것을 고르시오.

① How Embarrassing! Injury During the Race!
② Too Far Behind to Win a Medal!
③ Finishing a Marathon? It's Full of Pain!
④ What I Must Give Up Is to Give Up!
⑤ No Afghan Athletes? How Sad It Is!

[21~22] 다음 글을 읽고 물음에 답하시오.

> **Reporter:** Were you running marathons then?
> **Wasiqi:** No. I started running after Barcelona. I ran in lots of races. Finally I won a marathon in Germany. As a result, I was able to come to Atlanta.
> **Reporter:** How do you feel now?
> **Wasiqi:** ⓐI am proud of me and proud to be from Afghanistan. For me and my country, it was important not to give up. I didn't come here to win. For me, it was enough to be here and to finish the race.

21 위 글의 밑줄 친 ⓐ에서 어법상 틀린 부분을 찾아 고치시오.

_____ ➡ _____

22 According to the passage, which is NOT true?

① Wasiqi started running after the Barcelona Olympics.
② Wasiqi participated in a lot of races before he won a marathon in Germany.
③ After the marathon ended, Wasiqi was proud of himself and proud to be from Afghanistan.
④ To win in the Atlanta Olympics was important for Wasiqi and his country.
⑤ Wasiqi didn't come to Atlanta to win.

[23~24] 다음 글을 읽고 물음에 답하시오.

> **I Have a Goal to Run a 5 Kilometer Marathon**
> I want to take part in and complete a 5 (A) [kilometer / kilometers] marathon. I have a lot of time to exercise and a strong will to do my best in every activity. However, I run too slowly to finish the race within the limited amount of time (B)[giving / given]. ⓐNot to fall behind the other runners, I will practice (C) [running / to run] faster every morning.

23 위 글의 괄호 (A)~(C)에서 문맥이나 어법상 알맞은 낱말을 골라 쓰시오.

➡ (A) _____ (B) _____ (C) _____

24 위 글의 밑줄 친 ⓐ를 In order that을 사용하여 고치시오.

➡ _____

[01~03] 다음 대화를 읽고 물음에 답하시오.

> B: How was Thomas Edison able to invent so many things?
>
> G: Many people think that he ___(A)___ things on his first try, but that's not true.
>
> B: Oh, really?
>
> G: Yes. ___(B)___ (~할 때마다) he invented something, he experimented many times.
>
> B: (C)아마 그것이 그토록 많은 사람들이 그를 존경하는 이유일 것이다. (maybe, admire)

01 빈칸 (A)에 들어가기에 적절한 단어를 쓰시오.

➡ _____

02 (B)에 주어진 뜻에 어울리는 단어를 쓰시오. (한 단어)

➡ _____

03 밑줄 친 (C)의 우리말에 해당하는 영어 문장을 주어진 단어를 이용하여 쓰시오. (8 words)

➡ _____

04 다음 우리말을 괄호 안에 주어진 어휘를 이용하여 영작하시오.

(1) 우리는 너무 바빠서 산책하러 나갈 수가 없다. (go out, busy, too)

➡ _____

(2) Jin은 너무 늦어서 9시 기차를 탈 수 없다. (take the 9 o'clock train, that)

➡ _____

(3) 사과들이 따야 할 만큼 익었다. (be picked, the apples, ripe, to)

➡ _____

(4) 이 경기장은 천 명의 사람들을 수용할 만큼 크다. (this stadium, people, hold, large, so, that)

➡ _____

(5) Ellen은 체중이 늘지 않기 위해서 매일 운동한다. (exercises, gain weight)

➡ _____

(6) 그 소녀는 한 단어도 놓치지 않기 위해서 주의 깊게 수업을 들었다. (listened, miss, carefully, in class)

➡ _____

05 다음 문장에서 어법상 어색한 것을 바르게 고치시오.

(1) Andrew promised me to be late never for the meeting again.

➡ _____
_____

(2) In order to not forget certain events with my dog, I always take pictures with her.

➡ _____

(3) I will practice running every morning not so as to fall behind the other runners.

➡ _____
_____

(4) I was too busy going to bed before midnight.

➡ _____
_____

(5) No wonder my grade was so low for me to pass the exam.

➡ _____
_____

Someone shouted, "Look! ⓐAnother runner comes there!" A runner was just entering the stadium, but there was something wrong with his legs. Still, he kept going toward the finish line. The band and the volunteers stopped their preparations for the closing ceremony. All eyes were on the runner.

Suddenly, the band started playing celebration music, and the volunteers cheered. "Go! Go! Go for it!" Two volunteers ran to the finish line with a tape. Finally, the runner ran through the tape and then fell to the ground. His name was Abdul Baser Wasiqi. He was from Afghanistan.

06 위 글의 밑줄 친 ⓐ의 there를 문두로 이동시켜 강조하는 문장을 쓰시오.

➡ _____

07 본문의 내용과 일치하도록 다음 빈칸 (A)와 (B)에 알맞은 단어를 쓰시오.

> Though there was (A)_____ _____ with his legs, Wasiqi didn't give up racing and kept running for so long that when he entered the stadium, the band and the volunteers were preparing for the (B)_____ _____.

08 Why did two volunteers run to the finish line with a tape? Fill in the blanks with suitable words.

> Because they wanted to hold the tape for Wasiqi to _____ _____ it.

Reporters came up to Wasiqi and started asking him questions.

Reporter: What happened to you?

Wasiqi: I injured my leg (A)[during / while] a practice run. The injury got worse during the race, but I couldn't give up.

Reporter: Why not? You knew that you were too far (B)[ahead / behind] to win a medal.

Wasiqi: I am the only athlete here representing Afghanistan. There was no way I could give up.

Reporter: Afghanistan is still at war, isn't it?

Wasiqi: Yes, we have been at war (C)[during / for] 16 years. ⓐThat's why we were not able to send athletes to the Barcelona Olympics four years ago. I was sad for my country back then when I could see no Afghan athletes in the opening ceremony.

09 위 글의 괄호 (A)~(C)에서 문맥이나 어법상 알맞은 낱말을 골라 쓰시오.

➡ (A) _____ (B) _____ (C) _____

10 위 글의 밑줄 친 ⓐ를 다음과 같이 바꿔 쓸 때 빈칸에 들어갈 알맞은 한 단어를 쓰시오.

➡ For that _____, we were not able to send athletes to the Barcelona Olympics four years ago.

창의사고력 서술형 문제

01 리포터가 인터뷰한 후에 작성한 기사를 완성해 봅시다.

> ### A Little Big Hero from Afghanistan
>
> There was a _____ race at the end of the 1996 Atlanta Summer Olympics. When most runners _____ racing, and the officials started to prepare for the _____ ceremony, a runner entered the stadium. The runner finally _____ the tape and then fell to the ground. His name was Abdul Baser Wasiqi, and he was the only athlete _____ Afghanistan. He did not give up running the race for his country.

> finished   closing   marathon   representing   ran through

02 다음 그림을 참고하여 대화의 빈칸을 알맞게 채우시오.

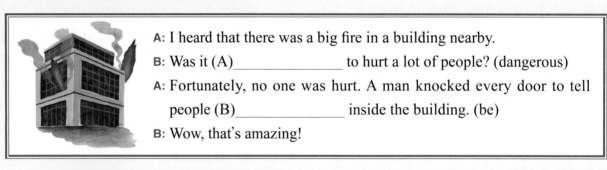

A: I heard that there was a big fire in a building nearby.

B: Was it (A)_____ to hurt a lot of people? (dangerous)

A: Fortunately, no one was hurt. A man knocked every door to tell people (B)_____ inside the building. (be)

B: Wow, that's amazing!

03 다음 내용을 바탕으로 기억 상자에 넣을 다짐의 글을 쓰시오.

> **My Goal**   I want to run a 5 km marathon
> **Strength**   a lot of time to exercise, a strong will
> **Weakness**   run slowly
> • I run too slowly to finish the race within the limited amount of time given.
> → I will practice running faster every morning.

> ### I Have a Goal to Run a 5 Kilometer Marathon
>
> I want to take part in and complete a (A)_____. I have (B)_____ and a strong will to do my best in every activity. However, I run (C)_____ to finish the race (D)_____. Not to fall behind the other runners, I will practice (E)_____.

단원별 모의고사

01 다음 짝지어진 두 단어의 관계가 같도록 빈칸에 알맞은 말을 쓰시오.

> invite : invitation – transport : _____

02 다음 영영풀이에 해당하는 단어로 적절한 것은?

> a strong emotion or feeling

① author
② passion
③ information
④ foundation
⑤ cheer

03 다음 〈보기〉에서 알맞은 말을 골라 써 넣어 문장을 완성하시오.

> ┤ 보기 ├
> stadium   cheered   celebration   war

(1) The two countries have been at _____ for many years.
(2) The Olympic _____ was filled with people.
(3) We had a big _____ for his son's first birthday.
(4) My classmates _____ for me and shouted my name.

04 다음 빈칸에 들어갈 말로 적절한 것은?

> It wasn't easy to sing in _____.

① public
② mind
③ plan
④ officials
⑤ place

[05~07] 다음 대화를 읽고 물음에 답하시오.

> G: How was Hyeon Chung ____(A)____ one of the final four players in the tennis competition?
> B: (B)He could do it only after years of hard training.
> G: I see. When did he start playing tennis?
> B: He started to play tennis when he was seven.

05 빈칸 (A)에 적절한 것은?

① can do
② able to be
③ would like to
④ become to
⑤ aware of

06 밑줄 친 (B)를 다음과 같이 바꾸어 쓸 때 빈칸에 적절한 단어를 쓰시오.

➡ He had trained hard for years _____ he could do it.

07 위 대화의 내용과 일치하지 <u>않는</u> 것은?

① Hyeon Chung was a tennis player.
② Hyeon Chung trained hard for years.
③ Hyeon Chung was the winner of the tennis competition.
④ Hyeon Chung started to play tennis at seven.
⑤ The girl wanted to know about Hyeon Chung.

[08~10] 다음 대화를 읽고 물음에 답하시오.

> G: Have you heard of Eui Hyun Sin, the skier?
> B: No. Who is he?
> G: He's a Paralympian skier. (A) He won the first gold medal for Korea in the 2018 Winter Paralympics. (B)
> B: Wow! That's great. (C)

G: He was in a car accident in his early twenties and hurt his legs. (D)

B: How was he able to become a skier?

G: (E) Then he became especially interested in skiing.

B: Skiing is not easy. (가)많은 사람들이 스키를 잘 타는 것은 아니다.

G: That's why he's so respected.

08 (A)~(E) 중에서 다음 문장이 들어가기에 적절한 곳은?

> After his accident, he tried several different sports to get better.

① (A)　② (B)　③ (C)　④ (D)　⑤ (E)

09 밑줄 친 (가)의 우리말과 같은 뜻이 되도록 빈칸에 알맞은 말을 쓰시오.

➡ _____ many people are _____ _____ skiing.

10 Which one is TRUE according to the dialogue?

① Eui Hyun Sin won the first gold medal for Korea for the first time.

② Eui Hyun Sin participated in the 2018 Winter Olympics.

③ Eui Hyun Sin hurt his legs in a car accident.

④ He was interested in skiing before he tried several different sports.

⑤ Skiing is not easy, so he respects many skiers.

[11~12] 다음 대화를 읽고 물음에 답하시오.

B: Sora, have you heard about the fire last night? (A)

G: Yes, I heard that there was a big fire in a building nearby. (B)

B: No, one man saved ten people who were in the building. (C)

G: Oh, really? How was he able to save so many people? (D)

B: He knocked on every door to tell people to leave the building. (E)

G: Wow, that's amazing!

11 다음 문장이 들어가기에 적절한 곳은?

> Was anybody hurt?

① (A)　② (B)　③ (C)　④ (D)　⑤ (E)

12 위 대화의 내용과 일치하는 것은?

① Sora didn't hear about the fire.

② The boy didn't know who was hurt.

③ No one saved people in the building.

④ A man knocked on every door.

⑤ There weren't any people in the building.

13 다음 문장과 같은 의미로 쓰인 것은?

> The subway I was going to take was too crowded to get on.

① The subway I was going to take was so crowded that I can get on.

② The subway I was going to take was so crowded that I can't get on.

③ The subway I was going to take was so crowded that I could get on it.

④ The subway I was going to take was so crowded that I could get on it.

⑤ The subway I was going to take was so crowded that I couldn't get on it.

14 다음 중 어법상 바르지 않은 것은?

① The last runner ran as fast as possible not to fall behind.
② I always try hard not to wake up late.
③ I told him to never tell a lie again.
④ We booked the concert tickets in advance not to miss the chance to see the idol.
⑤ The boy told a lie to his mom not to disappoint her.

15 두 문장의 의미가 같도록 빈칸을 완성하시오. (6 단어)

I couldn't solve the problem because it was very difficult.
= The problem was _____.

➡ _____

16 우리말과 같은 의미가 되도록 괄호 안의 단어를 바르게 배열하시오.

(1) Sally는 감기에 걸리지 않기 위해서 따뜻한 옷을 입었다. (Sally, clothes, not, a, wore, catch, warm, cold, to)

➡ _____
_____

(2) 사람들은 공공장소에서 다른 사람들을 방해하지 않기 위해 조용히 있어야 한다. (people, places, others, disturb, should, not, stay, quiet, public, to, in)

➡ _____
_____

(3) Amy는 너무 아파서 친구들과 놀 수 없었다. (her, Amy, friends, sick, too, play, was, to, with)

➡ _____
_____

17 다음 중 어법상 바른 문장은?

① The song is too difficult to singing.
② The question was enough easy to answer.
③ My mother was too busy to pick me up.
④ You must remember to not make a loud noise.
⑤ She is intelligent enough to not miss a trick.

[18~19] 다음 글을 읽고 물음에 답하시오.

Someone shouted, "Look! There comes another runner!" A runner was just entering the stadium, but there was something wrong with his legs. Still, he kept going toward the finish line. The band and the volunteers stopped their _____ⓐ_____ for the closing ceremony. All eyes were on the runner.

Suddenly, the band started playing celebration music, and the volunteers cheered. "Go! Go! Go for it!" Two volunteers ran to the finish line with a tape. Finally, the runner ran through the tape and then fell to the ground. His name was Abdul Baser Wasiqi. He was from Afghanistan.

18 위 글의 빈칸 ⓐ에 prepare를 알맞은 형태로 쓰시오.

➡ _____

19 위 글의 주제로 알맞은 것을 고르시오.

① something wrong with a marathon runner
② the true sportsmanship which never gives in to hardship
③ the surprise that the band and the volunteers felt
④ hot cheering of the band and the volunteers
⑤ a hard day of an exhausted marathon runner

[20~22] 다음 글을 읽고 물음에 답하시오.

Reporters came up to Wasiqi and started asking him questions.

Reporter: What happened to you?

Wasiqi: (①) I injured my leg during a practice run. The injury got worse during the race, but I couldn't give up.

Reporter: (②) You knew that you were too far behind to win a medal.

Wasiqi: (③) I am the only athlete here representing Afghanistan. (④) There was no way I could give up.

Reporter: (⑤) Afghanistan is still at war, isn't it?

Wasiqi: Yes, we have been at war for 16 years. That's why we were not able to send athletes to the Barcelona Olympics four years ago. I was sad for my country back then when I could see no ___@___ athletes in the opening ceremony.

20 위 글의 빈칸 @에 Afghanistan을 알맞은 형태로 쓰시오.

➡ _____

21 위 글의 흐름으로 보아, 주어진 문장이 들어가기에 가장 적절한 곳은?

Why not?

①   ②   ③   ④   ⑤

22 Why was Wasiqi sad for his country at the time when the Barcelona Olympics were held? Fill in the blanks (A) and (B) with suitable words.

Because at that time Afghanistan was not able to (A)_____ _____ to the Barcelona Olympics because of the war, so there were no athletes representing Afghanistan in the (B)_____ ceremony.

[23~25] 다음 글을 읽고 물음에 답하시오.

A Little Big Hero from Afghanistan

There was a marathon race at the end of the 1996 Atlanta Summer Olympics. When most runners finished racing, and the officials started to prepare for the closing ceremony, a runner entered the stadium. The runner finally ran through the tape and then fell to the ground. His name was Abdul Baser Wasiqi, and he was the only athlete representing Afghanistan. He did not give up ___@___ the race for his country.

23 위 글의 빈칸 @에 run을 알맞은 형태로 쓰시오.

➡ _____

24 주어진 영영풀이에 해당하는 단어를 본문에서 찾아 쓰시오.

people who hold a position of authority in an organization

➡ _____

25 위 글을 읽고 답할 수 없는 질문을 고르시오.

① When did Wasiqi enter the stadium?
② Did Wasiqi run through the tape?
③ Were there any other athletes representing Afghanistan except Wasiqi?
④ For what did Wasiqi keep running the race?
⑤ How long did Wasiqi run?

Teens' Worries

🎙 의사소통 기능

- 동의나 이의 여부 표현하기
  A: I think listening to music helps you relax.
  B: I agree.

- 안심시키기
  A: I'm worried about making friends at my new school.
  B: Don't worry. I'm sure you'll make a lot of friends there.

🎙 언어 형식

- 분사구문
  Daeho, **thinking that new things will make him more popular,** often wants new things just because his friends have them.

- 명사절을 이끄는 접속사 'if'
  You should just ask her **if** there is something wrong.

Words & Expressions

Key Words

- **advise** [ədváiz] 동 충고하다
- **afraid** [əfréid] 형 걱정하는, 불안한
- **agree** [əgríː] 동 동의하다
- **avoid** [əvɔ́id] 동 피하다
- **counselor** [káunsələr] 명 카운슬러, 상담역
- **decide** [disáid] 동 결정하다
- **disagree** [dìsəgríː] 동 동의하지 않다
- **else** [els] 형 다른
- **experiment** [ikspérəmənt] 명 실험
- **festival** [féstəvəl] 명 축제
- **final** [fáinl] 명 결승, 기말고사 형 마지막의
- **fun** [fʌn] 명 재미
- **guy** [gai] 명 (비격식) 녀석, 남자
- **hate** [heit] 동 매우 싫어하다
- **helpful** [hélpfəl] 형 도움이 되는
- **hurt** [həːrt] 동 다치다
- **if** [if] 접 ~인지 아닌지
- **latest** [léitist] 형 최신의
- **management** [mǽnidʒmənt] 명 관리
- **match** [mætʃ] 명 시합
- **matter** [mǽtər] 명 문제
- **mistake** [mistéik] 명 실수
- **misunderstand** [misəndərstǽnd] 동 오해하다
- **number** [nʌ́mbər] 동 번호를 매기다
- **P.E. teacher** 체육 교사
- **part** [paːrt] 명 부분, 배역, 역할
- **popular** [pápjulər] 형 인기 있는
- **project** [prádʒekt] 명 과제
- **protein** [próutiːn] 명 단백질
- **prove** [pruːv] 동 증명하다, 입증하다
- **recently** [ríːsntli] 부 최근에
- **relax** [rilǽks] 동 쉬다
- **snap** [snæp] 명 찰칵하는 소리를 내며 움직이는 것
- **sneakers** [sníːkərz] 명 운동화
- **speech contest** 웅변대회
- **still** [stil] 부 아직도
- **stress** [stress] 명 스트레스
- **strict** [strikt] 형 엄격한
- **teenager** [tíːnèidʒər] 명 청소년
- **try** [trai] 동 시도하다
- **upset** [ʌ́pset] 형 기분이 상한
- **vocabulary** [voukǽbjulèri] 명 어휘
- **worry** [wɔ́ːri] 명 걱정 동 걱정하다

Key Expressions

- **a couple of** 두서너 개의, 몇 개의, 몇 사람의
- **a lot of** 많은
- **ask A for B** A에게 B를 요청하다
- **ask somebody out** ~에게 데이트를 신청하다
- **be asked out** 데이트 신청을 받다
- **be nervous about** ~에 대하여 불안하다
- **be ready for** ~에 준비가 되다
- **be worried about** ~에 대해 걱정하다
- **do one's job** ~의 일을 하다
- **do one's part** ~의 역할을 하다
- **end up -ing** 결국 ~하게 되다
- **focus on** 집중하다
- **for a long time** 오랫동안
- **for now** 당분간은, 현재로는
- **get started** 시작하다
- **get together** 모이다
- **get 목적어 to 동사원형** ~에게 … 하도록 하다
- **have a hard time -ing** ~하는 데 어려움이 있다
- **in style** 유행하는, 유행되는
- **Is something wrong?** 뭐가 잘못되었나요?
- **look worried** 걱정스러워 보이다
- **make friends** 친구를 사귀다
- **no longer** 더 이상 ~가 아닌
- **not ~ anymore** 더 이상 ~가 아닌
- **not yet** 아직 ~가 아닌
- **take time** 시간이 걸리다
- **without -ing** ~하지 않고, ~ 없이
- **write down** 기록하다

Word Power

※ 서로 비슷한 뜻을 가진 어휘

☐ **afraid** 걱정하는, 불안한 : **nervous** 불안한

☐ **decide** 결정하다 : **determine** 결정하다

☐ **hurt** 다치다 : **injure** 부상을 입다

☐ **project** 과제 : **task** 과제

☐ **avoid** 피하다 : **evade** 피하다

☐ **hate** 매우 싫어하다 : **detest** 몹시 싫어하다

☐ **part** 배역, 역할 : **role** 역할

☐ **strict** 엄격한 : **rigid** 엄격한

※ 서로 반대되는 뜻을 가진 어휘

☐ **afraid** 걱정하는 ↔ **unafraid** 걱정하지 않는

☐ **avoid** 피하다 ↔ **face** 마주하다

☐ **agree** 동의하다 ↔ **disagree** 동의하지 않다

☐ **hate** 매우 싫어하다 ↔ **like** 좋아하다

※ 같은 형태로 동사와 명사로 쓰이는 낱말

☐ **worry** 동 걱정하다 명 걱정

☐ **need** 동 필요하다 명 필요

☐ **act** 동 행동하다 명 행동

☐ **design** 동 다자인하다 명 디자인

☐ **rain** 동 비 내리다 명 비

☐ **answer** 동 대답하다 명 대답

☐ **raise** 동 인상하다 명 인상

☐ **address** 동 주소를 쓰다 명 주소

☐ **fight** 동 싸우다 명 싸움

☐ **use** 동 사용하다 명 사용

☐ **hope** 동 희망하다 명 희망

☐ **taste** 동 맛보다 명 맛

☐ **care** 동 돌보다 명 돌봄

☐ **help** 동 돕다 명 도움

☐ **visit** 동 방문하다 명 방문

※ 동사 - 명사

☐ **relax** 쉬다 - **relaxation** 휴식

☐ **agree** 동의하다 - **agreement** 동의, 일치

☐ **prove** 입증하다 - **proof** 증거

☐ **manage** 관리하다 - **management** 관리

English Dictionary

☐ **a couple of** 두서너 개의, 몇 개의, 몇 사람의
→ two people or things of the same category
같은 유형의 두 사람 또는 두 개

☐ **agree** 동의하다
→ to have the same opinion as someone about a topic
어떤 주제에 대하여 다른 사람과 같은 의견을 가지다

☐ **counselor** 카운슬러, 상담역
→ someone whose job is to provide help and advice to people with problems
문제가 있는 사람에게 도움이나 조언을 제공하는 직업을 가진 사람

☐ **disagree** 동의하지 않다
→ to have a different opinion 다른 의견을 가지다

☐ **hate** 매우 싫어하다
→ to dislike something strongly 어떤 것을 강하게 싫어하다

☐ **latest** 최신의
→ most recent and newest 가장 새롭고 가장 최근의

☐ **mistake** 실수
→ something that you do wrong without wanting to
원치 않으면서 저지르는 잘못

☐ **prove** 증명하다, 입증하다
→ to show that something is true
어떤 것이 사실이라는 것을 보여주다

☐ **recently** 최근에
→ not long ago 얼마 전에

☐ **sneakers** 운동화
→ soft sided sports shoes 부드러운 소재의 운동화

☐ **teenager** 청소년
→ a person who is between the ages of 13 and 19
13세에서 19세 사이의 사람

☐ **vocabulary** 어휘
→ words that are used in a language
어떤 언어에서 사용되는 단어

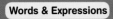

서답형

01 〈보기〉와 같은 관계가 되도록 빈칸에 알맞은 말을 쓰시오. (주어진 철자로 시작할 것)

┌─ 보기 ─┐
decide : determine
└────────┘

(1) hate : d_____

(2) afraid : n_____

02 다음 주어진 문장의 빈칸에 들어갈 단어를 사용하여 자연스러운 문장을 만들 수 있는 것은?

> Ella _____ to the judge that she hadn't stolen the money.

① I _____ with you about our field trip.
② Clair _____ Mason out, and they went to a movie.
③ Many people _____ with Mr. Smith.
④ He _____ that he didn't make the mistake.
⑤ The two boys _____ each other.

03 다음 중 밑줄 친 부분의 뜻풀이가 바르지 않은 것은?

① Daniel is afraid of going to the dentist. (두려운)
② The counselor advised me to get more sleep. (상담역)
③ Jack bought the latest model of the car. (마지막의)
④ Lucas got a C on the math test because he made too many mistakes. (실수)
⑤ Ryan misunderstood what I said. (오해했다)

중요

04 다음 중 〈보기〉에 있는 단어를 사용하여 자연스러운 문장을 만들 수 없는 것은?

┌─ 보기 ─┐
hate   guy   end   a couple of
└────────┘

① I saw _____ boys playing catch ball.
② If you do not leave now, you will _____ up being late.
③ Lucas is a nice _____ because he has good manners.
④ I _____ jelly because of its texture.
⑤ Luna wants to buy a dress that is _____ style.

05 다음 밑줄 친 부분과 의미가 가장 가까운 것을 고르시오.

> I think he will decide to travel with us.

① avoid   ② act
③ design   ④ answer
⑤ determine

중요

06 다음 빈칸에 공통으로 들어가기에 알맞은 것은?

> • You have to _____ started by the count of 10.
> • I hope that you _____ better soon.

① take   ② get   ③ hold
④ make   ⑤ grow

01 주어진 단어를 이용해 빈칸을 완성하시오.

> Time _____ is an important skill for them to learn.

➡ _____ (manage)

02 다음 짝지어진 단어의 관계가 같도록 빈칸에 알맞은 말을 쓰시오.

> relax : relaxation = prove : _____

[03~04] 빈칸에 공통으로 들어갈 단어를 쓰시오.

03
> • The house stood empty _____ a long time.
> • The plane is ready _____ take-off.

04
> • I was asked _____ to dinner.
> • She went _____ of the room.

05 빈칸에 알맞은 단어를 〈보기〉에서 골라 쓰시오.

> ┌ 보기 ┐
> style   end   about   now

(1) I'm worried _____ the safety of the project.

(2) I always _____ up eating too much during the holidays.

(3) The project of the team has been stopped for _____.

(4) Short skirts are in _____ these days.

06 다음 우리말에 맞게 빈칸에 알맞은 말을 쓰시오.

(1) 영어 수업의 팀 프로젝트는 시간이 많이 걸리고 있다.
  ➡ The team project for English class is _____ a lot of time.

(2) 나는 새로운 영어 단어를 배우느라 어려움을 겪고 있어.
  ➡ I'm _____ a hard time learning new English words.

(3) 그는 일어나서 아무에게도 말하지 않고 떠났다.
  ➡ He stood up and left _____ telling anyone.

(4) 가족과 친구들이 모여 그의 생일을 축하해 주었다.
  ➡ His family and friends got _____ and celebrated his birthday.

Conocation

교과서

Conversation

① 동의나 이의 여부 표현하기

> **A** I think listening to music helps you relax.
> 나는 음악을 듣는 것이 긴장을 푸는 데 도움이 된다고 생각해.
>
> **B** I agree. 동의해.

- 상대방의 말이나 의견에 동의할 때는 "I agree with you." 또는 "You can say that again."이라고 한다. 상대방의 말에 동의하지 않을 때는 "I don't agree."라고 한다.

- 상대방에게 자신의 말에 대하여 동의를 구할 때 간단하게는 부가의문문을 덧붙여서 나타낼 수 있지만, 다른 영어 표현으로 "Don't you agree (with me)?"가 있다. "(제 생각에) 동의하지 않으세요?"의 의미로 "Don't you think so?"라고 할 수도 있다.

- 상대방의 의견에 동의할 때는 '나도 그래.'의 의미로 "Me, too." 또는 "So+동사+주어."의 형태를 쓴다. 이때 사용하는 동사는 be동사, do, does, did를 포함하는 조동사들이다. 부정문에 이어지는 경우에는 so 대신 neither를 사용하여 "Neither+동사+주어."라고 하거나, "Me neither."라고 할 수 있다. 동의하지 않는 것을 좀 더 공손하게 표현할 때 "I'm afraid."를 덧붙여 말할 수도 있다.

동의나 이의 여부를 나타내는 표현

〈동의하기〉
- I agree (with you). 동의해.
- So am/do I. / Me, too. / Me, neither. 나도 마찬가지야.
- Same here. 나도 마찬가지야.
- You can say that again. 네 말이 맞아.
- That's a neat/good/great idea. 그거 좋은 생각이야.

〈이의 제기하기〉
- I don't agree. 저는 동의하지 않아요.
- I don't believe so. 그렇게 생각하지 않습니다.
- I don't think so. 그렇게 생각하지 않아요.
- I disagree with you. 저는 동의하지 않습니다.

동의하는지 묻는 표현

- Don't you agree (with me)? 동의하지 않으세요?
- Don't you think so? 그렇게 생각하지 않으세요?

핵심 Check

1. 다음 빈칸에 들어갈 말로 적절하지 <u>않은</u> 것을 고르시오.

> **G:** I think reading history comic books is helpful.
>
> **B:** _____ I learn a lot from them.

① I agree.　　　② Same here.　　　③ So do I.
④ I think so too.　　　⑤ Don't you think so?

② 안심시키기

A I'm worried about making friends at my new school.
난 새로운 학교에서 친구를 사귀는 것이 걱정이 돼.

B Don't worry. I'm sure you'll make a lot of friends there.
걱정하지 마. 네가 거기에서 많은 친구를 사귈 것이라고 확신해.

■ 상대방이 걱정스러워 보이거나 불안해 보일 때 상대를 안심시키는 말은 "Don't worry."(걱정하지 마.), "It's all right. Don't worry."(괜찮아, 걱정하지 마.) 등이다. 보통 시험이나 시합 또는 새로운 일을 앞두고 불안해 할 때 걱정하지 말라고 안심시키는 말을 하거나, "잘할 거라고 확신한다."는 의미로 "I'm sure you will fine.", "I'm sure it will be okay." 또는 "I'm sure you'll do better." 등의 표현을 사용한다.

■ worry를 사용하는 표현 이외에 안심시키는 표현은 "That's/It's all right.", "That's/It's okay.", "Everything will be okay." 등으로 상대의 마음을 편하게 해주는 표현이다. 보통 상대가 불안하다는 의사 표현을 했을 때 거기에 대하여 적절한 해결책을 제시하고 "Everything will be all right.", "Everything will be okay." 등의 표현을 사용한다.

■ 걱정하는 내용에 따라서 상대가 잘할 거니까 걱정하지 말라고 안심을 시키는 경우에는 "Cheer up. I'm sure that you will do better next time.", "I'm confident that you will succeed.", "I'm sure that you'll pass the exam." 등으로 나타낼 수 있다.

안심시키기

- Everything will be okay. 모든 게 잘 될 거야.
- Take it easy. Everything will be all right. 마음 편히 가져. 모든 일이 좋아질 거야.
- Don't sweat it. Nothing to worry about. 괜찮아, 걱정할 것 하나도 없어.
- Never mind, it'll be all right. 신경쓰지 마, 괜찮을 거야.
- Cheer up. I'm sure that you will do better next time. 힘내. 너는 다음 번에는 더 잘할 거라고 확신해.
- I'm confident that you will succeed. 네가 성공할 거라고 확신해.

핵심 Check

2. 다음 밑줄 친 말과 바꿔 쓸 수 있는 것은?

B: I have a big soccer match tomorrow. I'm nervous.
G: Don't worry. I'm sure you'll play very well.

① I'm all right.　　　　② Everything will be all right.
③ I don't think so.　　　④ Have you ever played soccer?
⑤ You have heard of it.

Real-Life Zone

B: The team project for English class is ❶taking a lot of time.

G: I agree. I have a problem. One of the people on our team isn't ❷doing his part.

B: That's not good. Everybody on the team has to do their job.

G: I know, but I don't know how to get him to do his part.

B: Maybe he doesn't know how to get started or doesn't like his part.

G: Then what should I do?

B: Talk to him. Ask him ❸why he's not doing his part. Then tell him you'll help him if he wants.

G: Okay. I'll try that.

B: I'm sure he'll do better after you talk to him. Good luck with your project.

G: Thanks.

B: 영어 수업의 팀 프로젝트는 시간이 많이 걸려.

G: 나도 동의해. 나 문제가 있어. 우리 팀의 한 사람이 자기 역할을 다하지 않아.

B: 좋지 않네. 팀의 모든 사람들은 자신들의 일을 해야 해.

G: 알아. 하지만 어떻게 그가 그의 역할을 하게 할지 모르겠어.

B: 어쩌면 그는 시작하는 법을 모르거나 자기 역할을 좋아하지 않을 수도 있어.

G: 그러면 나는 무엇을 해야 할까?

B: 그에게 말해. 그에게 왜 자신의 역할을 안 하는지 물어봐. 그리고 나서 원한다면 네가 도와주겠다고 말해.

G: 그래. 한번 해 볼게.

B: 나는 네가 말하고 나면 그가 더 잘할 거라고 확신해. 네 프로젝트가 잘 되길 바랄게.

G: 고마워.

❶ take a lot of time = 많은 시간이 걸리다
❷ do one's part = 자신의 역할을 하다
❸ "why he's not doing his part"는 ask의 직접목적어로 쓰인 간접의문문이다.

Check(√) True or False

(1) Some of the members on the girl's team aren't doing their part.　　T ☐ F ☐

(2) The girl will ask the student why he isn't doing his part.　　T ☐ F ☐

Wrap Up

G: What's the matter, Dongha? You look worried.

B: I'm not ready for the finals. I sit at my desk to study but ❶end up doing something else.

G: Well, time management is not easy.

B: I agree. What should I do?

G: ❷Number the things you have to do. Then write down how much time you need to finish each one.

B: Thank you, Emily. I'll try your idea.

G: I'm sure that will be helpful for you. Good luck with your finals.

G: 동하야, 무슨 일이야? 걱정스러워 보여.

B: 기말고사 준비가 안 됐어. 나는 공부하기 위해 책상에 앉지만 결국 다른 것을 하게 돼.

G: 음, 시간 관리가 쉽지 않지.

B: 나도 동의해. 내가 어떻게 해야 할까?

G: 해야 할 일에 번호를 매겨. 그리고 나서 각 항목을 끝내는 데 필요한 시간을 적어봐.

B: 고마워, 에밀리. 네 방안을 한번 해 볼게.

G: 나는 그것이 너에게 도움이 될 거라고 확신해. 기말고사 잘 보길 바랄게.

❶ end up -ing = 결국 ~하게 되다
❷ 이 문장의 "Number"는 동사로 쓰여서 "번호를 매기다"의 뜻이다.

Check(√) True or False

(3) Dongha sits at the desk to study but ends up doing something else.　　T ☐ F ☐

(4) Dongha disagrees that time management is not easy.　　T ☐ F ☐

Listen & Speak 1 Listen

1. **G:** ❶I think listening to music helps you relax.
   B: I agree.
2. **G:** I think ❷reading history comic books is helpful.
   B: I agree. I learn a lot from them.
3. **G:** Our school festival is going to be a lot of fun.
   B: I agree.
4. **B:** Our P.E. teacher is too strict. ❸Don't you agree?
   G: No, I don't agree. ❹I don't think he's too strict.

❶ helps의 목적격보어로 원형부정사 relax가 쓰였다. to relax라고도 할 수 있다.
❷ 종속절의 주어 "reading history comic books"는 단수 취급해서 동사 is가 쓰였다.
❸ "Don't you agree?"는 상대에게 동의 여부를 묻는 말이다.
❹ "I don't think ∼."는 "∼라고 생각하지 않는다."의 뜻으로 이의를 나타낸다.

 Listen & Speak 1 A-1

G: Mom told me ❶I could use the computer for only one hour a day. She thinks that's enough time.
M: I agree with her.
G: Sometimes, ❷when doing my homework, I need to use it for a long time.
M: Hmm. Then maybe we should all get together and talk about it.
G: Thanks for your understanding, Dad.

❶ 동사 told의 직접목적어로 쓰인 명사절의 접속사 that이 생략되었다.
❷ "when doing my homework"는 시간의 부사절에 "주어+be동사"가 생략된 형태이다.

 Listen & Speak 1 A-2

B: I just talked about the science project with Jinho and Mina.
G: ❶Has your team decided what you will do?
B: No, not yet. Jinho wants to visit a science museum, but Mina wants to do an experiment.
G: ❷Who do you agree with, Jinho or Mina?
B: ❸I agree with Mina because I think the experiment would be more interesting.

❶ 완료를 나타내는 현재완료이며, "what you will do"는 간접의문문이다.
❷ 의문사 Who는 전치사 with의 목적어에 해당한다. Whom을 써도 좋다.
❸ "agree with+사람", "agree to+의견"이다.

 Listen & Speak 2 Listen

1. **B:** I have a big soccer match tomorrow. I'm nervous.
   G: Don't worry. ❶I'm sure you'll play very well.
2. **G:** ❷I'm nervous about tomorrow's speech contest.
   B: I'm sure you'll do fine. Don't worry.
3. **G:** I'm worried about making friends at my new school.
   M: Don't worry. I'm sure you'll make a lot of friends there.

❶ "I'm sure ∼"는 상대를 안심시키기 위해서 확신을 주는 말이다.
❷ "be nervous about ∼"는 "be worried about ∼"처럼 불안, 염려를 나타낸다.

 Listen & Speak 2 A-1

B: You look worried. ❶Is something wrong?
G: Yes, ❷my sister is upset with me.
B: Why? What did you do?
G: I wore one of her shirts without asking.
B: Tell her you're sorry. I'm sure she'll understand.

❶ "Is something wrong?"은 "What's the matter?"처럼 상대가 안 좋아 보일 때 무슨 문제가 있는지 묻는 말이다.
❷ "be upset with"는 "∼에게 화내다"의 뜻이다.

 Listen & Speak 2 A-2

B: ❶I'm having a hard time learning new English words.
G: I had the same problem, ❷so I asked my English teacher for advice.
B: What did he say?
G: ❸He advised me to use an English vocabulary app. It has helped me a lot. I'm sure it would work for you, too.

❶ "have a hard time -ing"는 "have trouble -ing" 또는 "have a difficult time -ing"처럼 "∼하는 데 어려움을 겪다"라는 의미이다.
❷ so는 원인에 이어서 결과를 유도하는 등위 접속사이다.
❸ "∼에게 … 하도록 충고하다"는 "advise+목적어+to부정사"이다.

● 다음 우리말과 일치하도록 빈칸에 알맞은 말을 쓰시오.

Listen & Speak 1 Listen

1. B: I think _____ to music _____ you _____.
   G: I _____.

2. G: I think _____ history comic books is _____.
   B: I agree. I _____ a lot _____ them.

3. G: Our school _____ is going to be a lot of _____.
   B: I agree.

4. B: Our P.E. _____ is too _____. Don't you _____?
   G: No, I _____ agree. I don't think he's too _____.

Listen & Speak 1 A

1. G: Mom _____ me I could _____ the computer _____ only one hour a _____. She thinks that's _____ time.
   M: I _____ _____ her.
   G: Sometimes, when _____ my homework, I _____ to use it _____ a long time.
   M: Hmm. Then maybe we should all _____ together and _____ about it.
   G: Thanks _____ your understanding, Dad.

2. B: I _____ talked _____ the science _____ with Jinho and Mina.
   G: Has your team _____ what you will _____?
   B: No, _____ yet. Jinho wants to _____ a science museum, but Mina _____ to do an _____.
   G: Who do you agree _____, Jinho or Mina?
   B: I agree _____ Mina because I think the _____ would be more _____.

Listen & Speak 2 Listen

1. B: I _____ a big soccer _____ tomorrow. I'm _____.
   G: Don't _____. I'm _____ you'll _____ very well.

2. G: I'm _____ about tomorrow's _____ contest.
   B: I'm sure you'll _____ fine. Don't _____.

3. G: I'm _____ about making _____ at my new _____.
   M: Don't worry. I'm _____ you'll _____ a lot of _____ there.

해석

1. B: 나는 음악을 듣는 것이 긴장을 푸는 데 도움이 된다고 생각해.
   G: 나도 동의해.
2. G: 나는 역사 만화책을 읽는 것이 도움이 된다고 생각해.
   B: 나도 동의해. 나는 그것들로부터 많은 것을 배워.
3. G: 우리 학교 축제는 아주 재미있을 거야.
   B: 나도 동의해.
4. B: 우리 체육 선생님은 너무 엄격하셔. 너도 동의하지 않니?
   G: 응, 난 동의하지 않아. 나는 그가 너무 엄격하다고 생각하지 않아.

1. G: 엄마는 제가 하루에 한 시간만 컴퓨터를 사용할 수 있다고 말씀하셨어요. 그녀는 그게 충분한 시간이라고 생각하세요.
   M: 나도 그녀의 말에 동의한단다.
   G: 숙제를 할 때 그것을 오래 사용할 필요가 있어요.
   M: 음. 그러면 아마 우리는 다 같이 모여 그것에 대해 이야기를 해야 할 것 같구나.
   G: 이해해 줘서 고마워요, 아빠.
2. B: 나는 진호랑 미나랑 과학 프로젝트에 대해 방금 이야기했어.
   G: 너희 팀은 무엇을 할지 결정했니?
   B: 아니, 아직. 진호는 과학 박물관을 방문하고 싶어하지만, 미나는 실험을 하고 싶어해.
   G: 너는 진호나 미나 중에 누구에게 동의해?
   B: 나는 실험이 더 흥미로울 거라고 생각해서 미나의 말에 동의해.

1. B: 내일 큰 축구 경기가 있어. 긴장돼.
   G: 걱정하지 마. 난 네가 아주 잘 경기할 거라고 확신해.
2. G: 내일 있을 말하기 대회 때문에 긴장돼.
   B: 난 네가 잘할 거라고 확신해. 걱정하지 마.
3. G: 새 학교에서 친구를 사귀는 게 걱정돼요.
   M: 걱정하지 마. 난 네가 그곳에서 많은 친구들을 사귈 거라고 확신해.

Listen & Speak 2 A

1. **B:** You look _____. Is something _____?
   G: Yes, my sister is _____ with me.
   B: _____? What did you _____?
   G: I _____ one of her shirts _____ asking.
   B: Tell her you're _____. I'm sure she'll _____.

2. **B:** I'm _____ a hard time _____ new English words.
   G: I _____ the same problem, so I _____ my English _____ for advice.
   B: _____ did he say?
   G: He _____ me to _____ an English _____ app. It has helped me a lot. I'm _____ it would work for you, too.

Real-Life Zone

B: The team _____ for English class is _____ a lot of time.
G: I _____. I have a problem. _____ of the _____ on our team isn't _____ his part.
B: _____ not good. Everybody on the _____ has to do their job.
G: I _____, but I don't _____ how to _____ him _____ do his part.
B: Maybe he _____ know how to get _____ or doesn't _____ his _____.
G: Then _____ should I _____?
B: Talk _____ him. Ask him _____ he's not _____ his part. _____ tell him _____ help him _____ he _____.
G: Okay. I'll _____ that.
B: I'm _____ he'll do _____ after you _____ to him. Good luck with your _____.
G: Thanks.

Wrap Up

G: What's the _____, Dongha? You _____ worried.
B: I'm not _____ for the _____. I sit at my _____ to _____ but end _____ doing _____ else.
G: Well, time _____ is not _____.
B: I _____. What _____ I do?
G: _____ the things you _____ to do. _____ write how _____ time _____ need to _____ each one.
B: Thank you, Emily. I'll _____ your idea.
G: I'm sure _____ will be helpful for you. Good luck _____ your finals.

해석

1. **B:** 걱정스러워 보여. 무슨 일 있니?
   G: 응, 우리 언니가 나한테 화가 났어.
   B: 왜? 무엇을 했니?
   G: 내가 묻지도 않고 언니의 셔츠 중에 하나를 입었어.
   B: 그녀에게 미안하다고 말해. 나는 그녀가 이해해 줄 거라고 확신해.
2. **B:** 나는 새로운 영어 단어를 배우는 데 어려움을 겪고 있어.
   G: 나도 같은 문제가 있어서 영어 선생님께 조언을 구했어.
   B: 그가 뭐라고 하셨어?
   G: 그는 나에게 영어 어휘 앱을 사용하라고 조언해 주셨어. 그것은 나에게 큰 도움이 됐어. 나는 그것이 너에게도 효과가 있을 거라고 확신해.

B: 영어 수업의 팀 프로젝트는 시간이 많이 걸려.
G: 나도 동의해. 나 문제가 있어. 우리 팀의 한 사람이 자기 역할을 다하지 않아.
B: 좋지 않네. 팀의 모든 사람들은 자신들의 일을 해야 해.
G: 알아. 하지만 어떻게 그가 그의 역할을 하게 할지 모르겠어.
B: 어쩌면 그는 시작하는 법을 모르거나 자기 역할을 좋아하지 않을 수도 있어.
G: 그러면 나는 무엇을 해야 할까?
B: 그에게 말해. 그에게 왜 자신의 역할을 안 하는지 물어봐. 그러고 나서 원한다면 네가 도와주겠다고 말해.
G: 그래. 한번 해 볼게.
B: 나는 네가 말하고 나면 그가 더 잘할 거라고 확신해. 네 프로젝트가 잘 되길 바랄게.
G: 고마워.

G: 동하야, 무슨 일이야? 걱정스러워 보여.
B: 기말고사 준비가 안 됐어. 나는 공부하기 위해 책상에 앉지만 결국 다른 것을 하게 돼.
G: 음, 시간 관리가 쉽지 않지.
B: 나도 동의해. 내가 어떻게 해야 할까?
G: 해야 할 일에 번호를 매겨. 그러고 나서 각 항목을 끝내는 데 필요한 시간을 적어 봐.
B: 고마워, 에밀리. 네 방안을 한번 해 볼게.
G: 나는 그것이 너에게 도움이 될 거라고 확신해. 기말고사 잘 보길 바랄게.

[01~02] 다음 대화의 빈칸에 들어갈 말로 알맞은 것은?

01

> G: Mom told me I could use the computer for only one hour a day. She thinks that's enough time.
> M: I _____ her.
> G: Sometimes, when doing my homework, I need to use it for a long time.
> M: Hmm. Then maybe we should all get together and talk about it.
> G: Thanks for your understanding, Dad.

① agree with   ② approve   ③ am anxious about
④ am worried about   ⑤ am ready for

02

> B: You look worried. Is something wrong?
> G: Yes, my sister is upset with me.
> B: Why? What did you do?
> G: I wore one of her shirts without asking.
> B: Tell her you're sorry. _____

① You don't worry about her.
② I don't know why you were worried.
③ I will make her not be upset with you.
④ I'm sure she'll understand.
⑤ I'm pleased with her shirt.

03 대화에 이어지기에 적절하게 배열된 순서를 고르시오.

> B: I just talked about the science project with Jinho and Mina.
> G: Has your team decided what you will do?
> (A) I agree with Mina because I think the experiment would be more interesting.
> (B) Who do you agree with, Jinho or Mina?
> (C) No, not yet. Jinho wants to visit a science museum, but Mina wants to do an experiment.

① (A) – (C) – (B)   ② (B) – (A) – (C)   ③ (B) – (C) – (A)
④ (C) – (A) – (B)   ⑤ (C) – (B) – (A)

01 다음 빈칸에 적절한 말은?

> G: I think reading history comic books is helpful.
>
> B: I agree. _____

① I learn a lot from them.

② I don't like reading comic books.

③ Reading comic books is wasting time.

④ Why do you like reading comic books?

⑤ I won't read comic books any more.

[02~03] 다음 대화를 읽고 물음에 답하시오.

> B: I ____(가)____ learning new English words.
>
> G: I had the same problem, so I asked my English teacher for advice.
>
> B: What did he say?
>
> G: He advised me to use an English vocabulary app. It has helped me a lot. I'm sure it would work for you, too.

02 빈칸 (가)에 들어가기에 적절한 것은?

① have always enjoyed

② didn't really mind

③ wouldn't like

④ look forward to

⑤ am having a hard time

03 위 대화의 내용과 일치하지 <u>않는</u> 것은?

① The boy wants to improve his English.

② The girl has a hard time learning new English words.

③ The girl had the same problem.

④ The girl asked her teacher for advice.

⑤ The girl thinks using an English vocabulary app helped her.

[04~06] 다음 대화를 읽고 물음에 답하시오.

> G: What's the matter, Dongha? ____(가)____
>
> B: I'm not ready for the finals. I sit at my desk to study but end up doing something else. (A)
>
> G: Well, time management is not easy.
>
> B: I agree. What should I do? (B)
>
> G: Number the things you have to do. (C)
>
> B: Thank you, Emily. (D) I'll try your idea.
>
> G: I'm sure that will be helpful for you. (E) Good luck with your finals.

04 다음 중 빈칸 (가)에 들어가기에 적절한 것은?

① You look delighted.

② You look worried.

③ Didn't you know about the finals?

④ Are you aware of the finals?

⑤ You have too much work to do.

05 (A)~(E) 중에서 다음 문장이 들어가기에 가장 적절한 곳은?

> Then write down how much time you need to finish each one.

① (A)　② (B)　③ (C)　④ (D)　⑤ (E)

06 Which one CANNOT be answered from the dialogue above?

① Who is preparing for the finals?

② What is the problem Dongha has?

③ Why is time management important?

④ What does Emily advise Dongha to do?

⑤ What will Dongha do for his time management?

[07~09] 다음 대화를 읽고 물음에 답하시오.

B: The team project for English class is taking a lot of time.

G: I agree. I have a problem. One of the people on our team isn't doing his part.

B: That's not good. Everybody on the team has to do their job.

G: I know, but I don't know how to ___(A)___ him to do his part.

B: Maybe he doesn't know how to ___(B)___ started or doesn't like his part.

G: Then what should I do?

B: Talk to him. Ask him why he's not doing his part. Then tell him you'll help him if he wants.

G: Okay. I'll try that.

B: I'm sure he'll do better after you talk to him. Good luck with your project.

G: Thanks.

서답형

07 위 대화에서 다음 영어 설명에 해당하는 단어를 찾아 쓰시오.

> to have the same opinion as someone about a topic

➡ _____

08 위 대화의 빈칸 (A), (B)에 공통으로 들어가기에 적절한 것은?

① grow
② make
③ get
④ have
⑤ help

09 위 대화의 내용과 일치하지 <u>않는</u> 것은?

① 영어 조별 과제는 시간이 많이 걸린다.
② 소녀의 조원 중 한 명에게 문제가 있다.
③ 소녀의 조원은 모두 자기 역할을 다하고 있다.
④ 소년은 소녀에게 충고를 하고 있다.
⑤ 소녀는 문제가 있는 조원과 이야기를 할 것이다.

[10~12] 다음 대화를 읽고 물음에 답하시오.

B: You look ___(가)___. Is something wrong?

G: Yes, my sister is upset with me.

B: Why? ___(나)___ did you do?

G: I wore one of her shirts without ___(A)___.

B: Tell her you're sorry. (B)<u>I'm sure she'll understand.</u>

10 위 대화의 빈칸 (가), (나)에 들어가기에 가장 적절한 것은?

① surprised – Who
② fun – How
③ worried – What
④ tired – Why
⑤ pleased – How

11 다음 중 빈칸 (A)에 들어가기에 가장 적절한 것은?

① asked
② asks
③ ask
④ to ask
⑤ asking

12 밑줄 친 문장 (B)가 의도하는 것은?

① 방법 묻기
② 동의하기
③ 걱정 표현하기
④ 설명 요청하기
⑤ 안심시키기

01 다음 우리말에 어울리는 영어 문장을 완성하시오.

> B: I have a big soccer match tomorrow. I'm nervous.
> G: Don't worry. <u>나는 네가 시합을 매우 잘할 거라고 확신해.</u> (play, very well, 6 words)

➡ _____

02 다음 주어진 대화의 빈칸에 들어가기에 적절한 한 단어를 쓰시오.

> B: Our P.E. teacher is too strict. Don't you _____?
> G: No, I don't _____. I don't think he's too strict.

➡ _____

[03~05] 다음 대화를 읽고 물음에 답하시오.

> B: (A)<u>나는 새로운 영어 단어를 배우는 데 어려움을 겪고 있어.</u> (a hard time)
> G: I had the same problem, so I asked my English teacher for advice.
> B: What did he say?
> G: He advised me to use an English vocabulary app. It has helped me a lot. I'm sure it would work against you, too.

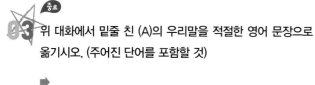

03 위 대화에서 밑줄 친 (A)의 우리말을 적절한 영어 문장으로 옮기시오. (주어진 단어를 포함할 것)

➡ _____

_____

04 위 대화에서 다음 설명에 해당하는 단어를 찾아 쓰시오.

> words that are used in a language

➡ _____

05 위 대화에서 흐름상 어색한 한 단어를 찾아 쓰고 적절한 단어로 바꾸시오.

_____ ➡ _____

[06~07] 다음 대화를 읽고 물음에 답하시오.

> B: The team project for English class is taking a lot of time.
> G: I agree. I have a problem. One of the people on our team isn't doing his (A)part.
> B: That's not good. Everybody on the team has to do their job.
> G: I know, but I don't know how to get him to do his part.
> B: Maybe he doesn't know how to get started or doesn't like his part.
> G: Then what should I do?
> B: Talk to him. Ask him why he's not doing his part. Then tell him you'll help him if he wants.
> G: Okay. I'll try that.
> B: (B)<u>나는 네가 그와 이야기한 이후로 그가 더 잘할 것이라고 확신해.</u> Good luck with your project.
> G: Thanks.

06 밑줄 친 (A)와 같은 의미로 바꾸어 쓸 수 있는 단어를 본문에서 찾아 쓰시오.

➡ _____

07 밑줄 친 (B)의 우리말을 적절한 영어 문장으로 옮기시오. (better, talk to 포함) (10 words)

➡ _____

교과서

Grammar

① 분사구문

> • Daeho, **thinking that new things will make him more popular**, often wants new things just because his friends have them. 대호는 새 물건이 그를 더 인기 있게 만들어 줄 것이라고 생각해서 단지 친구들이 그것을 가지고 있다는 이유로 종종 새 물건을 사기를 원합니다.

■ 분사가 이끄는 구를 분사구문이라고 하며, 이유, 조건, 시간, 동시동작, 양보 등의 뜻을 나타낸다. 분사구문은 '접속사+주어+동사'로 이루어진 부사절의 주어가 주절의 주어와 일치할 때 접속사와 주어를 생략하고 동사를 분사(동사원형+-ing)로 만든 구문이다. 이때 생략되는 접속사에 따라 뜻이 달라진다.

- He was lying in an armchair, as he watched TV. → He was lying in an armchair, **watching TV**. (시간) 그는 TV를 보며 안락의자에 누워 있었다.

■ 부사절과 주절의 주어가 다를 때는 부사절의 주어를 생략하지 않고 사용하며 이것을 독립분사구문이라고 한다.

- As it was fine, I went for a walk in the park. → **It being fine**, I went for a walk in the park. 날씨가 좋아서 나는 공원으로 산책하러 갔다.

■ 분사구문에서 Being이나 Having been은 보통 생략한다.

- I broke a tooth when I was eating something hard. → I broke a tooth (**being**) **eating something hard**. 딱딱한 것을 먹고 있을 때 이가 부러졌습니다.

■ 분사구문의 부정은 분사 앞에 'not'이나 'never'를 쓴다.

- As he didn't prepare for the exam, he got a bad grade. → **Not preparing for the exam**, he got a bad grade. 그가 시험을 위해 준비하지 않았기 때문에 나쁜 성적을 얻었다.

■ 분사구문의 뜻을 명확히 하기 위해 접속사를 생략하지 않기도 한다.

- **After taking a quick shower**, I make my own bed. 재빨리 샤워를 한 후에, 저는 잠자리를 준비합니다.

■ 과거분사로 시작되는 분사구문은 being이 생략된 것으로 수동의 의미를 갖는다.

- **Disappointed with the news** she went to him and explained her difficulty. 그 소식에 실망해서 그녀는 그에게 가서 자신의 어려움을 설명했다.

핵심 Check

1. 다음 괄호 안에서 알맞은 말을 고르시오.

(1) He had some chips, (watch / watching) the TV.

(2) (Listening / listened) to the music, he was reading a comic book.

② 명사절을 이끄는 접속사 if

- **You should just ask her if there is something wrong.**
  뭔가 잘못된 것이 있는지 그녀에게 물어봐.

- **Do you know if he's married?** 그가 결혼을 했는지 아니?

■ if나 whether는 '~인지 (아닌지)'라는 의미의 접속사로 어떠한 사실의 여부를 확인하거나 불확실함을
나타낼 때 쓰이며, 주로 ask, be not sure, find out, know, see, tell, wonder 등의 동사의 목적어 역할
을 하는 명사절을 이끈다. if[whether] 뒤에 오는 절은 의문사가 없는 간접의문문으로 'if[whether]+주
어+동사'의 어순으로 쓴다. if는 주어나 보어가 되는 명사절을 이끌 수 없다.

- I'm not sure **if[whether]** he's coming. 그가 올지 확실히 모르겠어. 〈목적어〉
- **Whether** he will come (or not) is not certain. 그가 올지 안 올지 확실치 않다. 〈주어〉
- The most important thing is **whether** you answered appropriately or not. 가장 중요한 것은 네가 적절
  하게 대답을 했는지 안 했는지이다. 〈보어〉
- I wonder. + He is at home.
  → I wonder **if** he is at home. 그가 집에 있을지 모르겠다.

■ if가 명사절을 이끄는 접속사로 그 명사절이 문장 내에서 동사의 목적어로 쓰일 때는 whether로 바
꿔 쓸 수 있다. whether 다음에는 or not을 바로 붙여 쓸 수 있지만, if는 바로 붙여 쓸 수 없다.

- I'll ask **if** it's all right to park here. 여기에 주차를 해도 괜찮은지 물어 볼게.
  = I'll ask **whether** it's all right to park here.
- I don't know **whether** or not it was true. 전 그게 사실이었는지 아닌지 몰라요.
  = I don't know **if** or not it was true. (×)

cf. 보통 if가 조건의 부사절을 이끌 때는 '만약 ~라면'이라는 의미로 쓰이며, whether가 부사절을 이끌
경우에는 '~이든 (아니든)'이라는 '양보'의 의미로 쓰인다.

- **If** metal gets hot, it expands. 금속은 열을 받으면 팽창한다. 〈조건〉
- **Whether** you agree or not, I will help them. 네가 동의하든 말든 그들을 돕겠다. 〈양보〉

핵심 Check

2. 다음 빈칸에 들어갈 말을 〈보기〉에서 골라 쓰시오.

┌─ 보기 ┄─────────────────────────────────┐

whether   if   that

└──┘

(1) When they asked me _____ I wanted the job, I said yes.

(2) I'm not sure _____ I can do it.

(3) They have never decided _____ or not he was murdered.

Grammar 시험대비 기본평가

01 다음 빈칸에 들어갈 말로 알맞은 것은?

> _____ me, he smiled brightly.

① Seeing   ② Seen   ③ Sees
④ Saw   ⑤ See

02 다음 괄호 안에서 알맞은 말을 고르시오.

(1) Lisa listens to music, (walk / walking) around the park.

(2) (Knowing not / Not knowing) her, I kept silent.

(3) He asked me (if / that) I could solve the puzzle.

(4) I am not sure (if / whether) or not he is going to the dance Friday night.

03 다음 우리말에 맞게 빈칸에 알맞은 것은?

> 다른 선택이 있는지 모르겠어요.
> = I don't know _____ I have another choice.

① which   ② that   ③ what
④ unless   ⑤ if

04 다음 우리말에 맞게 주어진 어휘를 바르게 배열하시오.

(1) 나를 바라보면서, 그녀는 환하게 미소를 지었다.

(she, me, looking, smiled, brightly, at)

➡ _____

(2) 회사에서 집으로 걸어오는 중에 이 근사한 빵집을 발견했어.

(work, this, home, while, bakery, I, walking, found, great, from)

➡ _____

(3) 소문이 사실인지 확인해 볼 필요가 있다

(the rumor, we, need, is, find, true, if, out, to)

➡ _____

01 다음 중 어법상 어색한 것은?

① Feeling tired, she went to bed early.

② Aaron danced with great joy, singing in the rain.

③ Mike was standing outside the house, wait for her.

④ While working together in the field, they became friends.

⑤ Turning left there, you will find the building.

02 다음 중 어법상 어색한 것은?

① I want to ask her if she likes chocolate cake.

② I'm not sure whether I can go to the concert or not.

③ He couldn't tell if she was laughing or crying.

④ I just wanted to know that everything was all right.

⑤ I'm wondering whether you could help me.

03 다음 빈칸에 알맞은 말이 바르게 짝지어진 것은?

> • I'd like to know _____ Sora likes spicy food.
> • _____ his homework, the boy played computer games.

① if – Finishing

② that – Finishing

③ if – Finished

④ that – Finished

⑤ whether – Finish

서답형

04 다음 괄호 안에서 알맞은 말을 고르시오.

(1) Do you know (that / if) Kate will come back soon?

(2) A number of factors decide (whether / that) a movie will be successful or not.

(3) You can find out online (whether / if) or not they have the book.

(4) (Neglect / Neglecting) his duty, he was fired.

(5) You need to watch your tongue when (talk / talking) to your boss.

(6) (Getting not / Not getting) a message from her, he just waited there.

05 주어진 두 문장을 한 문장으로 바꿀 때 옳지 <u>않은</u> 것은?

> • He came back from the trip.
> • He looked like a beggar.

① When he came back from the trip, he looked like a beggar.

② As he came back from the trip, he looked like a beggar.

③ Coming back from the trip, he looked like a beggar.

④ When coming back from the trip, he looked like a beggar.

⑤ When came back from the trip, he looked like a beggar.

06 빈칸 (A)와 (B)에 알맞은 것으로 짝지어진 것은?

> • You did not tell me ___(A)___ you would come to the party.
> • ___(B)___ or not this company will succeed depends on the outcome of the project.

	(A)	(B)
①	whether	If
②	which	If
③	if	Whether
④	which	Whether
⑤	if	While

07 다음 문장의 밑줄 친 부분 중 어법상 어색한 것은?

> Daeho, ⓐthinks that new things ⓑwill make him more popular, often ⓒwants new things just ⓓbecause his friends have ⓔthem.

① ⓐ   ② ⓑ   ③ ⓒ

④ ⓓ   ⑤ ⓔ

08 다음 밑줄 친 부분과 바꿔 쓸 수 있는 것은?

> I don't know if Bora has the key.

① unless   ② that   ③ what

④ which   ⑤ whether

서답형

09 다음 두 문장을 한 문장으로 바꿔 쓸 때 빈칸에 알맞은 말을 쓰시오.

> • I was lonely.
> • I decided to make some friends.
> = _____ lonely, I decided to make some friends.

10 다음 우리말을 바르게 영작한 것을 고르시오.

> Justine은 내가 영어 시험에서 좋은 점수를 받았는지 물어본다.

① Justine asks me if I get a good grade in the English test.

② Justine asks me if I got a good grade in the English test.

③ Justine asks me that I got a good grade in the English test.

④ Justine asks me because I got a good grade in the English test.

⑤ Justine asks me if or not I got a good grade in the English test.

11 밑줄 친 부분의 쓰임이 주어진 문장과 같은 것은?

> Getting hot, metal expands.

① You should not blink your eyes when taking pictures.

② Turning to the right, you will find the post office.

③ Having nothing to do, I went to see a film.

④ He kept on reading, while eating snacks.

⑤ Being nervous, she said it was a good experience.

서답형

12 다음 문장에서 생략할 수 있는 것을 찾아 쓰시오.

(1) Though I was sleepy, I forced myself to stay awake.

➡ _____

(2) He got interested in politics when he was in college.

➡ _____

13 주어진 문장의 틀린 부분을 찾아 바르게 고치지 <u>않은</u> 것을 고르시오.

> I wonder that our flight will leave today or not.

① I wonder whether our flight will leave today.

② I wonder whether our flight will leave today or not.

③ I wonder whether or not our flight will leave today.

④ I wonder if or not our flight will leave today.

⑤ I wonder if our flight will leave today or not.

서답형

14 다음 문장에서 어법상 어색한 것을 바르게 고쳐 다시 쓰시오.

(1) We don't know if Mark succeeds.

➡ _____

_____

(2) If I believe you or not is not important now.

➡ _____

_____

(3) Ridden a bike, he always wears his helmet.

➡ _____

_____

(4) Feeling not good about it, he wrote a letter to her.

➡ _____

_____

(5) Disappointing with the result, she walked out of her room.

➡ _____

_____

15 다음 우리말을 바르게 영작한 것을 고르시오.

> 좋은 점수를 받고 싶어서, 그는 공부를 열심히 하기로 결심했다.

① Wanted to get good grades, he decides to study hard.

② Wants to get good grades, he decides to study hard.

③ Want to get good grades, he decided to study hard.

④ Wanted to get good grades, he decided to study hard.

⑤ Wanting to get good grades, he decided to study hard.

16 다음 중 어법상 어색한 것을 <u>모두</u> 고르시오.

① I want to know if you can help me with my math homework.

② That depends on if you send it by air or ship.

③ He didn't decide if to go or stay.

④ Try these tips, and then let me know if they work for you.

⑤ Why don't you ask her if there is anything wrong?

서답형

17 다음 두 문장을 한 문장으로 바꿔 쓰시오.

> • She advises Sohui to ask Hayeon.
> • Is there something wrong?

➡ _____

_____

01 주어진 문장을 분사구문으로 바꿔 쓰시오.

(1) As he was so upset, he went out without saying anything.

➡ _____

_____

(2) If you cancel the order, you will lose your money.

➡ _____

_____

(3) Although I am tired of a lot of homework, I won't give up.

➡ _____

_____

(4) Because I didn't feel good, I stayed in bed all morning.

➡ _____

_____

(5) If it is fine, I will start tomorrow.

➡ _____

_____

02 if를 이용하여 다음 두 문장을 한 문장으로 바꿔 쓰시오.

(1) • He couldn't tell.

• Was she laughing or crying?

➡ _____

_____

(2) • I'm not sure.

• Did he explain everything about your compensation?

➡ _____

_____

03 다음 우리말에 맞게 주어진 단어를 바르게 배열하시오.

(1) 이 기차를 탄다면, 너는 오후 1시에 부산에 도착할 거야. (you'll, this train, 1 p.m., Busan, get, taking, at, to)

➡ _____

(2) 바쁠지라도, Amy는 항상 기꺼이 나를 도와주려 한다. (Amy, me, always, busy, is, being, help, willing, to)

➡ _____

(3) 나는 그가 이 근처에 사는지 궁금하다. (I, he, here, wonder, lives, near, if)

➡ _____

(4) 나는 그가 아직도 나를 기억하고 있는지 잘 모르겠어. (I, me, he, sure, am, remembers, not, still, if)

➡ _____

04 다음 문장에서 <u>잘못된</u> 것을 알맞게 고쳐 다시 쓰시오.

(1) If he will continue to be successful in future is open to doubt.

➡ _____

_____

(2) Some friends asked me if or not I had an accident.

➡ _____

_____

(3) I was debating in my mind if to go or not.

➡ _____

_____

05 그림을 보고 주어진 어휘를 이용하여 빈칸을 알맞게 채우시오.

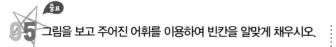

Mina   John   Suzie

(1) Mina wonders _____
at her new school. (can, she, make friends)

(2) John is not sure _____
well at the soccer match. (can, he, play)

(3) Suzie worries about _____
fine at the speech contest. (can, do, she)

06 그림을 보고 접속사 없이 주어진 어휘를 이용하여 빈칸을 알맞게 채우시오.

Minho   Jane   Don

(1) _____, Minho dropped his bag
and it opened. (do, check-in)

(2) Jane checked her schedule, _____
with Tom. (have a talk)

(3) _____ of the airport, Don felt
very cold. (come, out)

07 다음 우리말을 괄호 안의 지시대로 영작하시오.

(1) 그는 아파서 하루 종일 집에 있었다.

➡ _____

(분사구문을 써서)

➡ _____

(접속사를 써서)

(2) 길을 걸으면서 너의 전화기를 보지 마라.

➡ _____

(분사구문을 써서)

➡ _____

(접속사를 써서)

(3) 표를 가지고 계신지 여쭤봐도 될까요?

➡ _____

(접속사를 써서)

(4) 나는 그가 그 시험을 합격할 수 있을지 궁금하다.

➡ _____

(접속사를 써서)

08 다음 문장에서 어법상 <u>어색한</u> 것을 분사구문을 이용하여 바르게 고쳐 다시 쓰시오.

(1) Writing in haste, this book has a lot of mistakes.

➡ _____

_____

(2) There was no train left, he had to stay at a hotel.

➡ _____

_____

Reading

What Should I Do?

Everyone has worries. When you have things you worry about, what
단수 취급   have(×)   things와 you 사이에 목적격 관계대명사 that 생략
do you do? Here are some things that three teenagers worry about.
        Here are+복수 명사: '여기에 ~이 있다'

Sohui thought Hayeon was her best friend, but now, Sohui feels that

Hayeon has changed and she is avoiding her.
현재완료(결과 용법): 과거에 행해진 어떤 행동의 결과가 현재까지 영향을 미칠 때 사용

Sohui: (To her older sister) You know my friend Hayeon, don't you?
                                            일반동사가 있을 때: 부가의문문은 do(es)나 did를 사용해서 만든다.

Sister: Yeah. Why? What about her?
                    ~이 어때?

Sohui: I feel she's avoiding me. When I see her at school, she turns

around and walks away from me.

Sister: I'm sorry to hear that. Do you have any idea why she does that?
        to부정사의 부사적 용법(원인)   간접의문문(의문사+주어+동사)

Sohui: No. I don't think I've done anything wrong. It just feels like
                                    '-thing'으로 끝나는 대명사는 형용사가 뒤에서 수식

she doesn't like me anymore.
      = she no more likes me

Sister: Maybe you should just ask her if there is something wrong.
                            명사절을 이끄는 접속사: ~인지 아닌지

Sohui: Maybe I should. I still want to be friends with her.

---

everyone 모든 사람

worry 걱정거리, 걱정(되는 일); 걱정하다

teenager 청소년(나이가 13–19세인 사람)

avoid 피하다

turn around 돌아서다

not ~ anymore 더 이상 ~ 않다

avoid 피하다

if ~인지 아닌지

maybe 아마도

still 아직도

확인문제

● 다음 문장이 본문의 내용과 일치하면 T, 일치하지 <u>않으면</u> F를 쓰시오.

1 Sohui thought Hayeon was her best friend. ☐

2 Now, Hayeon feels that Sohui has changed and she is avoiding her. ☐

3 When Sohui sees Hayeon at school, Hayeon turns around and walks away from Sohui. ☐

4 Sohui thinks she has done something wrong. ☐

5 Sohui's sister advises Sohui to ask Hayeon if there is something wrong. ☐

6 Sohui doesn't want to be friends with Hayeon anymore. ☐

Daeho, thinking that new things will make him more popular, often wants new things just because his friends have them.

Daeho: Seongjin, look at my new sneakers. What do you think?

Seongjin: They're nice, but didn't you just buy new sneakers a couple of months ago?

Daeho: Yeah, but they're no longer in style. I look cooler in these, right?

Seongjin: Daeho, wearing the latest fashion doesn't make you cooler or more popular. People like you because you're you, not because of your clothes.

Daeho: Yeah?

Seongjin: Listen, you're a great guy. You don't need new sneakers to prove it.

Recently, Minkyeong was asked out by a boy in her class. She wants to say no but does not want to hurt his feelings.

Minkyeong: I need your advice. A boy in my class asked me out. I like him, but for now I don't want to go out with him. I need to focus on my studies. What should I do?

Counselor: Why don't you tell him why you can't go?

Minkyeong: I'm afraid I might hurt his feelings.

Counselor: If you don't tell him soon, he will misunderstand your feelings, and you may end up hurting him even more.

Minkyeong: Maybe you're right. Thanks for the advice.

---

sneakers 운동화

latest 최신의

guy (비격식) 녀석, 남자

prove 증명하다, 입증하다

a couple of 두서너 개의, 몇 개의, 몇 사람의

in style 유행하는, 유행되는

recently 최근에

afraid 걱정하는, 불안한

counselor 카운슬러, 상담역

misunderstand 오해하다

ask somebody out ~에게 데이트를 신청하다

end up 결국 ~하게 되다

📎 확인문제

● 다음 문장이 본문의 내용과 일치하면 T, 일치하지 않으면 F를 쓰시오.

1 Daeho thinks that new things will make him more popular. ☐

2 Seongjin doesn't like Daeho's new sneakers. ☐

3 Seongjin says wearing the latest fashion doesn't make Daeho cooler or more popular. ☐

4 Daeho needs new sneakers to prove he is a great guy. ☐

5 Recently, a boy in Minkyeong's class asked Minkyeong out. ☐

6 Minkyeong doesn't want to go out with him because she doesn't like him. ☐

우리말을 참고하여 빈칸에 알맞은 말을 쓰시오.

1 What _____ I Do?

2 Everyone _____ worries.

3 When you have things you worry about, _____ _____ _____ _____?

4 _____ _____ _____ _____ that three teenagers worry about.

5 Sohui thought Hayeon was _____ _____ _____, but now, Sohui feels that Hayeon _____ _____ and she _____ _____ her.

6 Sohui: (To her older sister) You know my friend Hayeon, _____ _____?

7 Sister: Yeah. Why? _____ _____ her?

8 Sohui: _____ _____ she's avoiding me.

9 When I see her at school, she _____ _____ and _____ _____ _____ me.

10 Sister: I'm sorry _____ _____ _____.

11 Do you have any idea _____ _____ _____ _____?

12 Sohui: No. I don't think _____ _____ _____.

13 It just _____ _____ she doesn't like me anymore.

14 Sister: Maybe you _____ just ask her _____ there is _____ _____.

15 Sohui: Maybe I should. I _____ want to be friends _____ her.

16 Daeho, _____ that new things will make him more popular, often wants new things _____ _____ his friends have them.

17 Daeho: Seongjin, look at my _____ _____.

18 _____ do you think?

1	제가 어떻게 해야 할까요?
2	누구나 고민은 있습니다.
3	여러분은 걱정되는 것이 있을 때 무엇을 하나요?
4	여기 세 명의 청소년이 걱정하는 것들이 있습니다.
5	소희는 하연이가 그녀의 가장 친한 친구라고 생각했지만, 지금은 하연이가 변했고 그녀를 피한다고 느낍니다.
6	소희: (그녀의 언니에게) 내 친구 하연이 알지, 그렇지?
7	언니: 응. 왜? 그녀가 어떤데?
8	소희: 나는 그녀가 나를 피하고 있다고 느껴.
9	학교에서 내가 그녀를 볼 때 그녀는 돌아서서 나로부터 멀리 걸어가.
10	언니: 그거 참 안타깝구나.
11	너는 그녀가 왜 그렇게 하는지 아니?
12	소희: 아니. 나는 내가 잘못한 것이 있다고 생각하지 않아.
13	단지 그녀가 더 이상 나를 좋아하지 않는다고 느껴져.
14	언니: 혹시 모르니 뭔가 잘못된 것이 있는지 그녀에게 물어봐.
15	소희: 아마 그래야겠어. 나는 여전히 그녀와 친구로 지내고 싶거든.
16	대호는 새 물건이 그를 더 인기 있게 만들어 줄 것이라고 생각해서 단지 친구들이 그것을 가지고 있다는 이유로 종종 새 물건을 사기를 원합니다.
17	대호: 성진아, 내 새 운동화 봐.
18	어떠니?

19 **Seongjin:** They're nice, but _____ _____ just buy new sneakers a _____ _____ months ago?

20 **Daeho:** Yeah, but they're no longer _____ _____.

21 I look cooler _____ _____, right?

22 **Seongjin:** Daeho, _____ the latest fashion doesn't make you _____ or _____ _____.

23 People like you _____ _____ _____, not because of your clothes.

24 **Daeho:** Yeah?

25 **Seongjin:** Listen, you're _____ _____ _____.

26 You don't need new sneakers _____ _____ _____.

27 Recently, Minkyeong _____ _____ _____ by a boy in her class.

28 She wants to say no but does not want _____ _____ _____ _____.

29 **Minkyeong:** I need your _____.

30 A boy in my class _____ _____ _____.

31 I like him, but _____ _____ I don't want to _____ _____ _____ him.

32 I need to _____ _____ my studies.

33 What _____ I do?

34 **Counselor:** _____ _____ _____ tell him why you can't go?

35 **Minkyeong:** _____ _____ I might hurt his feelings.

36 **Counselor:** _____ _____ _____ _____ him soon, he will misunderstand your feelings, and you may _____ _____ _____ him even more.

37 **Minkyeong:** Maybe _____ _____.

38 _____ _____ the advice.

19 성진: 멋지다. 그런데 너 겨우 몇 달 전에 새 운동화 사지 않았니?

20 대호: 응, 하지만 그건 더 이상 유행이 아니야.

21 이걸 신으니까 더 멋져 보이지, 그렇지?

22 성진: 대호야, 최신 유행하는 것을 입는 것이 너를 더 멋지고 더 인기 있게 만들어 주지는 않아.

23 사람들은 네가 너이기 때문에 너를 좋아하는 것이지, 네 옷 때문이 아니야.

24 대호: 그래?

25 성진: 들어봐. 너는 멋진 사람이야.

26 그것을 증명하기 위해 새 운동화가 필요하지 않아.

27 최근에 민경이는 그녀의 반 남자아이에게 데이트 신청을 받았습니다.

28 그녀는 거절하고 싶지만 그의 감정을 상하게 하고 싶지는 않습니다.

29 민경: 저는 선생님의 조언이 필요해요.

30 같은 반 남자아이가 저에게 데이트 신청을 했어요.

31 저는 그를 좋아하지만 당분간은 그와 데이트하고 싶지 않아요.

32 저는 공부에 집중해야 해요.

33 제가 어떻게 해야 할까요?

34 상담 선생님: 왜 네가 데이트를 할 수 없는지 그에게 말하는 것은 어떨까?

35 민경: 제가 그의 감정을 상하게 할까 봐 걱정돼요.

36 상담 선생님: 네가 그에게 빨리 말하지 않으면, 그는 네 감정을 오해할 것이고, 너는 그를 더 아프게 할 수도 있단다.

37 민경: 선생님 말씀이 맞는 것 같아요.

38 조언 감사합니다.

● 우리말을 참고하여 본문을 영작하시오.

1 제가 어떻게 해야 할까요?
➡ _____

2 누구나 고민은 있습니다.
➡ _____

3 여러분은 걱정되는 것이 있을 때 무엇을 하나요?
➡ _____

4 여기 세 명의 청소년이 걱정하는 것들이 있습니다.
➡ _____

5 소희는 하연이가 그녀의 가장 친한 친구라고 생각했지만, 지금은 하연이가 변했고 그녀를 피한다고 느낍니다.
➡ _____

6 소희: (그녀의 언니에게) 내 친구 하연이 알지, 그렇지?
➡ _____

7 언니: 응. 왜? 그녀가 어떤데?
➡ _____

8 소희: 나는 그녀가 나를 피하고 있다고 느껴.
➡ _____

9 학교에서 내가 그녀를 볼 때 그녀는 돌아서서 나로부터 멀리 걸어가.
➡ _____

10 언니: 그거 참 안타깝구나.
➡ _____

11 너는 그녀가 왜 그렇게 하는지 아니?
➡ _____

12 소희: 아니. 나는 내가 잘못한 것이 있다고 생각하지 않아.
➡ _____

13 단지 그녀가 더 이상 나를 좋아하지 않는다고 느껴져.
➡ _____

14 언니: 혹시 모르니 뭔가 잘못된 것이 있는지 그녀에게 물어봐.
➡ _____

15 소희: 아마 그래야겠어. 나는 여전히 그녀와 친구로 지내고 싶거든.
➡ _____

16 대호는 새 물건이 그를 더 인기 있게 만들어 줄 것이라고 생각해서 단지 친구들이 그것을 가지고 있다는 이유로 종종 새 물건을 사기를 원합니다.
➡ _____
_____

17 대호: 성진아, 내 새 운동화 봐.
➡ _____

18 어떠니?
➡ _____

19 성진: 멋지다. 그런데 너 겨우 몇 달 전에 새 운동화 사지 않았니?

➡ _____

20 대호: 응, 하지만 그건 더 이상 유행이 아니야.

➡ _____

21 이걸 신으니까 더 멋져 보이지, 그렇지?

➡ _____

22 성진: 대호야, 최신 유행하는 것을 입는 것이 너를 더 멋지고 더 인기 있게 만들어 주지는 않아.

➡ _____

23 사람들은 네가 너이기 때문에 너를 좋아하는 것이지, 네 옷 때문이 아니야.

➡ _____

24 대호: 그래?

➡ _____

25 성진: 들어봐. 너는 멋진 사람이야.

➡ _____

26 그것을 증명하기 위해 새 운동화가 필요하지 않아.

➡ _____

27 최근에 민경이는 그녀의 반 남자아이에게 데이트 신청을 받았습니다.

➡ _____

28 그녀는 거절하고 싶지만 그의 감정을 상하게 하고 싶지는 않습니다.

➡ _____

29 민경: 저는 선생님의 조언이 필요해요.

➡ _____

30 같은 반 남자아이가 저에게 데이트 신청을 했어요.

➡ _____

31 저는 그를 좋아하지만 당분간은 그와 데이트하고 싶지 않아요.

➡ _____

32 저는 공부에 집중해야 해요.

➡ _____

33 제가 어떻게 해야 할까요?

➡ _____

34 상담 선생님: 왜 네가 데이트를 할 수 없는지 그에게 말하는 것은 어떨까?

➡ _____

35 민경: 제가 그의 감정을 상하게 할까 봐 걱정돼요

➡ _____

36 상담 선생님: 네가 그에게 빨리 말하지 않으면, 그는 네 감정을 오해할 것이고, 너는 그를 더 아프게 할 수도 있단다.

➡ _____

37 민경: 선생님 말씀이 맞는 것 같아요.

➡ _____

38 조언 감사합니다.

➡ _____

[01~03] 다음 글을 읽고 물음에 답하시오.

Daeho, (A)thinking that new things will make him more popular, often wants new things just because his friends have them.

Daeho: Seongjin, look at my new sneakers. What do you think?

Seongjin: They're nice, but didn't you just buy new sneakers a couple of months ago?

Daeho: Yeah, but they're no longer ⓐ style. I look cooler ⓑ these, right?

Seongjin: Daeho, wearing the latest fashion doesn't make you cooler or more popular. People like you because you're you, not because of your clothes.

Daeho: Yeah?

Seongjin: Listen, you're a great guy. You don't need new sneakers to prove (B)it.

서답형

01 위 글의 빈칸 ⓐ와 ⓑ에 공통으로 들어갈 알맞은 전치사를 쓰시오.

➡ _____

02 위 글의 밑줄 친 (A)thinking과 문법적 쓰임이 같은 것을 모두 고르시오.

① Just thinking about her makes me happy.

② She answered the questions thinking carefully.

③ I turned left without thinking anything.

④ We need to start thinking globally.

⑤ I didn't lose hope thinking positively.

서답형

03 위 글의 밑줄 친 (B)it이 가리키는 것을 본문에서 찾아 쓰시오.

➡ _____

[04~05] 다음 글을 읽고 물음에 답하시오.

Recently, Minkyeong was asked out by a boy in her class. She wants to say no but does not want to hurt his feelings.

Minkyeong: I need your advice. A boy in my class asked me out. I like him, but for now I don't want to go out with him. I need to focus on my studies. What should I do?

Counselor: ⓐWhy don't you tell him why you can't go?

Minkyeong: I'm afraid I might hurt his feelings.

Counselor: If you don't tell him soon, he will misunderstand your feelings, and you may end up hurting him even more.

Minkyeong: Maybe you're right. Thanks for the advice.

서답형

04 위 글의 밑줄 친 ⓐ를 다음과 같이 바꿔 쓸 때 빈칸에 들어갈 알맞은 말을 두 단어로 쓰시오.

➡ _____ telling him why you can't go?

05 위 글의 제목으로 알맞은 것을 고르시오.

① Wow! Minkyeong Is Very Popular!

② Sorry, But You're Not My Type!

③ Sorry! For Now I Need to Focus on My Studies!

④ How about Telling Him You Like Him, Too?

⑤ Time to Say Hello and Goodbye

[06~07] 다음 글을 읽고 물음에 답하시오.

Everyone has worries. When you have things you worry ⓐ , what do you do? Here are some things that three teenagers worry ⓑ .

서답형

06 위 글의 빈칸 ⓐ와 ⓑ에 공통으로 들어갈 알맞은 전치사를 쓰시오.

➡ _____

07 위 글의 뒤에 올 내용으로 가장 알맞은 것을 고르시오.

① the most common concerns of people
② the way to give effective advice
③ the importance of friendship
④ the worries of three teenagers
⑤ the routine of most teenagers

[08~10] 다음 글을 읽고 물음에 답하시오.

Sohui thought Hayeon was ①her best friend, but now, Sohui feels that Hayeon has changed and she is avoiding ②her.
Sohui: (To ③her older sister) You know ④my friend Hayeon, don't you?
Sister: Yeah. Why? What about ⑤her?
Sohui: I feel she's avoiding me. When I see her at school, she turns around and walks away from me.
Sister: I'm sorry ⓐto hear that. Do you have any idea why she does that?
Sohui: No. I don't think I've done anything wrong. It just feels like she doesn't like me anymore.
Sister: Maybe you should just ask her if there is something wrong.
Sohui: Maybe I should. I still want to be friends with her.

중요

08 밑줄 친 ①~⑤ 중에서 가리키는 대상이 나머지 넷과 다른 것은?

① ② ③ ④ ⑤

09 다음 부사적 용법의 to부정사들 중에서 위 글의 밑줄 친 ⓐ to hear와 쓰임이 같은 것을 고르시오.

① He grew up to be a scientist.
② She must be smart to say so.
③ She was surprised to hear the news.
④ He is rich enough to buy a car of his own.
⑤ I got up early to catch the first train.

10 According to the passage, which is NOT true?

① Sohui feels Hayeon is avoiding her.
② When Sohui sees Hayeon at school, Sohui turns around and walks away from Hayeon.
③ Sohui doesn't think she has done anything wrong.
④ Sohui's sister advises Sohui to ask Hayeon if there is something wrong.
⑤ Sohui still wants to be friends with Hayeon.

[11~12] 다음 글을 읽고 물음에 답하시오.

Daeho, thinking that new things will make him more popular, often wants new things just because his friends have them.
Daeho: Seongjin, look at my new sneakers. What do you think?
Seongjin: They're nice, but didn't you just buy new sneakers a couple of months ago?
Daeho: Yeah, but ⓐthey're no longer in style. I look cooler in these, right?

Seongjin: Daeho, wearing the latest fashion doesn't make you cooler or more popular. People like you because you're you, not because of your clothes.

Daeho: Yeah?

Seongjin: Listen, you're a great guy. You don't need new sneakers to prove it.

서답형

11 다음 빈칸에 알맞은 단어를 넣어 위 글의 밑줄 친 ⓐthey가 가리키는 것을 완성하시오.

> the _____ _____ that Daeho bought a couple of months ago

중요

12 위 글의 '대호'를 설명할 수 있는 말로 가장 알맞은 것을 고르시오.

① old-fashioned   ② sociable

③ modest   ④ trendy

⑤ frugal

[13~15] 다음 글을 읽고 물음에 답하시오.

(A)Recently, Minkyeong was asked out by a boy in her class. She wants to say no but does not want to hurt his feelings.

Minkyeong: I need your advice. A boy in my class asked me out. I like him, but _____ⓐ_____ now I don't want to go out with him. I need to focus _____ⓑ_____ my studies. What should I do?

Counselor: Why don't you tell him why you can't go?

Minkyeong: I'm afraid I might hurt his feelings.

Counselor: If you don't tell him soon, he will misunderstand your feelings, and you may end up hurting him (B)even more.

Minkyeong: Maybe you're right. Thanks for the advice.

13 위 글의 빈칸 ⓐ와 ⓑ에 들어갈 전치사가 바르게 짝지어진 것은?

    ⓐ   ⓑ   ⓐ   ⓑ

① for – about   ② in – to

③ at – on   ④ for – on

⑤ at – to

서답형

14 위 글의 밑줄 친 (A)를 능동태로 고치시오.

➡ _____

중요

15 위 글의 밑줄 친 (B)even과 같은 의미로 쓰인 것을 고르시오.

① He never even opened the letter.

② You know even less about it than I do.

③ You need an even surface to work on.

④ Even a child can understand it.

⑤ Our scores are now even.

[16~18] 다음 글을 읽고 물음에 답하시오.

Daeho, thinking that new things will make him more popular, often wants new things just because his friends have ⓐthem.

Daeho: Seongjin, look at my new sneakers. What do you think?

Seongjin: They're nice, but didn't you just buy new sneakers a couple of months ago?

Daeho: Yeah, but they're no longer in style. I look cooler _____ⓑ_____ these, right?

Seongjin: Daeho, wearing the latest fashion doesn't make you cooler or more popular. ⓒ사람들은 네가 너이기 때문에 너를 좋아하는 것이지, 네 옷 때문이 아니야.

Daeho: Yeah?

Seongjin: Listen, you're a great guy. You don't need new sneakers to prove it.

서답형

16 위 글의 밑줄 친 ⓐthem이 가리키는 것을 본문에서 찾아 쓰시오.

➡ _____

17 위 글의 빈칸 ⓑ에 알맞은 것을 고르시오.

① on　　　　② to　　　　③ in
④ for　　　　⑤ with

서답형

18 위 글의 밑줄 친 ⓒ의 우리말에 맞게 한 단어를 보충하여, 주어진 어휘를 알맞게 배열하시오.

your clothes / like / because / not / you /
you / because / people / you're / ,

➡ _____
_____

[19~21] 다음 글을 읽고 물음에 답하시오.

Sohui thought Hayeon was her best friend, but now, Sohui feels that Hayeon ⓐhas changed and she is avoiding her.

Sohui: (To her older sister) You know my friend Hayeon, don't you?

Sister: Yeah. Why? What about her? (①)

Sohui: (②) I feel she's avoiding me. (③) When I see her at school, she turns around and walks away from me.

Sister: (④) Do you have any idea why she does that?

Sohui: (⑤) No. I don't think I've done anything wrong. It just feels like she doesn't like me anymore.

Sister: Maybe you should just ask her if there is something wrong.

Sohui: Maybe I should. I still want to be friends with her.

19 위 글의 흐름으로 보아, 주어진 문장이 들어가기에 가장 적절한 곳은?

I'm sorry to hear that.

①　　　②　　　③　　　④　　　⑤

20 위 글의 밑줄 친 ⓐhas changed와 현재완료의 용법이 같은 것을 모두 고르시오.

① I have spent all the money, so I have no money.

② I have known her for 5 years.

③ How many times have you seen it?

④ She has gone to Paris.

⑤ How long have you been in Korea?

21 위 글의 제목으로 알맞은 것을 고르시오.

① Yes, I Mean It. A Friend in Need Is a Friend Indeed.

② That's Enough! She Is No More My Best Friend!

③ Don't Worry Too Much! Every Dog Has His Day!

④ You've Changed. I Wonder If There's Something Wrong.

⑤ Why Don't You Also Ignore Her?

[01~03] 다음 글을 읽고 물음에 답하시오.

Recently, Minkyeong was asked out by a boy in her class. She wants to say no but does not want to hurt his feelings.

Minkyeong: I need your advice. A boy in my class asked me out. I like him, but for now I don't want to go out with him. I need to focus on my studies. What should I do?

Counselor: Why don't you tell him why you can't go?

Minkyeong: I'm afraid I might hurt his feelings.

Counselor: (A)If you don't tell him soon, he will misunderstand your feelings, and you may end up ⓐ him even more.

Minkyeong: Maybe you're right. Thanks for the advice.

01 위 글의 빈칸 ⓐ에 hurt를 알맞은 형태로 쓰시오.

➡ _____

02 위 글의 밑줄 친 (A)를 다음과 같이 바꿔 쓸 때 빈칸에 들어갈 알맞은 말을 두 단어로 쓰시오.

➡ _____ _____ tell him soon, he will misunderstand your feelings.

03 본문의 내용과 일치하도록 다음 빈칸 (A)와 (B)에 알맞은 단어를 쓰시오.

A boy in Minkyeong's class asked her (A)_____, but she wants to turn him down without (B)_____ _____ _____.

[04~06] 다음 글을 읽고 물음에 답하시오.

Daeho, ⓐthinking that new things will make him more popular, often wants new things just because his friends have them.

Daeho: Seongjin, look at my new sneakers. What do you think?

Seongjin: They're nice, but didn't you just buy new sneakers a couple of months ago?

Daeho: Yeah, but they're no longer in style. I look cooler in these, right?

Seongjin: Daeho, wearing the latest fashion doesn't make you cooler or more popular. ⓑPeople like you because you're you, not because your clothes.

Daeho: Yeah?

Seongjin: Listen, you're a great guy. You don't need new sneakers to prove it.

04 위 글의 밑줄 친 ⓐ를 부사절로 고치시오.

➡ _____

_____

05 위 글의 밑줄 친 ⓑ에서 어법상 틀린 부분을 찾아 고치시오.

_____ ➡ _____

06 본문의 내용과 일치하도록 다음 빈칸 (A)와 (B)에 알맞은 단어를 쓰시오.

Daeho often wants new things just because (A)_____ _____ have them, and he bought new sneakers again, thinking the sneakers that he bought a couple of months ago are no longer (B)_____ _____.

[07~09] 다음 글을 읽고 물음에 답하시오.

Daeho, thinking that new things will make him more popular, often wants new things just because his friends have them.

Daeho: Seongjin, look at my new sneakers. (A)[How / What] do you think?

Seongjin: They're nice, but didn't you just buy new sneakers a couple of months ago?

Daeho: Yeah, but they're no longer in style. I look cooler in ⓐthese, right?

Seongjin: Daeho, wearing the (B)[last / latest] fashion doesn't make you cooler or more popular. People like you because you're you, not because of your (C)[cloths / clothes].

Daeho: Yeah?

Seongjin: Listen, you're a great guy. You don't need new sneakers to prove it.

07 위 글의 괄호 (A)~(C)에서 문맥이나 어법상 알맞은 낱말을 골라 쓰시오.

➡ (A) _____ (B) _____ (C) _____

08 위 글의 밑줄 친 ⓐthese가 가리키는 것을 본문에서 찾아 쓰시오.

➡ _____

09 Does Seongjin think wearing the latest fashion makes Daeho cooler or more popular? Answer in English in a full sentence. (3 words)

➡ _____

[10~12] 다음 글을 읽고 물음에 답하시오.

Sohui thought Hayeon was her best friend, but now, Sohui feels that Hayeon has changed and she is avoiding her.

Sohui: (To her older sister) You know my friend Hayeon, don't you?

Sister: Yeah. Why? What about her?

Sohui: I feel she's avoiding me. When I see her at school, she turns around and walks away from me.

Sister: I'm sorry to hear that. Do you have any idea _____ ⓐ _____?

Sohui: No. I don't think I've done anything wrong. It just feels like she doesn't like me anymore.

Sister: Maybe you should just ask her if there is something wrong.

Sohui: Maybe I should. I still want to be friends with her.

10 위 글의 빈칸 ⓐ에 다음 문장을 알맞은 형태로 쓰시오.

| Why does she do that? |

➡ _____

11 다음 문장에서 위 글의 내용과 다른 부분을 찾아서 고치시오. (두 군데)

| Sohui thinks she has done something wrong. |

➡ _____, _____

12 다음 빈칸 (A)~(C)에 알맞은 단어를 넣어 소희의 고민과 그에 알맞은 조언을 완성하시오.

- **Sohui's worry:** I feel like my best friend Hayeon (A)_____ _____ and she (B)_____ _____ me.
- **Advice:** Why don't you ask her if there is anything (C)_____?

Communication Task

A: I think school should start later in the morning.
동사 think 뒤에는 접속사 that이 생략되었다.

B: I agree with you. We can get more sleep if school starts later.
조건을 나타내는 if절에서는 미래시제를 쓰지 않고 현재시제를 쓴다.

A: I think school should start later in the morning.

B: I don't agree with you. School will finish later if it starts later.
"agree with+사람"이다.

구문해설 • **later**: 더 늦게 • **get sleep**: 잠을 자다

Writing Workshop

Hena's World

I want to grow taller. I do not feel good being the shortest in the group. I'd like
분사구문(= as[because] I am)

to know how I can get taller.
간접의문문(의문사+주어+동사)

tallboy1201

I heard you are wondering if you can get taller. I suggest you eat foods
명사절을 이끄는 접속사(~인지 아닌지)   = should eat(suggest that+주어+(should)+동사원형)

like eggs, milk, and beans. These foods, having lots of protein and calcium,
like(전치사: ~와 같은) = such as   분사구문(= as they have)

can help you grow taller. Also, you should sleep at least eight hours every
help의 목적격보어(= to grow)

night. I hope these tips will be helpful to you.
= advice

구문해설 • **at least**: 적어도

After You Read B

• I feel like my best friend avoids me.

Why don't you ask her if there is anything wrong?
Why don't you 동사원형 ~?: ~하는 게 어때? if: ~인지 아닌지

• I need new clothes. They'll make me more popular.
= new clothes

People like you because you're you, not because of your clothes.
because+주어와 동사로 이루어진 절, because of+명사(구)

• How can I say no without hurting his feelings?
전치사 without+동명사

Why don't you tell him why you can't go?
의문사가 이끄는 명사절로 'tell'의 목적어. 간접의문문(why+주어+동사)

구문해설 • **avoid**: ~을 피하다 • **if**: ~인지 아닌지 • **clothes**: 옷, 의복 • **hurt**: 다치게[아프게] 하다

해석

A: 나는 학교가 아침에 더 늦게 시작해야 한다고 생각해.

B: 나도 네 말에 동의해. 학교가 늦게 시작하면 우리는 더 많이 잠을 잘 수 있어.

A: 나는 학교가 아침에 더 늦게 시작해야 한다고 생각해.

B: 나는 동의하지 않아. 학교가 늦게 시작하면 더 늦게 끝날 거야.

Hena의 세계

나는 키가 더 크고 싶어. 나는 그룹에서 키가 가장 작아서 기분이 안 좋아. 나는 내가 키가 더 클 수 있는 방법을 알고 싶어.

tallboy1201

나는 네가 키가 더 클 수 있는지 궁금해한다고 들었어. 나는 네가 달걀, 우유, 콩 같은 음식을 먹을 것을 제안해. 이 음식들은 많은 단백질과 칼슘을 갖고 있어서 네가 키가 더 크는 것을 도와줄 수 있어. 또한 너는 매일 밤 적어도 8시간을 자야 해. 이 조언들이 네게 도움이 되기를 바라.

• 내 가장 친한 친구가 나를 피하고 있다고 느껴.
뭔가 잘못된 것이 있는지 그녀에게 물어보는 게 어때?

• 나는 새 옷이 필요해. 그것들은 나를 더 인기 있게 만들어 줄 거야.
사람들은 네가 너이기 때문에 너를 좋아하는 것이지, 네 옷 때문이 아니야.

• 어떻게 그의 감정을 상하게 하지 않으면서 거절할 수 있을까?
왜 네가 데이트를 할 수 없는지 그에게 말하는 것은 어떨까?

01 다음 빈칸에 들어가기에 적절한 단어를 고르시오.

> Daeho, thinking that new things will make him more _____, often wants new things just because his friends have them.

① inventive ② careful ③ healthy
④ recent ⑤ popular

02 다음 영영풀이에 해당하는 단어를 고르시오.

> someone whose job is to provide help and advice to people with problems

① counselor ② scientist ③ lawyer
④ teenager ⑤ designer

03 다음 두 문장에 공통으로 알맞은 것을 고르시오.

> • Can I ask you _____ some help?
> • I am not ready _____ the audition.

① with ② by ③ for
④ about ⑤ on

04 다음 밑줄 친 부분과 같은 뜻으로 쓰인 것은?

> One of the people on our team isn't doing his part.

① Which part of the movie is good?
② I have a small part in the play.
③ This part of the song is easy.
④ I like this part of the game.
⑤ In part, his success is by luck.

[05~06] 다음 우리말과 일치하도록 빈칸에 알맞은 말을 쓰시오.

05
G: Mom told me I could use the computer for only one hour a day. She thinks that's enough time.
M: I agree with her.
G: Sometimes, _____.
(숙제할 때 나는 그것을 오랫동안 사용할 필요가 있어요.) (doing, for 포함, 13단어)
M: Hmm. Then maybe we should all get together and talk about it.
G: Thanks for your understanding, Dad.

➡ _____
_____

06
G: I'm worried about making friends at my new school.
M: Don't worry. _____
(나는 네가 거기에서 많은 친구를 사귈 것이라고 확신해.) (sure, a lot of 포함, 9단어)

➡ _____
_____

07 다음 대화의 빈칸에 들어가기에 적절하지 <u>않은</u> 것은?

> G: I think our school festival is going to be a lot of fun.
> B: _____

① I agree.
② So do I.
③ That's your idea.
④ Same here.
⑤ You can say that again.

[08~10] 다음 대화를 읽고 물음에 답하시오.

> B: The team project for English class is taking a lot of time.
>
> G: I agree. I have a problem. ⓐOne of the people on our team isn't doing his part.
>
> B: That's not good. (A)팀의 모든 사람들은 자신들의 역할을 해야 해.
>
> G: ⓑI know, but I don't know how to get him to do his part.
>
> B: ⓒMaybe he doesn't know how to get started or doesn't like his part.
>
> G: Then _____(B)_____?
>
> B: Talk to him. ⓓAsk him why he's doing his part. Then tell him you'll help him if he wants.
>
> G: Okay. I'll try that.
>
> B: ⓔI'm sure he'll do better after you talk to him. Good luck with your project.
>
> G: Thanks.

08 밑줄 친 (A)의 우리말에 해당하는 것으로 적절한 것은?

① Everybody have to do our job on the team.

② Somebody on the team has to do their job.

③ Everybody on the team have to do their job.

④ Everybody on the team has to do their job.

⑤ Every job on the team has to do their part.

09 빈칸 (B)에 들어가기에 적절한 것은?

① where is he now

② who is not doing his part

③ why is he doing his best

④ what would you do

⑤ what should I do

10 위 대화의 밑줄 친 ⓐ~ⓔ 중에서 내용상 어색한 부분이 있는 문장을 찾아 번호를 쓰고 자연스러운 문장으로 고치시오.

➡ _____

[11~13] 다음 대화를 읽고 물음에 답하시오.

> G: What's the matter, Dongha? You look ⓐworried.
>
> B: I'm not ready ____(A)____ the finals. I sit at my desk ⓑto study but end ____(B)____ doing something else.
>
> G: Well, time management is not easy.
>
> B: I agree. ⓒWhat should I do?
>
> G: ⓓNumber the things you have to do. Then write down how much time you need to finish each ⓔones.
>
> B: Thank you, Emily. I'll try your idea.
>
> G: I'm sure that will be helpful ____(C)____ you. Good luck with your finals

11 빈칸 (A), (B), (C)에 들어가기에 알맞은 것을 〈보기〉에서 골라 쓰시오. (중복 가능)

┌─ 보기 ┤
  about with up on for
└──────

➡ (A) _____ (B) _____ (C) _____

12 위 대화의 ⓐ~ⓔ 중에서 어법상 어색한 것을 고르시오.

① ⓐ   ② ⓑ   ③ ⓒ   ④ ⓓ   ⑤ ⓔ

13 위 대화의 내용과 일치하지 않는 것은?

① Emily thinks Dongha looks worried.

② Dongha doesn't sit at the desk to study for the finals.

③ Dongha is going to take the finals.

④ Dongha is not good at time management.

⑤ Dongha agrees with Emily.

Grammar

14 다음 문장을 바꾸어 쓸 때 가장 적절한 것은?

> Finishing my homework, I will go to Amy's house.

① Though I finish my homework, I will go to Amy's house.

② After I finish my homework, I will go to Amy's house.

③ Before I will finish my homework, I will go to Amy's house.

④ If I will finish my homework, I will go to Amy's house.

⑤ I finish my homework, after I will go to Amy's house.

15 다음 밑줄 친 부분과 바꿔 쓸 수 있는 것은?

> Maybe you should ask her <u>if</u> there is something wrong.

① whether   ② unless   ③ what
④ that   ⑤ which

16 다음 문장 중에서 어법상 <u>어색한</u> 문장을 <u>고르시오</u>.

① Not arriving on time, we could not enter the theater.

② She does not feel good being the shortest in the group.

③ Becoming more tired, she made more errors in her work.

④ He broke down and wept hearing the news.

⑤ Making a name for himself, he became arrogant.

17 다음 그림을 보고 주어진 어휘를 활용하여 빈칸을 알맞게 채우시오.

Tom asked her _____ the race. (she, give up, will)

18 다음 문장을 바꿔 쓸 때 빈칸에 알맞은 말을 쓰시오.

(1) Listening to music, Minji walked into the classroom.

➡ _____, Minji walked into the classroom.

(2) He was smiling broadly being so happy.

➡ He was smiling broadly _____ so happy.

19 다음 중 밑줄 친 부분의 의미가 나머지와 <u>다른</u> 것은?

① <u>If</u> Wendy comes back, say I've got a headache.

② <u>If</u> he thinks it's easy to get a job, he's living in a dream world.

③ I doubt <u>if</u> she will like my present.

④ A fortune will come to you <u>if</u> you take this offer.

⑤ You will have to work hard <u>if</u> you are to succeed.

20 다음 ⓐ~ⓖ 중 어법상 옳은 것을 모두 고르시오.

ⓐ Chloe watched a movie, ate some popcorn.

ⓑ Knowing not what to do, he asked for my advice.

ⓒ Seeing from a distance, the rock looks like a rabbit.

ⓓ Being a Sunday, Mr. Edgar and all the servants went to church.

ⓔ Helping us see far, telescopes are still limited.

ⓕ I wonder that the rumor is true.

ⓖ I'd like to know if you use social networking sites.

➡ _____

21 다음 문장을 같은 의미의 문장으로 바르게 바꾼 것은?

If you turn to the right, you will find a white building on the left.

① Turn to the right, you will find a white building on the left.

② Turned to the right, you will find a white building on the left.

③ You turn to the right, you will find a white building on the left.

④ Turning to the right, you will find a white building on the left.

⑤ You turning to the right, you will find a white building on the left.

22 다음 중 어법상 잘못된 문장을 고르시오.

① I will see whether we can come up with a better solution.

② Check whether you agree or disagree.

③ Many people wonder if he resigns before the election.

④ I heard you are wondering if you can get taller.

⑤ I don't know if he will follow my advice or not.

23 다음 문장을 바르게 영작한 것은?

나는 돈이 부족해서 스마트폰을 살 수 없다.

① Having not enough money, I cannot buy the smartphone.

② Not having enough money, I cannot buy the smartphone.

③ Have not enough money, I cannot buy the smartphone.

④ I do not have enough money, I cannot buy the smartphone.

⑤ Though I don't have enough money, I cannot buy the smartphone.

Reading

[24~26] 다음 글을 읽고 물음에 답하시오.

Sohui thought Hayeon was her best friend, but now, Sohui feels that Hayeon has changed and she is avoiding her.

Sohui: (To her older sister) You know my friend Hayeon, don't you?

Sister: Yeah. Why? What about her?

Sohui: I feel she's avoiding me. When I see her at school, she turns around and walks away from me.

Sister: I'm sorry to hear ⓐthat. Do you have any idea why she does that?

Sohui: No. I don't think I've done anything wrong. It just feels ⓑlike she doesn't ⓒlike me anymore.

Sister: Maybe you should just ask her if there is something wrong.

Sohui: Maybe I should. I still want to be friends with her.

24 위 글의 밑줄 친 ⓐthat이 가리키는 것을 본문에서 찾아 쓰시오.

➡ _____

_____

25 위 글의 밑줄 친 ⓑlike, ⓒlike와 문법적 쓰임이 같은 것을 각각 고르시오.

① Do you <u>like</u> vegetables?

② No one sings the blues <u>like</u> she did.

③ It didn't turn out <u>like</u> I intended.

④ I <u>like</u> playing tennis.

⑤ <u>Like</u> I said, you're always welcome to stay.

➡ ⓑ와 같은 것: _____, ⓒ와 같은 것: _____

26 위 글을 읽고 대답할 수 <u>없는</u> 질문은?

① Why does Sohui feel that Hayeon has changed and she is avoiding her?

② Does Sohui's sister know Hayeon?

③ Does Sohui have any idea why Hayeon avoids her?

④ What does Sohui's sister advise Sohui to do?

⑤ Why does Hayeon no more like Sohui?

[27~28] 다음 글을 읽고 물음에 답하시오.

Daeho, thinking that new things will make him more popular, often wants new things just because his friends have them.

Daeho: Seongjin, look at my new sneakers. (①) What do you think?

Seongjin: (②) They're nice, but didn't you just buy new sneakers a couple of months ago?

Daeho: (③) I look cooler in these, right?

Seongjin: (④) Daeho, wearing the latest fashion doesn't make you cooler or more popular. (⑤) People like you because you're you, not because of your clothes.

Daeho: Yeah?

Seongjin: Listen, you're a great guy. You don't need new sneakers to prove it.

27 위 글의 흐름으로 보아, 주어진 문장이 들어가기에 가장 적절한 곳은?

| Yeah, but they're no longer in style. |

①   ②   ③   ④   ⑤

28 위 글의 제목으로 알맞은 것을 고르시오.

① Be More Popular by Buying New Things!

② Can New Things Really Make You More Popular?

③ Hey, These Look Cooler, Don't They?

④ No! People Like Me Because of My Clothes!

⑤ How to Prove You're a Great Guy

[29~30] 다음 글을 읽고 물음에 답하시오.

Recently, Minkyeong was asked out by a boy in her class. She wants to say no but does not want to hurt his feelings.

Minkyeong: I need your advice. A boy in my class asked me out. I like him, but for now I don't want to go out with him. I need to focus on my studies. What should I do?

Counselor: Why don't you tell him why you can't go?

Minkyeong: I'm afraid I might hurt his feelings.

Counselor: If you don't tell him soon, he will misunderstand your feelings, and you may end up hurting him even more.

Minkyeong: Maybe you're right. Thanks for the advice.

29 위 글에서 알 수 있는 '민경이'의 성격으로 알맞은 말을 <u>모두</u> 고르시오.

① selfish ② thoughtful
③ outgoing ④ talkative
⑤ considerate

30 Why does Minkyeong want to refuse to go out with the boy who asked her out? Answer in English beginning with "Because". (10 words)

➡ _____

_____

[31~33] 다음 글을 읽고 물음에 답하시오.

▽ Hena's World

I want to grow taller. I do not feel good being the shortest in the group. I'd like to know how I can get taller.

↳ ● tallboy1201

I heard you are wondering if you can get taller. I suggest you eat foods like eggs, milk, and beans. These foods, ⓐ<u>having lots of protein and calcium</u>, can help you grow taller. Also, you should sleep at least eight hours every night. I hope ⓑ<u>these tips</u> will be helpful to you.

31 What is Hena's worry? Fill in the blanks (A) and (B) with suitable words.

Hena wants to (A)_____ _____. She does not feel good being the (B)_____ in the group.

32 위 글의 밑줄 친 ⓐ를 부사절로 고치시오.

➡ _____

_____

33 위 글의 밑줄 친 ⓑ의 내용을 본문에서 찾아 우리말로 쓰시오.

➡ (1) _____
   (2) _____

단원별 예상문제

01 짝지어진 단어의 관계가 같도록 빈칸에 알맞은 말을 쓰시오. (주어진 철자로 시작할 것.)

strict : rigid = p_____ : task

02 다음 빈칸에 들어갈 말로 적절한 것은?

He's too shy to _____ her out.

① try
② prove
③ inform
④ hurt
⑤ ask

03 다음 빈칸에 들어가기에 적절한 말이 바르게 짝지어진 것은?

- Your skirt is in _____ these days.
- What did you _____ up doing last night?

① pride – try
② part – upset
③ relax – look
④ style – end
⑤ prove – get

04 다음 〈보기〉의 단어로 자연스러운 문장을 만들 수 없는 것은?

┤ 보기 ├
teenagers   sneakers   strict   snap

① She closed her purse with a _____.
② He wore old jeans and _____.
③ They were always very _____ with their children.
④ His _____ was due to inexperience.
⑤ Here are some things that three _____ worry about.

[05~07] 다음 대화를 읽고 물음에 답하시오.

B: You look worried. _____(가)_____
G: Yes, my sister is upset with me.
B: Why? What did you do?
G: I wore one of her shirts ___(A)___ asking.
B: Tell her you're sorry. I'm ___(B)___ she'll understand.
G: OK. I will.

05 빈칸 (가)에 들어가기에 적절하지 <u>않은</u> 것은?

① Is something wrong?
② What's the matter?
③ What's the occasion?
④ What's wrong with you?
⑤ What happened?

06 빈칸 (A)와 (B)에 들어가기에 알맞은 것으로 짝지어진 것은?

	(A)	(B)
①	with	sure
②	about	aware
③	for	worried
④	without	sure
⑤	by	confident

07 Which one of the following is NOT true according to the dialogue above?

① The boy looks worried.
② The girl's sister is upset.
③ The boy wants the girl not to worry.
④ The girl wore her sister's shirt.
⑤ The girl will say sorry to her sister.

[08~10] 다음 대화를 읽고 물음에 답하시오.

G: What's the matter, Dongha? ①You look worried.

B: I'm not ready for the finals. I sit at my desk to study but end up doing something else.

G: ②Well, time management is not easy.

B: (A)I agree. What should I do?

G: ③Number the things you have to do. Then write down how much time you need to finish each one.

B: Thank you, Emily. ④I'll try your idea.

G: ⑤I'm sure that will be useless for you. Good luck with your finals.

🖊 출제율 90%

08 밑줄 친 (A) 대신 쓸 수 있는 것은?

① Why did you say that?

② Neither do I.

③ So do I.

④ You can say that again.

⑤ Don't you agree?

🖊 출제율 95%

09 위 대화의 밑줄 친 ①~⑤ 중 흐름상 어색한 문장은?

① ② ③ ④ ⑤

🖊 출제율 100%

10 Which one CANNOT be answered from the dialogue above?

① Does Dongha have a problem?

② Why does Dongha look worried?

③ What will Dongha be ready for?

④ When will Dongha sit at the desk?

⑤ What will Dongha try?

[11~12] 다음 대화를 읽고 물음에 답하시오.

B: I just talked about the science project with Jinho and Mina.

G: (A)너희 팀은 무엇을 할지 결정했니?

B: No, not yet. Jinho wants to visit a science museum, but Mina wants to do an experiment.

G: Who do you agree with, Jinho or Mina?

B: I agree with Mina because I think the experiment would be more interesting.

🖊 출제율 90%

11 밑줄 친 (A)의 우리말에 해당하는 영어 문장으로 적절한 것은?

① Did your team know what will you do?

② Has your team decided what you will do?

③ Will your team decide what you will do?

④ Has your team decided what are you going to do?

⑤ What has your team decided you are going to do?

🖊 출제율 95%

12 위 대화의 내용과 일치하는 것은?

① The boy will do the science project with the girl.

② The girl wants to do an experiment for the science project.

③ The boy wants to do an experiment for the science project.

④ Jinho and Mina both want to visit a science museum.

⑤ Jinho will ask why Mina wants to do an experiment.

13 다음 문장에서 어법상 <u>어색한</u> 것을 바르게 고쳐 다시 쓰시오.

(1) My concern is if or not they are alive.

➡ _____

_____

(2) I'll check if he sees this painting.

➡ _____

_____

(3) Win the game, Ben is very happy.

➡ _____

_____

(4) Properly conducting, this business is not a public danger.

➡ _____

_____

14 다음 문장의 빈칸에 알맞은 말은?

> I'd like to know _____ Jongmin is good at soccer.

① if ② as ③ what
④ that ⑤ which

15 다음 문장을 분사구문을 이용한 문장으로 바꿔 쓰시오.

(1) As he felt tired, he took a warm bath.

➡ _____

(2) I make delicious food with a dream to be a cook.

➡ _____

(3) Although it was raining, 75 people were waiting for her.

➡ _____

16 다음 그림을 보고 주어진 어휘를 이용하여 빈칸을 알맞게 채우시오.

Do you know _____
for school today or not? (Minji, late)

17 다음 중 어법상 적절한 문장은?

① These foods, have lots of protein and calcium, can help you grow taller.
② Mason listened to the music, to take a shower.
③ When served in the army, he felt a strong tie with his colleagues.
④ Not having any money, I can't buy a car.
⑤ Being disappointing, I kept writing and now I'm a writer.

[18~20] 다음 글을 읽고 물음에 답하시오.

> Sohui thought Hayeon was her best friend, but now, Sohui feels that Hayeon has changed and she is avoiding her.
>
> Sohui: (To her older sister) You know my friend Hayeon, don't you?
>
> Sister: Yeah. Why? What about her?
>
> Sohui: I feel she's avoiding me. When I see her at school, she turns around and walks away from me.

Sister: I'm sorry to hear that. Do you have any idea why she does that?

Sohui: No. I don't think I've done anything wrong. ⓐIt just feels like she doesn't like me anymore.

Sister: Maybe you should just ask her ⓑif there is something wrong.

Sohui: Maybe I should. I still want to be friends with her.

18 위 글의 밑줄 친 ⓐ를 다음과 같이 바꿔 쓸 때 빈칸에 들어갈 알맞은 말을 두 단어로 쓰시오. 출제율 90%

➡ It just feels like she _____ _____ likes me.

19 위 글의 밑줄 친 ⓑif와 문법적 쓰임이 같은 것을 모두 고르시오. 출제율 95%

① He couldn't tell if she was laughing or crying.

② You can stay here for the weekend if you like.

③ I'll buy the car if you offer me more money.

④ Do you know if he's married?

⑤ I wonder if I should wear a coat.

20 위 글에서 알 수 있는 '소희'의 심경으로 가장 알맞은 것을 고르시오. 출제율 100%

① ashamed   ② relieved

③ upset   ④ frightened

⑤ bored

[21~23] 다음 글을 읽고 물음에 답하시오.

Daeho, thinking that new things will make him more popular, often wants new things just because his friends have them.

Daeho: Seongjin, look at my new sneakers. What do you think?

Seongjin: They're nice, but didn't you just buy new sneakers a couple of months ago?

Daeho: ⓐYeah, but they're no longer out of style. I look cooler in these, right?

Seongjin: Daeho, ⓑwearing the latest fashion doesn't make you cooler or more popular. People like you because you're you, not because of your clothes.

Daeho: Yeah?

Seongjin: Listen, you're a great guy. You don't need new sneakers to prove it.

21 위 글의 밑줄 친 ⓐ에서 흐름상 어색한 부분을 찾아 고치시오. 출제율 90%

_____ ➡ _____

22 아래 〈보기〉에서 위 글의 밑줄 친 ⓑwearing과 문법적 쓰임이 다른 것의 개수를 고르시오. 출제율 95%

┌─── 보기 ───┐

① She was wearing a cap.

② Do you know the man wearing a cap?

③ It is no use wearing a cap.

④ She is fond of wearing a cap.

⑤ I saw her wearing a cap.

① 1개   ② 2개   ③ 3개   ④ 4개   ⑤ 5개

23 Why does Seongjin think people like Daeho? Fill in the blanks (A) and (B) with suitable words.

> He thinks people like Daeho because (A)_____ _____, not because of (B)_____ _____.

[24~26] 다음 글을 읽고 물음에 답하시오.

> Recently, Minkyeong was asked out by a boy in her class. She wants to say no but does not want to hurt his feelings.
>
> Minkyeong: I need your advice. A boy in my class asked me out. I like him, but for now I don't want to go out with him. I need to focus on my studies. What should I do?
>
> Counselor: ⓐ왜 네가 데이트를 할 수 없는지 그에게 말하는 것은 어떨까?
>
> Minkyeong: I'm afraid I might hurt his feelings.
>
> Counselor: ⓑIf you won't tell him soon, he will misunderstand your feelings, and you may end up hurting him even more.
>
> Minkyeong: Maybe you're right. Thanks for the advice.

24 위 글의 밑줄 친 ⓐ의 우리말에 맞게 주어진 어휘를 이용하여 9 단어로 영작하시오.

> don't, why, can't go

➡ _____

25 위 글의 밑줄 친 ⓑ에서 어법상 틀린 부분을 찾아 고치시오.

_____ ➡ _____

26 According to the passage, which is NOT true?

① Recently, a boy in Minkyeong's class asked Minkyeong out.

② Minkyeong wants to refuse to go out with the boy because she doesn't like him.

③ Minkyeong does not want to hurt his feelings.

④ The counselor advises Minkyeong to tell the boy why she can't go.

⑤ The counselor says unless Minkyeong tells him soon, he will misunderstand her feelings.

[27~28] 다음 글을 읽고 물음에 답하시오.

> Don't worry. If you follow my advice, you will grow taller. I suggest you try not to get too stressed out. Too much stress can cause a decrease in growth hormone production. Also, you should try to get some exercise every day like swimming, jumping rope, or playing basketball. (A)These types of exercises can stimulate your growth plates, helping you to grow taller. Try these tips, and then let me know ____ⓐ____ they work for you. I hope these tips will be helpful.

27 위 글의 빈칸 ⓐ에 들어갈 알맞은 말을 모두 고르시오.

① that ② if

③ what ④ which

⑤ whether

28 위 글의 밑줄 친 (A)These types of exercises에 해당하지 않는 것을 모두 고르시오.

① 수영 ② 줄다리기

③ 줄넘기 ④ 농구

⑤ 야구

[01~03] 다음 대화를 읽고 물음에 답하시오.

B: The team project for English class is taking a lot of time.

G: I agree. I have a problem. One of the people on our team isn't doing his part.

B: That's not good. Everybody on the team ___(A)___ to do their job.

G: I know, but I don't know how to ___(B)___ him to do his part. (자기의 역할을 하도록 하다)

B: Maybe he doesn't know how to get started or doesn't like his part.

G: Then what should I do?

B: Talk to him. (가)그에게 왜 자신의 역할을 하지 않는지 물어봐.(doing, part) Then tell him you'll help him if he wants.

G: Okay. I'll try that.

B: I'm sure he'll do better after you talk to him. Good luck with your project.

G: Thanks.

01 빈칸 (A)에 들어가기에 적절한 한 단어를 쓰시오.

➡ _____

02 빈칸 (B)에 괄호 안의 우리말 뜻에 어울리는 한 단어를 쓰시오.

➡ _____

03 밑줄 친 (가)의 우리말에 해당하는 영어 문장을 쓰시오. (주어진 단어 포함, 8 words)

➡ _____

04 분사구문은 부사절로, 부사절은 분사구문으로 바꿔 쓰시오.

(1) Being interested in soccer, I joined a soccer club.

➡ _____
_____

(2) Emily opened her birthday present, smiling happily.

➡ _____
_____

(3) When she heard about the accident, she was shocked.

➡ _____
_____

(4) If it is cold tomorrow, I won't go there.

➡ _____
_____

05 다음 문장에서 어법상 어색한 것을 바르게 고쳐 다시 쓰시오.

(1) He can't decide if to buy it.

➡ _____
_____

(2) I don't know if she comes tomorrow.

➡ _____
_____

(3) Jane watched a baseball game on TV, had dinner.

➡ _____
_____

(4) Put eggs on the bread, Yena made the sandwiches more delicious.

➡ _____
_____

[06~08] 다음 글을 읽고 물음에 답하시오.

Sohui thought Hayeon was her best friend, but now, Sohui feels that Hayeon has changed and she is avoiding her.

Sohui: (To her older sister) You know my friend Hayeon, ____ⓐ____?

Sister: Yeah. Why? What about her?

Sohui: I feel she's avoiding me. When I see her at school, she turns around and walks away from me.

Sister: I'm sorry to hear that. Do you have any idea why she does ⓑthat?

Sohui: No. I don't think I've done anything wrong. It just feels like she doesn't like me anymore.

Sister: Maybe you should just ask her if there is something wrong.

Sohui: Maybe I should. I still want to be friends with her.

06 위 글의 빈칸 ⓐ에 들어갈 알맞은 부가의문문을 쓰시오.

➡ _____

07 위 글의 밑줄 친 ⓑthat이 가리키는 것을 우리말로 쓰시오.

➡ _____

_____

08 위 글의 내용을 다음과 같이 정리하고자 한다. 빈칸 (A)와 (B)에 들어갈 알맞은 단어를 쓰시오. (A)에는 철자 w로, (B)에는 철자 a로 시작하는 단어를 쓰시오.

> Sohui is (A)_____ that her best friend Hayeon has changed and she is avoiding her, and then her sister (B)_____ her to ask Hayeon if there is something wrong.

[09~11] 다음 글을 읽고 물음에 답하시오.

Daeho, thinking that new things will make him more popular, often wants new things just because his friends have them.

Daeho: Seongjin, look at my new sneakers. What do you think?

Seongjin: They're nice, but didn't you just buy new sneakers ⓐ몇 달 전에?

Daeho: Yeah, but they're no longer in style. I look cooler in these, right?

Seongjin: Daeho, wearing the latest fashion doesn't make you cooler or more popular. People like you because you're you, not because of your clothes.

Daeho: Yeah?

Seongjin: Listen, you're a great guy. You don't need new sneakers to prove it.

09 위 글의 밑줄 친 ⓐ의 우리말에 맞게 5 단어로 영작하시오.

➡ _____

10 다음 문장에서 위 글의 내용과 다른 부분을 찾아서 고치시오.

> Seongjin says Daeho needs new sneakers to prove he's a great guy.

_____ ➡ _____

11 다음 빈칸 (A)~(D)에 알맞은 단어를 넣어 대호의 고민과 그에 알맞은 조언을 완성하시오.

> • **Daeho's worry:** I need (A)_____ clothes. They'll make me (B)_____ _____.
> • **Advice:** People like you not (C)_____ _____ your clothes but (D)_____ you're you.

창의사고력 서술형 문제

01 주어진 그림과 다음 표현을 보고 if를 이용하여 다음 문장의 빈칸을 알맞게 채우시오.

- Does listening to music help you relax?
- Is reading history comic books helpful?
- Is our P.E. teacher too strict?
- Will our school festival be a lot of fun?

(1) I'd like to know _____.

(2) I'd like to know _____.

(3) I'd like to know _____.

(4) I'd like to know _____.

02 다음 내용을 바탕으로 헤나의 SNS에 고민 상담 댓글을 쓰시오.

> **Worry:** Hena wants to grow taller. She does not feel good being the shortest in the group.
> - Eat foods that help you grow taller, like eggs, milk, and beans.
> - Sleep at least eight hours every night.

> ▽ **Hena's World**
> I want to (A)_____. I do not feel good (B)_____ in the group. I'd like to know how I can get taller.
>
> ↳ 👤 **tallboy1201**
> I heard you are wondering if you can get taller. I suggest you eat foods like (C)_____. These foods, having lots of protein and calcium, can help you grow taller. Also, you should sleep at least (D)_____ every night. I hope these tips will be helpful to you.

단원별 모의고사

01 다음 짝지어진 두 단어의 관계가 같도록 빈칸에 알맞은 말을 쓰시오. (주어진 철자로 시작할 것.)

avoid : face = agree : d_____

02 다음 영영풀이에 해당하는 단어로 적절한 것은?

a person who is between the ages of 13 and 19

① counselor
② manager
③ athlete
④ teenager
⑤ author

03 다음 문장의 빈칸에 알맞은 것을 〈보기〉에서 찾아 쓰시오.

┌─ 보기 ─┐
relax   worry   avoid   agree

(1) I entirely _____ with you.
(2) I left early to _____ the rush hour.
(3) Just _____ and enjoy the movie.
(4) Don't _____ about the exam–just do your best.

04 다음 빈칸에 들어갈 말로 적절하지 <u>않은</u> 것은?

You will have _____ solving the problem.

① thought
② difficulty
③ a difficult time
④ trouble
⑤ a hard time

[05~07] 다음 대화를 읽고 물음에 답하시오.

B: The team project for English class is taking a lot of time.
G: I agree. I have a problem. (A) One of the people on our team isn't doing his part.
B: _____(가)_____ Everybody on the team has to do their job.
G: I know, but I don't know how to get him to do his part. (B)
B: Maybe he doesn't know how to get started or doesn't like his part.
G: Then what should I do? (C)
B: Talk to him. Ask him why he's not doing his part. (D)
G: Okay. I'll try that. (E)
B: I'm sure he'll do better after you talk to him. Good luck with your project.
G: Thanks.

05 빈칸 (가)에 들어가기에 적절한 것은?

① That's what I thought.
② That's a good idea.
③ That's not good.
④ I said it many times.
⑤ Is it your idea?

06 (A)~(E) 중에서 다음 문장이 들어가기에 적절한 곳은?

Then tell him you'll help him if he wants.

① (A)   ② (B)   ③ (C)   ④ (D)   ⑤ (E)

07 Which one is TRUE according to the dialogue?

① The boy thinks the team project is easy.
② One of the people on the girl's team isn't doing his part.
③ The girl doesn't like her part in the team project.
④ The girl doesn't know how to get started.
⑤ The boy will ask why he's not doing his part.

10 Which one of the following is NOT true according to the dialogue above?

① Emily thinks Dongha looks worried.
② Dongha didn't study hard for the finals.
③ Emily doesn't know how to manage her time.
④ Dongha agrees that time management is not easy.
⑤ Emily is sure that her idea will be helpful for Dongha.

[08~10] 다음 대화를 읽고 물음에 답하시오.

G: What's the matter, Dongha? You look worried.
B: I'm not ⓐready for the finals. I sit at my desk to study but ___(A)___ doing something else.
G: Well, time ⓑmanagement is not easy.
B: I agree. What should I do?
G: ⓒNumber the things you have to do. Then write down how much time ⓓdo you need to finish each one.
B: Thank you, Emily. I'll try your idea.
G: I'm sure ⓔthat will be helpful for you. Good luck with your finals.

11 다음 우리말을 주어진 어휘를 이용하여 영작하시오.

(1) 그 소식을 들었을 때, 그는 충격으로 바닥에 주저앉았다. (from, drop down on the floor, 11 단어)
➡ _____
_____

(2) 아버지께 말씀드리고 난 후, 나는 기분이 훨씬 나아졌다. (my dad, felt, talk, much, to, 9 단어)
➡ _____
_____

(3) 나는 네가 나를 기억하는지 확신하지 못한다. (sure, remember, not, 8 단어)
➡ _____
_____

08 빈칸 (A)에 적절한 것은?

① enjoy   ② dislike
③ end up   ④ mind
⑤ finish

(4) 집을 나갈 때 스토브가 꺼졌는지 확인해야 해. (the house, the stove, check, leave, should, if, off, 12 단어)
➡ _____
_____

09 밑줄 친 ⓐ~ⓔ 중에서 어법상 어색한 것은?

① ⓐ   ② ⓑ   ③ ⓒ   ④ ⓓ   ⑤ ⓔ

12 Which is grammatically WRONG?

① Could you check if everything is correct?

② Hansu is not sure if he closed all the windows.

③ The question is if or not I have the patience to read it through.

④ I wonder if Sue knows my secret.

⑤ Jay asked me if I could join his club.

13 다음 두 문장을 한 문장으로 바꿔 쓸 때 빈칸에 알맞은 말을 쓰시오.

(1) • Do you know?

　• Will he come to the party tonight?

　→ Do you know _____

　_____?

(2) • I wonder.

　• Does he like playing baseball?

　→ I wonder _____

　_____.

(3) • Please check.

　• Is dinner ready?

　→ Please check _____.

14 다음 중 어법상 옳은 문장을 <u>모두</u> 고르시오.

① Ms. Brown asked me if I knew the answer.

② Do you know if she comes back soon?

③ My mom always checks if I finish my homework.

④ It being Sunday, most shops were closed.

⑤ Writing too quickly, the letter had many mistakes.

⑥ Feeling not well, I came home early.

⑦ Listening to music, he drinks tea.

[15~17] 다음 글을 읽고 물음에 답하시오.

　Sohui thought Hayeon was her best friend, but now, Sohui feels that Hayeon has changed and she is avoiding her.

Sohui: (To her older sister) You know my friend Hayeon, don't you?

Sister: Yeah. Why? What about her?

Sohui: I feel she's avoiding me. When I see her at school, she turns around and walks away from me.

Sister: I'm sorry to hear that. Do you have any idea why she does that?

Sohui: No. ⓐ나는 내가 잘못한 것이 있다고 생각하지 않아. It just feels like she doesn't like me anymore.

Sister: ⓑ<u>Maybe you should just ask her that there is something wrong.</u>

Sohui: Maybe I should. I still want to be friends with her.

15 위 글의 주제로 알맞은 것을 고르시오.

① the way to give effective advice

② worry about friendship and advice

③ the common concerns of teenagers

④ the importance of friendship

⑤ worry about the school life and solution

16 위 글의 밑줄 친 ⓐ의 우리말에 맞게 주어진 어휘를 알맞게 배열하시오.

> done / wrong / I / think / I've / anything / don't

➡ _____

17 위 글의 밑줄 친 ⓑ에서 어법상 <u>틀린</u> 부분을 찾아 고치시오.

_____ ➡ _____

[18~20] 다음 글을 읽고 물음에 답하시오.

Daeho, thinking that new things will make ①him more popular, often wants new things just because his friends have them.

Daeho: Seongjin, look at ②my new sneakers. What do ③you think?

Seongjin: They're nice, but didn't ④you just buy new sneakers a couple of months ago?

Daeho: Yeah, but they're no longer in style. ⑤I look cooler in these, right?

Seongjin: Daeho, wearing the latest fashion doesn't make you cooler or more popular. People like you because you're you, not because of your clothes.

Daeho: Yeah?

Seongjin: Listen, you're a great guy. You don't need new sneakers ⓐto prove it.

18 밑줄 친 ①~⑤ 중에서 가리키는 대상이 나머지 넷과 다른 것은?

①　　　　②　　　　③　　　　④　　　　⑤

19 아래 〈보기〉에서 위 글의 밑줄 친 ⓐto prove와 to부정사의 용법이 같은 것의 개수를 고르시오.

┌──── 보기 ────┐
① She was pleased to prove it.
② He tried to prove it.
③ Tell me the way to prove it.
④ He was clever enough to prove it.
⑤ Was it easy to prove it?
└───────────────┘

① 1개　② 2개　③ 3개　④ 4개　⑤ 5개

20 According to the passage, which is NOT true?

① Daeho thinks that new things will make him more popular.

② Seongjin says Daeho's new sneakers are nice.

③ Daeho says the sneakers he bought a couple of months ago are out of style.

④ Seongjin says wearing the latest fashion makes Daeho cooler or more popular.

⑤ Seongjin says Daeho is a great guy.

[21~22] 다음 글을 읽고 물음에 답하시오.

Recently, Minkyeong was asked out by a boy in her class. She wants to say no but does not want to hurt his feelings. (①)

Minkyeong: I need your advice. (②) A boy in my class asked me out. (③) I like him, but for now I don't want to go out with him. (④) I need to focus on my studies. (⑤)

Counselor: Why don't you tell him why you can't go?

Minkyeong: I'm afraid I might hurt his feelings.

Counselor: If you don't tell him soon, he will misunderstand your feelings, and you may end up hurting him even more.

Minkyeong: Maybe you're right. Thanks for the advice.

21 위 글의 흐름으로 보아, 주어진 문장이 들어가기에 가장 적절한 곳은?

┌─────────────────────┐
│　　What should I do?　　│
└─────────────────────┘

①　　　　②　　　　③　　　　④　　　　⑤

22 다음 빈칸 (A)와 (B)에 알맞은 단어를 넣어 민경이의 고민과 그에 알맞은 조언을 완성하시오.

• **Minkyeong's worry:** How can I (A) _____ _____ without hurting his feelings?

• **Advice:** How about telling him why you (B)_____ _____?

Lesson 3

Healthy Living, a Happy Life

🎙 의사소통 기능

- 강조하기
  A: I think it's important to eat a good breakfast.
  B: I think so, too.

- 안타까움, 후회 표현하기
  A: Your bag is too small.
  B: Yes. I should have brought a bigger one.

📝 언어 형식

- 'the 비교급, the 비교급'
  The more sun you get, **the more** "happy hormone" the brain produces.

- It is ... that 강조 구문
  It is calcium **that** builds strong bones and teeth.

Words & Expressions

Key Words

- **already** [ɔːlrédi] 부 이미, 벌써
- **arrive** [əráiv] 동 도착하다
- **avoid** [əvɔ́id] 동 피하다
- **benefit** [bénəfit] 명 이득 동 이득을 보다
- **blanket** [blǽŋkit] 명 이불, 담요
- **bone** [boun] 명 뼈
- **brain** [brein] 명 뇌
- **calcium** [kǽlsiəm] 명 칼슘
- **calming** [kɑːmiŋ] 형 진정시키는
- **check** [tʃek] 동 점검하다
- **clearly** [klíərli] 부 또렷하게
- **create** [kriéit] 동 만들어 내다, 창조하다
- **decide** [disáid] 동 결심하다, 결정하다
- **direct** [dirékt] 형 직접적인, (열기나 빛이) 직접 닿는
- **effect** [ifékt] 명 효과
- **exercise** [éksərsàiz] 동 운동하다
- **finally** [fáinəli] 부 마침내
- **flight** [flait] 명 항공편, 비행
- **fortunately** [fɔ́ːrtʃənətli] 부 다행스럽게도
- **grade** [greid] 명 성적
- **hang** [hæŋ] 동 걸다
- **healthy** [hélθi] 형 건강한
- **hormone** [hɔ́ːrmòun] 명 호르몬
- **interestingly** [íntərəstiŋli] 부 흥미롭게도
- **journal** [dʒɔ́ːrnl] 명 일지, 일기

- **leave** [liːv] 동 떠나다
- **level** [lévəl] 명 수준, 수치
- **mood** [muːd] 명 기분, 감정
- **moreover** [mɔːróuvər] 부 게다가
- **nature-friendly** 형 자연친화적인
- **outdoors** [áutdɔrz] 부 야외에서
- **peak** [piːk] 형 절정의, 최고조의 명 절정, 최고조
- **produce** [prədjúːs] 동 만들어 내다
- **properly** [prɑ́pərli] 부 제대로
- **protect** [prətékt] 동 보호하다
- **reach** [riːtʃ] 동 도달하다
- **regret** [rigrét] 동 후회하다
- **regularly** [régjulərli] 부 규칙적으로
- **review** [rivjúː] 동 복습하다
- **role** [roul] 명 역할
- **safely** [séifli] 부 안전하게
- **serotonin** [serətóunin] 명 세로토닌
- **shine** [ʃain] 동 빛나다
- **skin** [skin] 명 피부
- **sunlight** [sʌ́nlait] 명 햇살
- **sunscreen** [sʌ́nskrìːn] 명 자외선 차단제
- **sunshine** [sʌ́nʃain] 명 햇볕, 햇빛
- **vitamin** [váitəmin] 명 비타민
- **weather** [wéðər] 명 날씨
- **wet** [wet] 형 젖은

Key Expressions

- **be good for** ~에 유익하다
- **both A and B** A와 B 둘 다
- **full of** ~로 가득 찬
- **get sleep** 잠자다
- **go up** 높아지다
- **have a snack** 간식을 먹다
- **keep ~ in mind** ~을 명심하다
- **make a world of difference** 큰 차이를 만들다
- **on time** 제시간에

- **play an important role in** ~에 중요한 역할을 하다
- **put on** 착용하다, 바르다
- **put out** 내놓다
- **should have p.p.** ~했어야 했는데
- **stay healthy** 건강을 유지하다
- **stay up** 깨어 있다
- **surf the Internet** 인터넷 검색을 하다
- **too ~ to ...** 너무 ~해서 …할 수 없다

112 Lesson 3. Healthy Living, a Happy Life

Word Power

※ 서로 비슷한 뜻을 가진 어휘

- □ **arrive** 도착하다 : **reach** 도착하다
- □ **exercise** 운동하다 : **work out** 운동하다
- □ **fortunately** 다행스럽게도 : **luckily** 운 좋게도
- □ **leave** 떠나다 : **depart** 떠나다
- □ **protect** 보호하다 : **cover** 보호하다

- □ **benefit** 이점 : **advantage** 이점, 장점
- □ **finally** 마침내 : **ultimately** 결국
- □ **grade** 성적 : **degree** 점수
- □ **properly** 제대로 : **suitably** 적절하게
- □ **role** 역할 : **part** 배역

※ 서로 반대되는 뜻을 가진 어휘

- □ **avoid** 피하다 ↔ **face** 마주하다
- □ **direct** 직접적인 ↔ **indirect** 간접적인
- □ **wet** 젖은 ↔ **dry** 건조한

- □ **clearly** 또렷하게 ↔ **vaguely** 모호하게
- □ **healthy** 건강한 ↔ **unhealthy** 건강하지 못한
- □ **regularly** 규칙적으로 ↔ **irregularly** 불규칙하게

※ 동사 - 명사

- □ **arrive** 도착하다 - **arrival** 도착
- □ **decide** 결심하다 - **decision** 결심
- □ **protect** 보호하다 - **protection** 보호

- □ **avoid** 피하다 - **avoidance** 회피
- □ **produce** 만들어 내다 - **production** 생산

English Dictionary

- □ **benefit** 이득을 보다
  → to take advantages from something
  무엇인가로부터 이득을 얻다

- □ **blanket** 이불, 담요
  → a large piece of cloth used as a covering for warmth
  따뜻하도록 덮개로 사용되는 큰 천

- □ **bone** 뼈
  → the hard part of the body that forms a framework inside people or animals
  사람이나 동물의 내부에서 골격을 형성하는 신체의 단단한 부분

- □ **brain** 뇌
  → the organ inside the head that control movements and feelings
  움직임과 감정을 조절하는 머리 속에 있는 기관

- □ **go up** 올라가다
  → to become higher or greater 더 높거나 크게 되다

- □ **journal** 일지, 일기
  → a book in which people regularly write about what has happened to them
  자신들에게 일어난 일을 규칙적으로 기록하는 책

- □ **mood** 기분, 감정
  → a temporary state of mind 일시적인 마음의 상태

- □ **peak** 절정, 최고조
  → the highest level or degree of excellence, quantity, activity, etc. 탁월함, 수량, 활동 등의 가장 높은 수준이나 정도

- □ **regularly** 규칙적으로
  → at the same time every day, week, month, or year
  매일, 매주, 매달, 매년 똑같은 시간에

- □ **role** 역할
  → the part assumed to be played by a person
  사람에 의해 수행되도록 떠맡겨지는 배역

- □ **skin** 피부
  → the outer layer of a person's or animal's body
  사람이나 동물 신체의 가장 바깥 층

- □ **sunshine** 햇빛
  → light and heat from the sun 태양으로부터의 빛과 열

- □ **wet** 젖은
  → covered or touched with water or another liquid
  물이나 다른 액체로 덮여 있거나 접촉한

01 다음 밑줄 친 부분과 의미가 가장 가까운 것을 고르시오.

> As you can see, sunshine has many <u>benefits</u>, but how can you enjoy its benefits safely?

① impacts   ② favors   ③ joys
④ events   ⑤ advantages

02 다음 문장의 빈칸에 들어갈 단어를 사용하여 문장을 자연스럽게 완성할 수 있는 것은?

> What are the positive and negative _____ of social networking sites?

① A letter _____ for you this morning.
② He tends to _____ all physical contact.
③ He has cracked a _____ in his arm.
④ The drug has some bad side _____.
⑤ People need _____ to have strong bones.

03 다음 빈칸에 공통으로 들어가기에 알맞은 것은?

> • Look at my face. I should have _____ on some sunscreen.
> • I _____ the blanket out in the sun this morning.

① got   ② had   ③ put
④ let   ⑤ left

---

04 〈보기〉와 같은 관계가 되도록 빈칸에 알맞은 말을 쓰시오.

> ┤ 보기 ├
> avoid : face

(1) wet : _____
(2) regular : _____

05 다음 중 밑줄 친 부분의 뜻풀이가 바르지 <u>않은</u> 것은?

① One of the <u>benefits</u> of a smartphone is that you can reach someone quickly in an emergency. (이점)
② This exercise helps increase growth <u>hormone</u>. (호르몬)
③ Some research has shown us that our sports ability is also related to our <u>brains</u>. (뇌)
④ This steak was cooked with <u>direct</u> heat. (즉각적인)
⑤ The house has a reasonable price. <u>Moreover</u>, the location is very good. (게다가)

06 다음 중 〈보기〉에 있는 단어를 사용하여 자연스러운 문장을 만들 수 <u>없는</u> 것은? (대 · 소문자 무시)

> ┤ 보기 ├
> difference mood outdoors fortunately

① _____, the typhoon weakened before getting to my town.
② When you are cold, wearing a muffler will make a world of _____.
③ This book talks about how to get out of a bad _____.
④ Children enjoy playing _____.
⑤ When is the _____ hour for electricity use?

[01~02] 빈칸에 공통으로 들어갈 단어를 쓰시오.

01
• A walk in the sun is good _____ both your mind and your body.
• I have decided to exercise on the weekend _____ my health.

02
• It's important to arrive at school _____ time.
• Serotonin helps you focus better _____ what you are doing.

03 밑줄 친 부분과 의미가 가장 가까운 단어를 주어진 철자로 시작하여 쓰시오.

I am not really <u>suitably</u> dressed for a party.

➡ p_____

04 주어진 단어를 이용해 빈칸을 완성하시오.

We apologize for the late _____ of the train.

➡ _____ (arrive)

05 다음 짝지어진 단어의 관계가 같도록 빈칸에 알맞은 말을 쓰시오.

healthy : unhealthy = direct : _____

06 빈칸에 알맞은 단어를 〈보기〉에서 골라 쓰시오. (어형 변화 가능)

┌ 보기 ┐
skin   produce   role   properly

(1) This factory _____ car parts.
(2) Managing your time _____ is the key to success.
(3) Sue has an important _____ in our group.
(4) I need to buy a facial cream for dry _____.

07 다음 우리말에 맞게 빈칸에 알맞은 말을 쓰시오.

(1) Davis 박사는 햇살이 피부에 끼치는 영향을 연구 중이다.
➡ Dr. Davis is studying the action of _____ on the skin.
(2) 그는 아시아 횡단 여행에 대해 일기를 썼다.
➡ He kept a _____ of his travels across Asia.
(3) 75점 이상의 점수에 대해서는 A 학점을 받는다.
➡ You get an A _____ for scores of 75 and over.
(4) 제가 한 말을 유의하시기 바랍니다.
➡ I hope you'll keep in _____ what I've told you.

Conversation

1 강조하기

> **A** I think it's important to eat a good breakfast. 아침을 잘 먹는 것이 중요하다고 생각해.
> **B** I think so, too. 나도 역시 그렇게 생각해.

- 전달하고자 하는 내용을 강조하는 표현은 다양하다. to부정사를 사용하여 부정사 부분을 강조할 때는 "It's important to V" 구문으로 나타내고, 절을 강조할 때에는 "It's important that S+V"의 형태를 취하고, "I think it's important to ~" 또는 "I think it's important that S+V"의 형태가 되기도 한다.

- "It's important to + 동사원형~"은 "~하는 것은 중요하다"라는 의미이고, 이 표현에서 it은 가주어이고 "to부정사"가 진주어이다. 이 표현은 to부정사 부분을 강조하는 표현이다. "It's important that S+V"의 형태에서는 that절이 강조되는 내용이다.

- to부정사를 강조할 때는 "important" 대신 necessary(필요한), essential(필수적인), crucial(중요한, 치명적인) 등을 이용하여 "It is necessary/important/essential/crucial to ~" 또는 "It is important/essential/crucial that S+V ~"라고 할 수도 있다.

- 그 외에 강조하는 표현으로는 강조할 내용에 따라, 동사를 강조할 때는 강조의 조동사 do, does, did를 사용하고, 문장의 어느 한 성분을 강조할 때는 "It is ~ that" 강조구문을 사용할 수 있다.

강조를 나타내는 표현

- It is important[necessary] to/that ~. ~하는 것이 중요/필요하다
- I want to stress that ~. ~을 강조하고 싶다
- It is essential to ~. ~하는 것이 필수적이다
- It's crucial[critical] to V ~. ~하는 것이 중요하다
- It's significant to V ~. ~하는 것이 중요하다

핵심 Check

1. 다음 밑줄 친 우리말에 해당하는 표현으로 적절하지 <u>않은</u> 것은?

   G: How can we stay healthy?

   B: Well, 아침을 잘 먹는 것이 중요해.

   ① I think it's important to eat a good breakfast
   ② it's important that you should eat a good breakfast
   ③ I want to stress that you eat a good breakfast
   ④ I think I will have a good breakfast, too
   ⑤ it's significant to have a good breakfast

2 안타까움, 후회 표현하기

A Your bag is too small. 네 가방이 너무 작아.

B Yes. I should have brought a bigger one. 맞아. 나는 더 큰 것을 가지고 왔어야 했는데.

■ 과거의 행위에 대한 안타까움, 후회 또는 유감을 나타낼 때는 "should have+과거분사"의 표현을 사용한다. "should have+과거분사"는 "~했어야 했는데(하지 못해 유감이다)"의 의미로 과거와 반대되는 상황을 나타내기 위하여 사용할 수 있다.

■ 이 표현에서는 "should"를 "ought to"로 바꾸어 "ought to have+과거분사"로 표현할 수 있다. "~하지 말았어야 했는데 (했다)"의 의미는 "should not have+과거분사" 또는 "ought not to have+과거분사"로 나타낸다.

■ 안타까움, 후회를 나타내는 비슷한 표현으로 "I had to ~, but I didn't.", "I (really) regret ~." 등이 있고, sorry를 사용하여 "I'm sorry that 주어+과거동사 ~"로 나타내기도 한다. "should have+과거분사"는 과거 사실에 대한 가정의 표현으로 "~했어야 했는데 (하지 않았다)"의 의미를 나타내어 과거에 하지 않은 일에 대해 후회하는 표현이다. should 대신 could를 사용하여 "could have+과거분사"가 되면 "~할 수 있었는데"의 의미가 될 수 있다.

■ "should have p.p."는 과거에 했어야 하는 일이나 하지 못한 일에 대한 후회, 유감, 안타까움을 표현하며 "~했어야 했는데 (못했다)"의 의미로 사용되고, "could/would have p.p."는 과거의 일에 대한 유감을 의미하여 "~할 수 있었는데(못했다), ~했어야 했는데(못했다)"의 의미로 가정법에 주로 사용된다. "must have p.p."는 과거에 대한 강한 추측을 나타내어 "~이었음에 틀림없다"의 의미로 사용되고, 그에 반해, "may have p.p."는 과거에 대한 약한 추측을 나타내어 "~했을지도 모른다"의 의미로 사용된다.

안타까움, 후회 표현하기

• 주어+should[shouldn't] have+과거분사 ~	~했어야[하지 말았어야] 했는데
• 주어+ought[ought not] to have+과거분사 ~	~했어야[하지 말았어야] 했는데
• I (really) regret (that) 주어+과거동사 ~	~한 것이 유감이다/후회한다
• I'm sorry that 주어+과거동사 ~	~한 것이 유감이다

핵심 Check

2. 다음 밑줄 친 말 대신 쓰기에 적절한 것은?

G: Aren't you cold?

B: Yes. <u>I should have worn a jacket.</u>

① Everything will be all right.　② You ought to wear a jacket.

③ I must have worn a jacket.　④ I am sorry that you wear a jacket.

⑤ I regret that I didn't wear a jacket.

 Real-Life Zone

G: Ben, you look full of energy today!

B: Do I? Maybe ❶that's because I finally got a good night's sleep last night.

G: Why? Don't you usually get enough sleep?

B: No, ❷I know it's really important to get a good night's sleep, but I always stay up late surfing the Internet or playing with my phone.

G: That sometimes happens to me too.

B: After I do that, I regret it the next morning and say, "I should have gone to bed earlier last night."

G: How was yesterday different?

B: Well, yesterday afternoon I climbed the mountain with my dad. I was really tired when I got home. I went to sleep right after I went to bed.

G: Outdoor activities are a great way ❸to help you get a good night's sleep.

G: 벤, 너 오늘 기운 차 보여!

B: 내가 그래? 그건 아마 내가 지난밤 마침내 잠을 잘 잤기 때문일 거야.

G: 왜? 평소에 충분한 잠을 자지 못하니?

B: 응, 잠을 잘 자는 것이 정말 중요하다는 것은 알지만 나는 언제나 인터넷 검색을 하거나 휴대폰을 가지고 놀면서 늦게까지 깨어 있어.

G: 그건 나에게도 가끔 일어나는 일이야.

B: 그러고 난 뒤에, 나는 다음 날 아침 후회하고 "지난밤에 더 일찍 잠들었어야 했는데."라고 말해.

G: 어제는 어떻게 달랐니?

B: 음, 어제 오후에 나는 아빠와 등산을 했어. 집에 왔을 때 나는 매우 피곤했어. 나는 침대에 가자마자 바로 잠들었어.

G: 야외 활동은 네가 잠을 잘 자도록 돕는 훌륭한 방법이구나.

❶ "that's because ~"는 "그것은 ~이기 때문이다"라는 뜻으로 이어지는 내용이 앞에 나온 것에 대한 이유가 된다.

❷ "I know" 뒤에는 명사절을 유도하는 접속사 that이 생략되어 있다.

❸ "to help"는 명사 way를 수식하는 형용사적 용법의 to부정사이다.

Check(√) True or False

(1) The boy didn't get a good night's sleep last night.   T ☐ F ☐

(2) Yesterday afternoon the boy climbed the mountain with his dad.   T ☐ F ☐

 Wrap Up 1

W: Oh, your blanket is wet from the rain! I should have checked the weather.

B: Did you wash it?

W: No. ❶I just put it out in the sun this morning.

B: Why didn't you wash it?

W: Hanging a blanket in the sun is ❷a nature-friendly way to keep the blanket clean.

B: Oh, I didn't know that. I'll remember that.

W: And it's also important to remember to do it regularly.

W: 오, 네 이불이 비에 젖었어! 내가 날씨를 확인했어야 했는데.

B: 그것을 빨았어요?

W: 아니. 오늘 아침에 그냥 햇볕에 널어놓았어.

B: 왜 빨지 않았어요?

W: 햇볕에 이불을 널어놓는 것은 이불을 깨끗하게 유지하는 친환경적인 방법이야.

B: 오, 저는 그것을 몰랐어요. 기억해 둘게요.

W: 그리고 정기적으로 그렇게 하는 것을 기억하는 것 또한 중요해.

❶ "put ~ out"은 "~을 밖에 내놓다"의 의미를 가진다.

❷ "a nature-friendly way to keep the blanket clean"에서 to keep은 way를 수식하는 형용사적 용법이다.

Check(√) True or False

(3) The woman regrets that she didn't wash the blanket.   T ☐ F ☐

(4) It is important to remember to wash a blanket regularly.   T ☐ F ☐

Listen & Speak 1 Listen

1. G: How can we stay healthy?
   B: Well, ❶it's important to eat a good breakfast.
2. B: What can we do to get good grades?
   G: It's important to review every day.
3. G: ❷I think it's important to write a journal after reading.
   B: I agree.
4. B: It's important to write down ❸what you spend your money on.
   G: I think so, too.

❶ "it's important to ～"에서 it은 가주어이고, to ～는 진주어이다.
❷ 강조하는 의미의 "It's important to ～"는 "I think it's important to ～"라고 할 수 있다.
❸ "what you spend ～"는 "무엇에 돈을 쓰는지"의 의미로 간접의문문이다.

Listen & Speak 1 A-1

B: What did you do on the weekend?
G: I played tennis. ❶I have decided to exercise on the weekend for my health.
B: Good for you. It's important to exercise regularly.
G: Right. ❷How about playing tennis with me?
B: Why not?

❶ 동사 decided의 목적어는 to부정사이다.
❷ "How about ～ing ?"는 "～하는 것이 어때?"의 의미로 상대에게 제안하는 표현이다.

Listen & Speak 1 A-2

M: John, you are late again.
B: I'm sorry. ❶I took the wrong bus.
M: ❷I think you need to leave home a little earlier.
B: I think so, too. Next time I won't be late.
M: It's important to arrive at school on time.

❶ take the wrong bus = 버스를 잘못 타다
❷ 동사 think의 목적어 역할을 하는 명사절에서 접속사 that이 생략되어 있다.

Listen & Speak 2 Listen

1. G: Your bag is too small.
   B: Yes. I should have brought a bigger one.

2. G: Aren't you cold?
   B: ❶Yes. I should have worn a jacket.
3. B: We ❷missed our flight.
   G: Oh, no. We should have come earlier.
4. G: Look at my face. I should have put on some sunscreen.
   B: Yes. You're right.

❶ "Aren't you ～?"에 해당하는 부정의 질문에 대한 대답은 대답이 긍정이면 Yes, 부정이면 No이다.
❷ miss flight = 항공편을 놓치다

Listen & Speak 2 A-1

B: Mina, ❶how was the movie?
G: I didn't enjoy it. It was boring.
B: What was bad about it?
G: I already knew the ending. I ❷shouldn't have read about it before seeing it.
B: Oh, I'm sorry you didn't like it.

❶ "how was the movie?"는 영화가 만족스러운지를 묻는 질문이다.
❷ "shouldn't have+과거분사"는 "～하지 말았어야 했는데"의 의미로 과거 사실에 대한 유감이나 후회를 나타낸다.

Listen & Speak 2 A-2

B: We still have 30 minutes ❶to go before we reach the top of the mountain. Let's sit down over there and have a snack.
G: Oh, I brought only water. I should have brought some snacks.
B: That's okay. I brought a lot. We can share.
G: I'll keep ❷it in mind to bring some snacks next time.

❶ "to go ～"는 minutes를 수식하는 형용사적 용법이다.
❷ it은 가목적어이고, to bring이 진목적어이다.

Wrap Up 2

G: Ryan, ❶are you okay? You look tired.
B: I couldn't sleep well last night.
G: Why is that? Did you have too much homework?
G: No. I ❷watched a movie on TV, and it didn't end until after 2:00.
G: Oh, you should have gone to bed earlier.

❶ "are you okay?"는 상대의 안부를 묻는 말이다.
❷ "watch a movie on TV"는 "TV로 영화를 보다"의 뜻이다.

● 다음 우리말과 일치하도록 빈칸에 알맞은 말을 쓰시오.

Listen & Speak 1 Listen

1. **G:** How _____ we _____ healthy?
   B: _____, it's _____ to eat a good _____.

2. **B:** _____ can we _____ to get good _____?
   G: It's _____ to review every day.

3. **G:** I _____ it's important to _____ a _____ after reading.
   B: I agree.

4. **B:** It's important to _____ _____ what you _____ your money _____.
   G: I _____ so, too.

Listen & Speak 1 A

1. **B:** _____ did you _____ on the _____?
   G: I _____ tennis. I have _____ to _____ on the weekend _____ my health.
   B: Good for _____. It's _____ to exercise _____.
   G: _____. How _____ playing tennis _____ me?
   B: Why not?

2. **M:** John, you are _____ again.
   B: I'm sorry. I _____ the wrong _____.
   M: I _____ you need to _____ home a little _____.
   B: I think so, _____. Next time I _____ be late.
   M: It's important to _____ at school _____ time.

Listen & Speak 2

1. **G:** Your bag is _____ small.
   B: Yes. I _____ have _____ a bigger _____.

2. **G:** Aren't you _____?
   B: Yes. I should _____ worn a jacket.

3. **B:** We _____ our flight.
   G: Oh, no. We should _____ come _____.

4. **G:** _____ at my face. I _____ have _____ _____ some sunscreen.
   B: Yes. You're _____.

해석

1. G: 우리는 어떻게 건강을 유지할 수 있을까?
   B: 음, 든든한 아침 식사를 하는 것이 중요해.
2. B: 좋은 점수를 받기 위해 우리는 무엇을 할 수 있을까?
   G: 매일 복습하는 것이 중요해.
3. G: 나는 독서 후에 일기를 쓰는 것이 중요하다고 생각해.
   B: 나도 동의해.
4. B: 네가 돈을 어디에 썼는지 적는 것은 중요해.
   G: 나도 그렇게 생각해.

1. B: 주말에 뭐 했니?
   G: 나는 테니스를 쳤어. 나는 건강을 위해 주말에 운동을 하기로 결정했어.
   B: 잘했어. 규칙적으로 운동하는 것은 중요해.
   G: 맞아. 나와 테니스 치는 것은 어때?
   B: 왜 안 되겠어?
2. M: 존, 또 지각이구나!
   B: 죄송해요. 버스를 잘못 탔어요.
   M: 나는 네가 집에서 좀 더 빨리 출발할 필요가 있다고 생각한단다.
   B: 저도 그렇게 생각해요. 다음번에는 늦지 않을 게요.
   M: 학교에 제시간에 오는 것은 중요하단다.

1. G: 네 가방은 정말 작아.
   B: 응. 난 더 큰 것을 가져왔어야 했어.
2. G: 춥지 않니?
   B: 응. 나는 재킷을 입었어야 했어.
3. B: 우리 비행기를 놓쳤어.
   G: 오, 안 돼. 우리는 더 빨리 왔어야 했어.
4. G: 내 얼굴 좀 봐. 나는 자외선 차단제를 발랐어야 했어.
   B: 그래. 네 말이 맞아.

Listen & Speak 2 A

1. **B:** Mina, _____ was the _____?
   G: I didn't _____ it. It _____ boring.
   B: _____ was bad _____ it?
   G: I already _____ the ending. I shouldn't _____ read about it _____ seeing it.
   B: Oh, I'm _____ you didn't _____ it.

2. **B:** We _____ have 30 _____ to go _____ we reach the _____ of the mountain. Let's sit _____ over there _____ have a _____.
   G: Oh, I _____ only water. I should have _____ some snacks.
   B: That's _____. I brought a lot. We can _____.
   G: I'll _____ it in _____ to bring _____ snacks next _____.

Real-Life Zone

G: Ben, you _____ full of _____ today!
B: Do I? Maybe that's _____ I finally _____ a good night's sleep _____ night.
G: Why? Don't you _____ get _____ sleep?
B: No, I _____ it's really _____ to get a good _____ sleep, but I _____ stay _____ late _____ the Internet or _____ with my _____.
G: That _____ happens to _____ too.
B: _____ I do that, I _____ it the next _____ and say, "I should _____ gone to bed _____ last night."
G: How was yesterday _____?
B: Well, yesterday afternoon I _____ the mountain with my _____. I was really _____ when I got _____. I went to _____ right _____ I went to bed.
G: _____ activities _____ a great _____ to help you _____ a good night's sleep.

Wrap Up 1

W: Oh, your _____ is _____ from the rain! I should have _____ the weather.
B: Did you _____ it?
W: No. I just _____ it out in the _____ this morning.
B: _____ didn't you _____ it?
W: Hanging a _____ in the sun is a nature-friendly _____ to _____ the blanket _____.
B: Oh, I didn't _____ that. I'll _____ that.
W: And it's also _____ to _____ to do it _____.

해석

1. B: 미나야, 영화 어땠니?
   G: 나는 그것을 즐기지 못했어. 지루했어.
   B: 무엇이 별로였니?
   G: 나는 이미 결말을 알고 있었어. 보기 전에 그것에 대해 읽지 말았어야 했는데.
   B: 오, 네가 좋아하지 않다니 유감이야.

2. B: 우리는 산 정상에 도착하기까지 아직 30분이 더 가야 해. 저기서 앉아서 간식 먹고 가자.
   G: 오, 난 물만 가져왔어. 간식을 가져왔어야 했는데.
   B: 괜찮아. 내가 많이 가져왔어. 우리는 같이 먹을 수 있어.
   G: 다음번에는 간식을 가져올 것을 명심할게.

G: 벤, 너 오늘 기운 차 보여!
B: 내가 그래? 그건 아마 내가 지난밤 마침내 잠을 잘 잤기 때문일 거야.
G: 왜? 평소에 충분한 잠을 자지 못하니?
B: 응, 잠을 잘 자는 것이 정말 중요하다는 것은 알지만 나는 언제나 인터넷 검색을 하거나 휴대폰을 가지고 놀면서 늦게까지 깨어 있어.
G: 그건 나에게도 가끔 일어나는 일이야.
B: 그러고 난 뒤에, 나는 다음 날 아침 후회하고 "지난밤에 더 일찍 잠들었어야 했는데."라고 말해.
G: 어제는 어떻게 달랐니?
B: 음, 어제 오후에 나는 아빠와 등산을 했어. 집에 왔을 때 나는 매우 피곤했어. 나는 침대에 가자마자 바로 잠들었어.
G: 야외 활동은 네가 잠을 잘 자도록 돕는 훌륭한 방법이구나.

W: 오, 네 이불이 비에 젖었어! 내가 날씨를 확인했어야 했는데.
B: 그것을 빨았어요?
W: 아니. 오늘 아침에 그냥 햇볕에 널어놓았어.
B: 왜 빨지 않았어요?
W: 햇볕에 이불을 널어놓는 것은 이불을 깨끗하게 유지하는 친환경적인 방법이야.
B: 오, 저는 그것을 몰랐어요. 기억해 둘게요.
W: 그리고 정기적으로 그렇게 하는 것을 기억하는 것 또한 중요해.

[01~02] 다음 대화의 빈칸에 들어갈 말로 알맞은 것은?

01

B: What did you do on the weekend?

G: I played tennis. I have decided to exercise on the weekend for my health.

B: Good for you. It's important to exercise regularly.

G: Right. _____ playing tennis with me?

B: Why not?

① How about   ② Will you avoid   ③ Do you like

④ Are you   ⑤ Why do you enjoy

02

M: John, you are late again.

B: I'm sorry. _____

M: I think you need to leave home a little earlier.

B: I think so, too. Next time I won't be late.

M: It's important to arrive at school on time.

① I won't leave home early.

② Will you say that again?

③ I'm sure you will be all right.

④ I can drive a car myself.

⑤ I took the wrong bus.

03 다음 대화에 이어지기에 적절하게 배열된 순서를 고르시오.

B: Mina, how was the movie?

G: I didn't enjoy it. It was boring.

(A) I already knew the ending. I shouldn't have read about it before seeing it.

(B) Oh, I'm sorry you didn't like it.

(C) What was bad about it?

① (A) – (C) – (B)   ② (B) – (A) – (C)   ③ (B) – (C) – (A)

④ (C) – (A) – (B)   ⑤ (C) – (B) – (A)

01 다음 빈칸에 적절한 말은?

> B: It's important to write down what you spend your money on.
> G: _____, too.

① You heard it　　② I don't know

③ I think so　　　④ We will do it

⑤ They are ready

[02~03] 다음 대화를 읽고 물음에 답하시오.

> B: What did you do on the weekend?
> G: I played tennis. I have decided to _____(A)_____ for my health.
> B: Good for you. It's important to exercise regularly.
> G: Right. How about playing tennis with me?
> B: Why not?

02 빈칸 (A)에 들어가기에 적절한 것은?

① be ready for my finals

② invite you to my house

③ watch a tennis match

④ exercise on the weekend

⑤ write down how much I spend

중요

03 위 대화를 읽고 알 수 없는 것은?

① The boy asked the girl what she did on the weekend.

② The girl played tennis on the weekday.

③ The girl decided to play tennis for the health.

④ The boy thinks it's important to exercise regularly.

⑤ The boy will play tennis with the girl.

[04~06] 다음 대화를 읽고 물음에 답하시오.

> G: Ben, you look full of energy today!
> B: Do I? Maybe that's because I finally got a good night's sleep last night.
> G: Why? Don't you usually get enough sleep?
> B: No, I know it's really important to get a good night's sleep, but I always _____ late surfing the Internet or playing with my phone. (A)
> G: That sometimes happens to me too.
> B: After I do that, I regret it the next morning and say, "I should have gone to bed earlier last night." (B)
> G: How was yesterday different? (C)
> B: Well, yesterday afternoon I climbed the mountain with my dad. (D) I went to sleep right after I went to bed.
> G: Outdoor activities are a great way to help you get a good night's sleep. (E)

04 위 대화의 빈칸에 들어가기에 가장 적절한 것은?

① make bed　　　② wake up

③ stay up　　　　④ call you

⑤ work out

중요

05 (A)~(E) 중에서 다음 주어진 문장이 들어가기에 적절한 곳은?

> I was really tired when I got home.

① (A)　② (B)　③ (C)　④ (D)　⑤ (E)

06 위 대화의 내용과 일치하지 <u>않는</u> 것은?

① Ben feels very good today.
② Ben slept well last night.
③ Ben will surf the Internet late at night.
④ Yesterday Ben climbed the mountain with his father.
⑤ Ben slept early last night.

[07~09] 다음 대화를 읽고 물음에 답하시오.

> B: ⓐMina, how was the movie?
> G: _____(A)_____ ⓑIt was boring.
> B: ⓒWhat was bad about it?
> G: I already knew the ending. ⓓI should have read about it before seeing it.
> B: ⓔOh, I'm sorry you didn't like it.

07 다음 중 빈칸 (A)에 들어가기에 적절한 것은?

① I didn't enjoy it.
② Do you like it?
③ How was the ending?
④ The story was very good.
⑤ Did you like it?

08 ⓐ~ⓔ 중에서 대화의 내용상 <u>어색한</u> 것은?

① ⓐ　　② ⓑ　　③ ⓒ　　④ ⓓ　　⑤ ⓔ

09 Which one CANNOT be answered from the dialogue above?

① What are they talking about right now?
② How did the girl think about the movie?
③ Did the girl know the ending of the movie?
④ Did the girl read about the movie?
⑤ Why didn't the boy like the movie?

[10~12] 다음 대화를 읽고 물음에 답하시오.

> B: We still have 30 minutes to go before we reach the top of the mountain. Let's sit down over there and have a snack.
> G: Oh, I brought only water. (A)<u>I should bring some snacks.</u>
> B: That's okay. I brought a lot. We can ___(B)___ .
> G: I'll ___(C)___ it in mind to bring some snacks next time.

10 위 대화의 밑줄 친 (A)를 흐름상 알맞은 문장으로 고치시오.

➡ _____

11 위 대화의 빈칸 (B), (C)에 들어가기에 적절한 것은?

	(B)		(C)
①	share	–	keep
②	take	–	make
③	keep	–	get
④	share	–	have
⑤	help	–	keep

12 위 대화의 내용과 일치하지 <u>않는</u> 것은?

① They are going up the mountain.
② They are going to take some rest.
③ They don't have enough snacks.
④ The girl didn't bring any snacks.
⑤ The girl says she will bring some snacks next time.

01 다음 우리말을 영어로 쓰시오.

> G: Aren't you cold?
> B: Yes. 나는 재킷을 입었어야 했어.

➡ _____

02 다음 대화의 순서를 올바르게 배열하시오.

> G: Ryan, are you okay? You look tired.
> B: I couldn't sleep well last night.
> (A) Oh, you should have gone to bed earlier.
> (B) Why is that? Did you have too much homework?
> (C) No. I watched a movie on TV, and it didn't end until after 2:00.

➡ _____

[03~05] 다음 대화를 읽고 물음에 답하시오.

> B: What did you do on the weekend?
> G: I played tennis. I have decided to ___(A)___ on the weekend for my health.
> B: Good for you. (B)규칙적으로 운동하는 것은 중요해.
> G: Right. How about (C)(play) tennis with me?
> B: Why not?

03 주어진 영영풀이를 참고하여 빈칸 (A)에 철자 e로 시작하는 단어를 쓰시오.

> to do physical activities in order to make yourself stronger and healthier

➡ _____

04 (B)에 주어진 우리말에 해당하는 영어 문장을 쓰시오.

➡ _____

05 (C)에 주어진 단어의 올바른 형태를 쓰시오.

➡ _____

[06~08] 다음 대화를 읽고 물음에 답하시오.

> B: Mina, how was the movie?
> G: I didn't enjoy it. It was boring.
> B: What was good about it?
> G: I already knew the ending. (A)(read, it, I shouldn't, before, have, seeing, about, it.)
> B: Oh, _____(B)_____ you didn't like it.

06 위 대화에서 (A)의 괄호 안에 주어진 단어를 적절하게 배열하시오.

➡ _____

07 내용상 빈칸 (B)에 들어가기에 적절한 표현을 쓰시오. (2 words)

➡ _____

08 위 대화에서 흐름상 어색한 한 단어를 찾아 쓰고 적절한 단어로 바꾸시오.

_____ ➡ _____

Grammar

① the 비교급, the 비교급

- **The more** sun you get, **the more** "happy hormone" the brain produces.
  여러분이 햇빛을 많이 쬐면 쬘수록 뇌는 행복 호르몬을 더 만들어 냅니다.

- **The stronger** will you have, **the more** you will learn.
  의지가 더 강하면 강할수록 더 많이 배울 것이다.

■ the 비교급+주어+동사 ~, the 비교급+주어+동사 …

- 의미: ~하면 할수록 더 …하다
- 형태: 'the 비교급+주어+동사 ~, the 비교급+주어+동사 …'

■ 'the 비교급+주어+동사 ~, the 비교급+주어+동사 …' 구문은 정도가 점점 더해지거나 덜해지는 것을 표현할 때 사용한다.

- **The more, the better.** 많으면 많을수록 더 좋다.

■ 최상급이 아닌 비교급임에도 the를 쓰는 것에 주의해야 하며, be동사나 반복되는 어구는 종종 생략된다. 이 구문에 쓰이는 'the'는 정관사가 아니라 부사이다.

- **The harder** you work, **the more** you get. 더 열심히 일할수록 더 많이 얻는다.
- **The less** my hope, **the hotter** my love. 내 희망이 적을수록 내 사랑은 더 뜨겁다.

■ 'the 비교급+주어+동사 ~, the 비교급+주어+동사 …' 구문은 'As+주어+동사+비교급 ~, 주어+동사 +비교급 …'으로 바꿔 쓸 수 있다.

- **The higher** we go up, **the colder** the air becomes.
  = **As** we go up **higher**, the air becomes **colder**. 높이 올라가면 올라갈수록 공기가 더욱 더 차가워진다.

cf. '비교급 and 비교급'은 '점점 더 …하다'의 뜻이다

- It is getting **colder and colder**. 날씨가 점점 더 추워지고 있다.

핵심 Check

1. 다음 괄호 안에서 알맞은 말을 고르시오.
   (1) The (long / longer) the soup cooks, the thicker it gets.
   (2) The more I want to get something done, the (less / least) I call it work.

2 It is[was] ... that 강조 구문

- **It** is calcium **that** builds strong bones and teeth. 튼튼한 뼈와 치아를 만드는 것은 칼슘입니다.
- **It** was his family **that** Sam wanted to meet before he died.
  샘이 죽기 전에 만나보고 싶은 것은 바로 그의 가족이었다.

■ 'It + is/was + 강조어(구) + that ...'의 형태로 특정 부분을 강조하여 나타낼 때 사용한다. 강조하고자 하는 부분을 'It is/was'와 'that' 사이에 쓰고, 나머지 부분을 that 뒤에 써서 주어, 목적어인 명사, 부사(구/절) 등을 강조한다. 'be'동사는 문장의 시제에 맞춰 'is'나 'was'를 사용한다.

- His laughter broke the silence in the room.
  - → **It was** his laughter **that** broke the silence in the room. (주어 강조)
  - → **It was** the silence **that** his laughter broke in the room. (목적어인 명사 강조)
  - → **It was** in the room **that** his laughter broke the silence. (부사구 강조)

■ 'It is[was] ~ that ...' 강조 구문에서 강조하는 대상이 명사일 경우, that 대신에 관계대명사 who[whom](사람일 경우) 또는 which(사물이나 동물일 경우)로 바꿔 쓸 수 있으며, 시간 또는 장소의 부사(구/절)일 경우, when(시간) 또는 where(장소)로 바꿔 쓸 수 있다.

- I bought the brush at the shop yesterday. 나는 어제 그 가게에서 빗을 샀다.
  - → **It was** I **that**[**who**] bought the brush at the shop yesterday.
  - → **It was** the brush **that**[**which**] I bought at the shop yesterday.
  - → **It was** yesterday **that**[**when**] I bought the brush at the shop.
  - → **It was** at the shop **that**[**where**] I bought the brush yesterday.

■ 'It is[was] ~ that ...' 강조 구문에서 강조하는 대상이 부사(구/절)일 경우 that 다음에 완전한 절이 나오지만 그 외의 경우에는 불완전한 절이 나오는 것에 유의한다. 또한 강조되는 부분에 형용사나 동사는 올 수 없다.

- **It was** a new smartphone **that**[**which**] I wanted to buy. 내가 사고 싶었던 것은 바로 새 스마트폰이었다. (that 다음에 buy의 목적어가 없는 불완전한 절)
- **It was** at the library **that**[**where**] I studied math. 내가 수학을 공부한 곳은 바로 그 도서실에서였다. (that 다음에 완전한 절)
- It is beautiful that she is. (형용사 강조 ×)
- It was bought that I the books yesterday. (동사 강조 ×)

핵심 Check

2. 다음 괄호 안에서 알맞은 말을 고르시오.

(1) It is Minjun (that / what) is playing basketball.

(2) (It / That) was in the morning that I got a call from Samuel.

(3) It was he (whom / which) they wanted for a king.

Grammar 시험대비 기본평가

01 다음 각 문장의 빈칸에 공통으로 들어갈 말로 알맞은 것은?

> • It is California _____ Layla comes from.
> • It was her wallet _____ Linda lost in the subway yesterday.

① where   ② when   ③ who

④ that   ⑤ what

02 다음 빈칸에 들어갈 말로 알맞은 것은?

> • The _____ you laugh, the happier you become!

① much   ② many   ③ more

④ few   ⑤ fewer

03 다음 중 어법상 바르지 <u>않은</u> 것은?

① It was Mike that stole the wallet.

② It was John which loved her.

③ It was Clair whom he met again.

④ It was in the library that we studied together.

⑤ It was on Friday when we had dinner together.

04 다음 우리말에 맞게 주어진 어휘를 바르게 배열하시오.

(1) 내가 사랑하는 건 바로 너야.

    (that, I, it, you, is, love)

    ➡ _____

(2) 튼튼한 뼈와 치아를 만드는 것은 칼슘입니다.

    (calcium, bones, teeth, that, it, builds, strong, is, and)

    ➡ _____

(3) 운동을 하면 할수록 나는 더 강해진다.

    (I, I, get, exercise, the, the, more, stronger)

    ➡ _____

(4) 많으면 많을수록 더 좋다.

    (the, the, better, more)

    ➡ _____

01 다음 중 어법상 <u>어색한</u> 것은?

① The more I read, the more I learn.
② The hot it gets, the hard it is to work.
③ The colder it gets, the more clothes you need.
④ It is the baby that she should take care of.
⑤ It was some flowers which he bought for her.

02 다음 중 어법상 옳은 것은?

① It was the shoes which Ted bought last Sunday.
② It was James which went to the shop to buy some bread.
③ It is on Sundays where Daniel and I meet.
④ The much I play, the much I want to play.
⑤ The older he gets, the wise he becomes.

03 다음 문장과 같은 뜻의 문장은?

> As I study harder, I learn more.

① Because I studied harder, I learned the more.
② I have studied the harder, so I have learned the more.
③ The hard I study, the much I learn.
④ The harder I study, the more I learn.
⑤ The hardest I study, the most I learn.

04 다음 밑줄 친 부분과 바꿔 쓸 수 있는 것은?

> It was James <u>that</u> went to Amy's birthday party last Friday.

① whether   ② what
③ it   ④ which
⑤ who

[05~06] 다음 우리말을 알맞게 영작한 것을 <u>모두</u> 고르시오.

05
> 여러분이 햇볕을 쬘수록 뇌는 행복 호르몬을 더 만들어 냅니다.

① More sun you get, more "happy hormone" the brain produces.
② The most sun you get, the most "happy hormone" the brain produces.
③ The more sun you get, the more "happy hormone" the brain produces.
④ Because you get more sun, the brain produces the more "happy hormone".
⑤ As you get more sun, the brain produces more "happy hormone".

06
> Tom이 매일 먹는 것은 바로 사과이다.

① It is an apple what Tom eats every day.
② It is an apple who Tom eats every day.
③ It is an apple which Tom eats every day.
④ It is an apple when Tom eats every day.
⑤ It is an apple where Tom eats every day.

07 다음 우리말과 일치하는 문장을 쓸 때, 빈칸에 알맞은 말은?

> 어두워질수록 우리의 두려움은 더 커졌다.
> = _____ it grew, the bigger our fear became.

① Dark

② Darker

③ Darkest

④ The darker

⑤ The darkest

08 다음 〈보기〉의 밑줄 친 that과 쓰임이 같은 것은?

> ┌─ 보기 ─
> It was in the library that Ryan met Suho yesterday.

① He isn't that rich.

② It was the cookies that Amy made for me yesterday.

③ That's a nice tie you are wearing.

④ That the earth is round is common knowledge today.

⑤ That fifty dollars helped me greatly.

09 다음 문장의 빈칸 (A), (B)에 들어갈 말로 가장 적절한 것은?

> _____ (A) _____ she grows, _____ (B) _____ she becomes.

	(A)	(B)
①	The older	the prettier
②	The older	prettier
③	The old	the pretty
④	Older	the prettier
⑤	Older	prettier

10 다음 문장의 빈칸에 알맞은 말을 모두 고르시오.

> It was a book _____ Eric lent me in the library yesterday.

① that ② what ③ when

④ which ⑤ where

---

11 다음 문장과 비슷한 뜻이 되도록 비교급을 사용하여 바꿔 쓰시오.

(1) As I went up higher, the air was fresher.

➡ _____

(2) If you walk much, you will get tired.

➡ _____

12 다음 중 It ~ that 쓰임이 나머지와 다른 하나는?

① It was in the park that I played soccer with my friends.

② It is essential that you have some experience.

③ It was yesterday that I met him in the park.

④ It was math that I studied at the library.

⑤ It was when Kate came into the room that the phone rang.

13 다음 문장을 어법에 맞게 고쳐 쓰시오.

(1) This red dress looks prettier of the two.

➡ _____
_____

(2) More water we use, drier our well will become.

➡ _____
_____

(3) Much stress I get, much emotional I become.

➡ _____
_____

[14~15] 다음 중 어법상 올바른 문장을 고르시오.

14
① That was a new smartphone which I wanted to buy.
② It is meet that Daniel and I on Sundays.
③ It was comfortable that you felt.
④ It is he who make decisions on the matter.
⑤ It is the blue shirt that Jay wants to buy.

15 중요
① The older the queen got, the ugly she got.
② The more slowly you drive, the more safe you are.
③ I believe the more often we laugh, the happier we will be.
④ My English is getting good and good.
⑤ My new computer was nicer of the two.

서답형
16 다음 문장에서 어법상 <u>어색한</u> 부분을 바르게 고치시오.

(1) It was because he was sick why we decided to return.

_____ ➡ _____

(2) It is a good breakfast who helps the brain work properly.

_____ ➡ _____

(3) It was July 26 when Gustav Jung was born.

_____ ➡ _____

서답형
17 괄호 안에서 알맞은 것을 고르시오.

(1) (The spicier / The spicy) the food is, (the more / the much) Kevin likes it.
(2) (The more / Much) Andy worked, (the more / much) money he earned.
(3) It was last Friday (which / when) James went to Amy's birthday party.
(4) It was under the bed (which / where) Tina found the wallet yesterday.
(5) It was William (whom / which) she wanted to see.

중요
18 주어진 문장을 'the movie'를 강조하는 문장으로 바르게 고친 것은?

James watched the movie with his girl friend last night.

① It is the movie what James watched with his girl friend last night.
② It was the movie which James watched with his girl friend last night.
③ It is the movie whom James watched with his girl friend last night.
④ It is the movie when James watched with his girl friend last night.
⑤ It was the movie who James watched with his girl friend last night.

19 다음 빈칸에 들어갈 수 <u>없는</u> 것은?

The finer the weather is, _____ I become.

① the more gloomy
② the happier
③ the brighter
④ the merrier
⑤ the more excited

01 다음 두 문장을 〈보기〉와 같이 한 문장으로 완성하시오.

┌─ 보기 ├─
- You get much sunlight.
- You feel happy and strong.
→ The more sunlight you get, the happier and stronger you feel.

(1) • A bird flies high.
  • It can see far.
  ➡ _____

(2) • They have much.
  • They want much.
  ➡ _____

02 다음 문장에서 어법상 <u>어색한</u> 것을 바르게 고쳐 다시 쓰시오.

(1) More stress I get, more emotional I become.
  ➡ _____
  _____

(2) Ryan thinks the much slowly he eats, the full he gets.
  ➡ _____
  _____

(3) Youngest you are, easiest it is to learn.
  ➡ _____
  _____

(4) This country is better of the two.
  ➡ _____

(5) It was Hamin which played basketball with Eric last Saturday.
  ➡ _____
  _____

(6) It is on Saturdays which there are lots of weddings.
  ➡ _____
  _____

(7) It was Hangang Park which Ms. Jones was at 2 p.m. last Saturday.
  ➡ _____
  _____

(8) It was Amy's house where James visited last Friday.
  ➡ _____
  _____

03 다음 그림을 보고 각 질문에 'It ~ that' 강조 구문을 사용하여 답하시오.

Jenny's family

(1) Who went to the beach last summer?
  ➡ _____

(2) Where did Jenny's family go last summer?
  ➡ _____

(3) When did Jenny's family go to the beach?
  ➡ _____

04 다음 문장과 비슷한 뜻이 되도록 비교급을 사용하여 바꿔 쓰시오.

(1) If I like her much, I will miss her much.

➡ _____

_____

(2) If you leave early, you will arrive there early.

➡ _____

(3) As you study harder for the exam, you will do better.

➡ _____

_____

(4) As you are more careful, you will make fewer mistakes.

➡ _____

_____

05 다음 문장을 주어진 단어를 강조하는 문장으로 고쳐 쓰시오. that은 사용하지 말 것.

Anna bought the dress on the Internet last Sunday.

(1) Anna

➡ _____

_____

(2) bought

➡ _____

_____

(3) the dress

➡ _____

_____

(4) on the Internet

➡ _____

_____

(5) last Sunday

➡ _____

_____

06 괄호 안에 주어진 어휘를 이용하여 빈칸에 알맞은 말을 쓰시오.

(1) The more you walk, _____

_____. (healthy, will, feel)

(2) The hotter the weather is, _____

_____. (hard, doing outdoor activities)

(3) The faster you drive, _____

_____. (dangerous, will, be)

07 다음 우리말과 일치하도록 괄호 안에 주어진 어휘를 이용하여 영작하시오.

(1) 공부를 많이 할수록, 너는 더 똑똑해질 것이다. (much, smart, become)

➡ _____

_____

(2) 당신이 돈을 덜 쓸수록, 당신은 당신의 계좌에 더 많은 돈을 갖게 될 것이다. (little, spend, have in your account)

➡ _____

_____

(3) Mr. Smith가 우리 아파트로 이사 온 것은 바로 5년 전이었다. (move to, apartment)

➡ _____

_____

(4) 내가 이 조리법을 배운 곳은 바로 그 이탈리아 식당이었다. (learned, this recipe)

➡ _____

_____

(5) Jack이 시장에서 잃어버린 것은 바로 그의 책이었다. (lost, at the market)

➡ _____

_____

Reading

Enjoy the Sunshine

How much time do you spend every day out in the sun? Not much, right? Most people are too busy at school or at work to spend much time

= Most people are so busy at school or at work that they cannot spend much time outdoors.
too ~ to부정사 = so ~ that 주어 cannot

outdoors. However, the sun plays an important role in your health. It

play an important role in: ~에서 중요한 역할을 하다   = the sun

helps you stay healthy.

help+목적어+목적격보어(to부정사 또는 동사원형)

Everyone feels happier when the sun shines. This is because of

Everyone: 단수 취급, 단수 동사

serotonin, the body's happy hormone. The more sun you get, the more

동격의 콤마, the body's happy hormone = serotonin   the 비교급 ~, the 비교급 …: ~할수록 …하다

"happy hormone" the brain produces. When your serotonin level goes

up, you feel happier and stronger. This helps you fight everyday stress.

비교급 and 비교급   = to fight

Serotonin also has a calming effect, helping you focus better on what

분사구문. and it helps you   = the thing(s) which[that]

you are doing. Moreover, serotonin helps you get a good night's sleep

= to get

because it helps the brain produce a sleep hormone.

= serotonin   = to produce

sunshine 햇빛
outdoors 야외에서
role 역할
hormone 호르몬
brain 뇌
produce 만들어 내다, 생산하다
effect 효과
moreover 게다가
go up 올라가다

 확인문제

- 다음 문장이 본문의 내용과 일치하면 T, 일치하지 않으면 F를 쓰시오.

1 Most people are so busy at school or at work that they cannot spend much time outdoors. ☐

2 The sun plays an insignificant role in your health. ☐

3 Everyone feels happier when the sun shines. ☐

4 As you get more sun, the brain produces less "happy hormone". ☐

5 Serotonin has a calming effect. ☐

6 Serotonin helps you get a good night's sleep because it helps the brain produce a calming hormone. ☐

Sunshine does not just <u>make you feel and sleep</u> better. It also
make(사역동사)+목적어+목적격보어(동사원형): ~에게 …하게 하다

helps build strong bones. <u>As</u> you all know, <u>it is calcium that builds</u>
help가 준사역동사로 사용된   as: ~한 것처럼, ~하다시피(접속사)   'it … that' 강조 구문: 강조하고자 하는 부분을 it과 that 사이에 쓰고,
문장으로, 목적어가 생략됨.   it 뒤에 오는 be동사는 문장의 시제에 맞춰 is나 was를 사용한다.

strong bones and teeth. However, <u>for the body</u> to use calcium properly,
for+목적격: to부정사의 의미상의 주어

it needs vitamin D. Interestingly, the skin creates vitamin D when

sunlight shines on it. The easiest way <u>to make</u> strong bones is <u>to go</u>
to부정사의 형용사적 용법   to부정사의 명사적 용법(보어)

outside and <u>enjoy</u> the sun.
enjoy 앞에 to가 생략된 것임.

As you can see, sunshine has many benefits, but how can you enjoy

its benefits safely? Fortunately, <u>getting</u> direct sunlight on your skin for
동명사 주어

10 to 20 minutes <u>a day</u> is <u>enough to</u> benefit from it. Try to go out into
하루에   enough+to부정사: ~하기에 충분한

the sun between classes or during lunch breaks and get sunshine on

your arms and hands. A walk in the sun, for <u>just</u> a few minutes every
= only

day, is good for <u>both</u> your mind <u>and</u> your body. However, avoid the
both A and B: 'A와 B 둘 다', A와 B는 문법적으로 성격과 형식이 같은 요소가 와야 한다.

sun during peak summer hours, between 11 and 3, and use sunscreen

<u>to protect</u> your face and neck. Enjoy the sun safely and see <u>how a little</u>
to부정사의 부사적 용법(목적: ~하기 위해)

<u>sunshine can make a world of difference in your health and your mood.</u>
간접의문문(의문사+주어+동사), see의 목적어   a[the] world of: 산더미 같은, 막대한

bone 뼈

properly 제대로, 적절하게

vitamin 비타민

skin 피부

sunlight 햇빛, 햇살

benefit 이득; 이득을 보다

fortunately 다행스럽게도

direct (열기나 빛이) 직접 닿는

peak 절정의, 최고조의

sunscreen 자외선 차단제

mood 기분, 감정

 확인문제

● 다음 문장이 본문의 내용과 일치하면 T, 일치하지 <u>않으면</u> F를 쓰시오.

1   Sunshine helps build strong bones as well as makes you feel and sleep better. ☐

2   For the body to use vitamin D properly, it needs calcium. ☐

3   The easiest way to make strong bones is to go outside and enjoy the sun. ☐

4   Getting direct sunlight on your skin for 10 to 20 minutes a day isn't enough to
benefit from it. ☐

5   A walk in the sun, for just a few minutes every day, is good for both your mind and
your body. ☐

6   A little sunshine can make a little difference in your health and your mood. ☐

● 우리말을 참고하여 빈칸에 알맞은 말을 쓰시오.

1 Enjoy the _____

2 How much time do you spend every day _____ _____ _____ _____ ?

3 _____ _____, right?

4 Most people are _____ _____ at school or at work _____ _____ much time _____.

5 However, the sun _____ _____ _____ _____ in your health.

6 It helps you _____ _____.

7 Everyone _____ _____ when the sun shines.

8 This is because of serotonin, _____ _____ _____ _____.

9 _____ _____ _____ you get, _____ _____ "_____ _____" the brain produces.

10 When your serotonin level _____ _____, you feel happier and stronger.

11 This helps you _____ _____ _____.

12 Serotonin also has a _____ _____, helping you focus better on _____ _____ _____ _____.

13 _____, serotonin helps you get _____ _____ _____ _____ because it helps the brain produce a sleep hormone.

14 Sunshine does _____ _____ make you feel and sleep better.

1 햇빛을 즐기세요

2 여러분은 매일 햇빛 속에서 얼마나 많은 시간을 보내나요?

3 많지 않죠, 그렇죠?

4 대부분의 사람들은 학교와 직장에서 너무 바빠서 많은 시간을 야외에서 보내지 못합니다.

5 그러나 햇빛은 여러분의 건강에 중요한 역할을 합니다.

6 그것은 여러분이 건강을 유지하는 데 도움을 줍니다.

7 모든 사람들은 해가 비칠 때 더 행복하게 느낍니다.

8 이것은 몸의 행복 호르몬인 세로토닌 때문입니다.

9 여러분이 햇빛을 쬘수록 뇌는 행복 호르몬을 더 만들어 냅니다.

10 여러분의 세로토닌 수치가 높아지면, 여러분은 더 행복하고 더 건강하게 느낍니다.

11 이것은 여러분이 매일의 스트레스를 이겨 내는 데 도움을 줍니다.

12 세로토닌은 또한 진정 효과가 있고, 여러분이 하는 일에 더 잘 집중할 수 있도록 도와줍니다.

13 게다가, 세로토닌은 뇌가 수면 호르몬을 생성하도록 도와주기 때문에 여러분이 숙면을 취하도록 해 줍니다.

14 햇빛은 단지 여러분이 더 기분 좋게 느끼고 잠을 더 잘 자게 하는 것만은 아닙니다.

15 It _____ helps _____ _____ _____.

16 _____ _____ _____ _____, it is calcium that builds strong bones and teeth.

17 H o w e v e r, _____ _____ _____ _____ _____ calcium properly, it needs vitamin D.

18 Interestingly, the skin creates vitamin D _____ _____ _____ on it.

19 The easiest way to make strong bones is _____ _____ _____ and enjoy the sun.

20 _____ _____ _____ _____, s u n s h i n e has many benefits, but how can you _____ _____ _____ _____?

21 Fortunately, _____ _____ _____ on your skin for 10 to 20 minutes a day is enough _____ _____ _____ _____.

22 _____ _____ _____ _____ _____ the sun between classes or during lunch breaks and _____ _____ _____ your arms and hands.

23 A walk in the sun, _____ _____ _____ _____, is good for both your mind and your body.

24 However, avoid the sun during peak summer hours, between 11 and 3, and use sunscreen _____ _____ _____ _____ _____ _____.

25 Enjoy the sun safely and see how _____ _____ _____ can _____ _____ _____ _____ _____ in your health and your mood.

15 그것은 또한 튼튼한 뼈를 만드는 것을 돕습니다.

16 여러분 모두가 알다시피, 튼튼한 뼈와 치아를 만드는 것은 칼슘입니다.

17 그러나 몸이 칼슘을 적절하게 사용하기 위해서는 비타민 D가 필요합니다.

18 흥미롭게도, 피부는 햇빛이 피부에 비칠 때 비타민 D를 만들어 냅니다.

19 튼튼한 뼈를 만드는 가장 쉬운 방법은 밖으로 나가서 햇빛을 즐기는 겁니다.

20 보시다시피, 햇빛은 많은 이점이 있지만, 어떻게 그것의 이점을 안전하게 즐길 수 있을까요?

21 다행히도, 하루에 10분에서 20분 동안 피부에 직사광선을 쪼이는 것은 햇빛으로부터 이점을 얻는 데 충분합니다.

22 수업 시간 사이나 점심시간에 햇빛을 쐬러 밖으로 나가서 팔과 손에 햇빛을 쐬어 보세요.

23 매일 단 몇 분 동안 햇살을 쐬며 걷는 것은 여러분의 마음과 몸 모두에 좋습니다.

24 그러나 여름 절정 시간인 11시에서 3시 사이에는 햇빛을 피하고, 얼굴과 목을 보호하기 위해 자외선 차단제를 사용하세요.

25 태양을 안전하게 즐기고 적은 양의 햇빛이 여러분의 건강과 기분에 얼마나 큰 차이를 만들어 내는지 보세요.

● 우리말을 참고하여 본문을 영작하시오.

1 햇빛을 즐기세요

➡ _____

2 여러분은 매일 햇빛 속에서 얼마나 많은 시간을 보내나요?

➡ _____

3 많지 않죠, 그렇죠?

➡ _____

4 대부분의 사람들은 학교와 직장에서 너무 바빠서 많은 시간을 야외에서 보내지 못합니다.

➡ _____

5 그러나 햇빛은 여러분의 건강에 중요한 역할을 합니다.

➡ _____

6 그것은 여러분이 건강을 유지하는 데 도움을 줍니다.

➡ _____

7 모든 사람들은 해가 비칠 때 더 행복하게 느낍니다.

➡ _____

8 이것은 몸의 행복 호르몬인 세로토닌 때문입니다.

➡ _____

9 여러분이 햇빛을 쬘수록 뇌는 행복 호르몬을 더 만들어 냅니다.

➡ _____

10 여러분의 세로토닌 수치가 높아지면, 여러분은 더 행복하고 더 건강하게 느낍니다.

➡ _____

11 이것은 여러분이 매일의 스트레스를 이겨 내는 데 도움을 줍니다.

➡ _____

12 세로토닌은 또한 진정 효과가 있고, 여러분이 하는 일에 더 잘 집중할 수 있도록 도와줍니다.

➡ _____

13 게다가, 세로토닌은 뇌가 수면 호르몬을 생성하도록 도와주기 때문에 여러분이 숙면을 취하도록
해 줍니다.

➡ _____

_____

14 햇빛은 단지 여러분이 더 기분 좋게 느끼고 잠을 더 잘 자게 하는 것만은 아닙니다.

➡ _____

15 그것은 또한 튼튼한 뼈를 만드는 것을 돕습니다.

➡ _____

16 여러분 모두가 알다시피, 튼튼한 뼈와 치아를 만드는 것은 칼슘입니다.

➡ _____

17 그러나 몸이 칼슘을 적절하게 사용하기 위해서는 비타민 D가 필요합니다.

➡ _____

18 흥미롭게도, 피부는 햇빛이 피부에 비칠 때 비타민 D를 만들어 냅니다.

➡ _____

19 튼튼한 뼈를 만드는 가장 쉬운 방법은 밖으로 나가서 햇빛을 즐기는 겁니다.

➡ _____

20 보시다시피, 햇빛은 많은 이점이 있지만, 어떻게 그것의 이점을 안전하게 즐길 수 있을까요?

➡ _____

21 다행히도, 하루에 10분에서 20분 동안 피부에 직사광선을 쪼이는 것은 햇빛으로부터 이점을 얻는 데 충분합니다.

➡ _____

_____

22 수업 시간 사이나 점심시간에 햇빛을 쬐러 밖으로 나가서 팔과 손에 햇빛을 쬐어 보세요.

➡ _____

_____

23 매일 단 몇 분 동안 햇살을 쬐며 걷는 것은 여러분의 마음과 몸 모두에 좋습니다.

➡ _____

24 그러나 여름 절정 시간인 11시에서 3시 사이에는 햇빛을 피하고, 얼굴과 목을 보호하기 위해 자외선 차단제를 사용하세요.

➡ _____

_____

25 태양을 안전하게 즐기고 적은 양의 햇빛이 여러분의 건강과 기분에 얼마나 큰 차이를 만들어 내는지 보세요.

➡ _____

_____

[01~04] 다음 글을 읽고 물음에 답하시오.

How much time do you spend every day out in the sun? Not much, right? (A)[Almost / Most] people are too busy at school or at work to spend much time (B)[outdoor / outdoors]. __ⓐ__, the sun plays an important ⓑrole in your health. It helps you stay (C) [healthy / healthily].

01 위 글의 빈칸 ⓐ에 들어갈 알맞은 말을 고르시오.

① Thus
② Moreover
③ For example
④ In other words
⑤ However

서답형
02 위 글의 괄호 (A)~(C)에서 문맥이나 어법상 알맞은 낱말을 골라 쓰시오.

➡ (A) _____ (B) _____ (C) _____

서답형
03 위 글의 밑줄 친 ⓑrole과 바꿔 쓸 수 있는 말을 쓰시오.

➡ _____

서답형
04 다음 문장에서 위 글의 내용과 다른 부분을 찾아서 고치시오.

Almost all the people spend much time outside a building or in the open air.

_____ ➡ _____

[05~06] 다음 글을 읽고 물음에 답하시오.

As you can see, sunshine has many benefits, but how can you enjoy its benefits safely? Fortunately, getting direct sunlight on your skin for 10 to 20 minutes a day is enough to benefit from it. Try to go out into the sun between classes or during lunch breaks and get sunshine on your arms and hands. A walk in the sun, for just a few minutes every day, is good for both your mind and your body. However, avoid the sun during peak summer hours, between 11 and 3, and use __ⓐ__ to protect your face and neck. Enjoy the sun safely and see how a little sunshine can make a world of difference in your health and your mood.

중요
05 위 글의 제목으로 알맞은 것을 고르시오.

① Sunshine and Our Everyday Activity
② How to Enjoy Many Benefits of Sunshine Safely
③ How to Get Direct Sunlight?
④ Take Advantage of Spare Time to Enjoy the Sun
⑤ Make a Difference in Your Health and Your Mood!

서답형
06 주어진 영영풀이를 참고하여 빈칸 ⓐ에 철자 s로 시작하는 단어를 쓰시오.

a cream that protects your skin from the sun's rays, especially in hot weather

➡ _____

[07~10] 다음 글을 읽고 물음에 답하시오.

Sunshine does not just make you feel and sleep better. It also helps build strong bones. As you all know, ⓐ튼튼한 뼈와 치아를 만드는 것은 칼슘입니다. However, for the body ⓑto use calcium properly, it needs vitamin D. Interestingly, the skin creates vitamin D when sunlight shines on it. The easiest way to make strong bones is to go outside and enjoy the sun.

서답형

07 위 글의 밑줄 친 ⓐ의 우리말에 맞게 주어진 어휘를 이용하여 9 단어로 영작하시오.

> it, that, builds

➡ _____

08 아래 〈보기〉에서 위 글의 밑줄 친 ⓑto use와 to부정사의 용법이 <u>다른</u> 것의 개수를 고르시오.

> ┤ 보기 ├
> ① I don't know how <u>to use</u> this machine.
> ② This machine is very simple <u>to use</u>.
> ③ Can you show me the way <u>to use</u> this machine?
> ④ It is easy <u>to use</u> this machine.
> ⑤ He is too old <u>to use</u> this machine.

① 1개 ② 2개 ③ 3개 ④ 4개 ⑤ 5개

중요

09 위 글의 주제로 알맞은 것을 고르시오.

① Sufficient calcium intake is very important to build strong bones.
② What's the nutritional value of vitamin D?
③ Are there any side effects caused by strong sunshine?
④ How much calcium is needed to build strong bones?

⑤ Sunshine is the easiest way to make strong bones.

서답형

10 What is necessary for the body to use calcium properly? Fill in the blanks with suitable words.

➡ _____ _____ is necessary.

[11~13] 다음 글을 읽고 물음에 답하시오.

As you can see, sunshine has many benefits, but how can you enjoy its benefits safely? (①) Fortunately, getting direct sunlight on your skin ___ⓐ___ 10 to 20 minutes a day is enough to benefit from it. (②) Try to go out into the sun between classes or during lunch (A)breaks and get sunshine on your arms and hands. (③) A walk ___ⓑ___ the sun, for just a few minutes every day, is good for both your mind and your body. (④) Enjoy the sun safely and see how a little sunshine can make a world of difference in your health and your mood. (⑤)

11 위 글의 빈칸 ⓐ와 ⓑ에 들어갈 전치사가 바르게 짝지어진 것은?

	ⓐ	ⓑ		ⓐ	ⓑ
①	for	– to	②	on	– in
③	for	– in	④	from	– to
⑤	from	– for			

중요

12 위 글의 흐름으로 보아, 다음 문장이 들어가기에 가장 적절한 곳은?

> However, avoid the sun during peak summer hours, between 11 and 3, and use sunscreen to protect your face and neck.

①   ②   ③   ④   ⑤

13 위 글의 밑줄 친 (A)breaks와 같은 의미로 쓰인 것을 고르시오.

① He breaks the chocolate in two.
② We could see the moon through breaks in the clouds.
③ He always breaks the speed limit.
④ Can you take coffee breaks whenever you want?
⑤ She breaks the silence by coughing.

[14~17] 다음 글을 읽고 물음에 답하시오.

Everyone feels happier when the sun shines. This is because of serotonin, the body's happy hormone. The more sun you get, the more "happy hormone" the brain produces. When your serotonin level goes up, you feel happier and stronger. This helps you fight everyday stress. Serotonin also has a calming effect, ⓐhelping you focus better on what you are doing. Moreover, serotonin helps you get a good night's sleep because ⓑit helps the brain produce a sleep hormone.

14 위 글의 밑줄 친 ⓐhelping과 문법적 쓰임이 같은 것을 모두 고르시오.

① Do you have a mentor helping you in your life?
② I will take pleasure in helping you.
③ I don't mind helping you if you can't find anyone else.
④ Jack listened to music, helping her sister do her homework.
⑤ Helping you has made my life meaningful.

서답형
15 위 글의 밑줄 친 ⓑit이 가리키는 것을 본문에서 찾아 쓰시오.

➡ _____

16 According to the passage, which is NOT true?

① Serotonin is the body's happy hormone.
② The brain produces more "happy hormone" as you get more sun.
③ If you want to feel happier and stronger, you had better lower your serotonin level.
④ Serotonin's calming effect helps you focus better on what you are doing.
⑤ Serotonin helps the brain produce a sleep hormone.

서답형
17 본문의 내용과 일치하도록 다음 빈칸 (A)와 (B)에 알맞은 단어를 쓰시오.

Thanks to (A)_____, you can have a good night's sleep. That's because it helps the brain produce a (B)_____ _____.

[18~20] 다음 글을 읽고 물음에 답하시오.

ⓐSunshine does not just make you feel and sleep better. ⓑIt also helps build strong bones. As you all know, it is calcium ⓒthat builds strong bones and teeth. However, for the body to use calcium properly, ⓓit needs vitamin D. Interestingly, the skin creates vitamin D when sunlight shines on it. The easiest way to make strong bones is to go outside and enjoy the sun.

서답형
18 위 글의 밑줄 친 ⓐ와 ⓑ를 as well as를 사용하여 한 문장으로 바꿔 쓰시오.

➡ _____
_____

19 위 글의 밑줄 친 ⓒthat과 문법적 쓰임이 같지 <u>않은</u> 것을 <u>모두</u> 고르시오.

① She was so tired <u>that</u> she couldn't think straight.
② It is you <u>that</u> are to blame.
③ What kind of work is it <u>that</u> you want?
④ It's possible <u>that</u> he has not received the letter.
⑤ It was an accident <u>that</u> changed my mind.

서답형

20 위 글의 밑줄 친 ⓓit이 가리키는 것을 본문에서 찾아 쓰시오.

➡ _____

[21~22] 다음 글을 읽고 물음에 답하시오.

ⓐ보시다시피, sunshine has many benefits, but how can you enjoy its benefits safely? Fortunately, getting direct sunlight on your skin for 10 to 20 minutes a day is enough to benefit from it. Try to go out into the sun between classes or during lunch breaks and get sunshine on your arms and hands. A walk in the sun, for just a few minutes every day, is good for both your mind and your body. However, avoid the sun during peak summer hours, between 11 and 3, and use sunscreen to protect your face and neck. Enjoy the sun safely and see how a little sunshine can make a world of difference in your health and your mood.

서답형

21 위 글의 밑줄 친 ⓐ의 우리말에 맞게 4 단어로 영작하시오.

➡ _____

22 다음 중 위 글의 내용을 바르게 이해하지 <u>못한</u> 사람을 고르시오.

① 진수: 햇빛의 이점들을 안전하게 즐길 수 있는 방법은 찾기 어려워.
② 영혜: 매일 단 몇 분 동안 햇빛을 쬐며 걷는 것은 우리의 마음과 몸 모두에 좋아.
③ 경호: 그러나 여름에 절정 시간인 11시에서 3시 사이에는 햇빛을 피해야 해.
④ 기철: 응, 그리고 얼굴과 목을 보호하기 위해 자외선 차단제를 사용해야 해.
⑤ 성미: 적은 양의 햇빛도 우리의 건강과 기분에 큰 차이를 만들어 낼 수 있어.

[23~24] 다음 글을 읽고 물음에 답하시오.

Everyone feels happier when the sun shines. This is because of serotonin, the body's happy hormone. The more sun you get, the more "happy hormone" the brain produces. When your serotonin level goes up, you feel happier and stronger. This helps you fight everyday stress. Serotonin also has a calming effect, ⓐ<u>helping you focus better on what you are doing</u>. Moreover, serotonin helps you get a good night's sleep because it helps the brain produce a sleep hormone.

서답형

23 위 글의 밑줄 친 ⓐhelping을 접속사를 사용하여 고쳐 쓰시오.

➡ _____

24 위 글의 제목으로 알맞은 것을 고르시오.

① What Makes You Feel Happy?
② The Difficulty of Increasing the Level of Serotonin
③ How to Fight Everyday Stress by Serotonin
④ Various Benefits of Serotonin
⑤ The Effect of Serotonin on Your Sleep Pattern

[01~03] 다음 글을 읽고 물음에 답하시오.

How much time do you spend every day out in the sun? Not much, right? ⓐMost people are too busy at school or at work to spend much time outdoors. However, the sun plays an important role in your health. ⓑIt helps you stay healthy.

중요

01 위 글의 밑줄 친 ⓐ를 복문으로 고치시오.

➡ _____

_____

02 위 글의 밑줄 친 ⓑit이 가리키는 것을 본문에서 찾아 쓰시오.

➡ _____

중요

03 본문의 내용과 일치하도록 다음 빈칸 (A)와 (B)에 알맞은 단어를 쓰시오.

The sun has an important effect on your (A)_____, helping you to stay (B)_____.

[04~06] 다음 글을 읽고 물음에 답하시오.

Everyone feels happier when the sun shines. This is because of serotonin, the body's happy hormone. ⓐThe more sun you get, the more "happy hormone" the brain produces. When your serotonin level goes up, you feel happier and stronger. This helps you fight everyday stress. Serotonin also has a calming effect, ⓑ여러분이 하는 일에 더 잘 집중할 수 있도록 도와줍니다. Moreover, serotonin helps you get a good night's sleep because it helps the brain produce a sleep hormone.

중요

04 위 글의 밑줄 친 ⓐ를 접속사 As를 사용하여, 고쳐 쓰시오.

➡ _____

_____

05 위 글의 밑줄 친 ⓑ의 우리말에 맞게 한 단어를 보충하여, 주어진 어휘를 알맞게 배열하시오.

better / helping / what / doing / are / you / focus / you

➡ _____

고난이도

06 본문의 내용과 일치하도록 다음 빈칸 (A)와 (B)에 알맞은 단어를 쓰시오.

When you are in the sun, (A)_____ _____ produces serotonin, and in proportion to its level, you can feel happier. So, you can call serotonin the body's (B)_____ _____.

*in proportion to: …에 비례하여

[07~09] 다음 글을 읽고 물음에 답하시오.

Sunshine does not just make you feel and sleep better. It also helps build strong bones. As you all know, it is calcium that builds strong bones and teeth. ⓐTherefore, for the body to use calcium properly, it needs vitamin D. Interestingly, the skin creates vitamin D when sunlight shines on ⓑit. The easiest way to make strong bones is to go outside and enjoy the sun.

07 Write the three benefits of sunshine in English.

➡ (1) _____

(2) _____

(3) _____

08 위 글의 밑줄 친 ⓐ에서 흐름상 어색한 부분을 찾아 고치시오.

_____ ➡ _____

09 위 글의 밑줄 친 ⓑit이 가리키는 것을 본문에서 찾아 쓰시오.

➡ _____

[10~11] 다음 글을 읽고 물음에 답하시오.

Sunshine does not just make you feel and sleep better. It also helps build strong bones. As you all know, it is calcium that builds strong bones and teeth. However, for the body to use calcium properly, it needs vitamin D. Interestingly, the skin creates vitamin D when sunlight shines on it. The easiest way to make strong bones is to go outside and enjoy the sun.

10 위 글의 내용을 다음과 같이 정리하고자 한다. 빈칸 (A)~(C)에 들어갈 알맞은 단어를 본문에서 찾아 쓰시오.

The body needs (A)_____ _____ to use calcium properly, which builds strong bones. The skin creates vitamin D when (B)_____ shines on it, so the easiest way to make strong bones is to go outside and (C)_____ _____ _____.

11 다음 문장에서 위 글의 내용과 다른 부분을 찾아서 고치시오.

Sunshine does not make you feel and sleep better.

_____ ➡ _____

[12~13] 다음 글을 읽고 물음에 답하시오.

As you can see, sunshine has many benefits, but how can you enjoy its benefits safely? Fortunately, getting direct sunlight on your skin for 10 to 20 minutes a day is enough to benefit from it. Try to go out into the sun between classes or during lunch breaks and get sunshine on your arms and hands. A walk in the sun, for just a few minutes every day, is good for both your mind and your body. However, avoid the sun (A)[during / for] peak summer hours, between 11 and 3, and use sunscreen to (B)[prevent / protect] your face and neck. Enjoy the sun safely and see how a little sunshine can make (C)[a number of / a world of] difference in your health and your mood.

12 위 글의 괄호 (A)~(C)에서 문맥이나 어법상 알맞은 낱말을 골라 쓰시오.

➡ (A) _____ (B) _____ (C) _____

13 In order to benefit from sunlight, how long do you need to get direct sunlight? Fill in the blanks with suitable words.

We need to get direct sunlight on our skin for _____ _____ _____ minutes a day to benefit from it.

Communication Task

A: I think it's important to exercise every day. Do you exercise every day?

B: Yes, I do.

B: No, I don't. But I'll try.
"시도하다, 노력하다"

A: Good for you.
잘했다

A: Okay.

해석

A: 나는 매일 운동하는 것
이 중요하다고 생각해.
너는 매일 운동하니?

B: 네, 그렇습니다.

A: 잘했다.

B: 아니요, 하지만 노력하겠
습니다.

A: 알았어.

After You Read A

The Benefits of Sunshine

1. Sunshine helps you deal with stress and feel happier.
= treat. handle

2. Sunshine helps you focus better on what you are doing.
= the thing(s) which

3. If you get enough sunshine, you will sleep better at night.
조건의 부사절에서 현재시제가 미래시제를 대신함.

4. When the sun shines on your skin, your skin produces vitamin D, which is
that(×)

needed for strong bones.

구문해설 • **benefit:** 혜택, 이득, 좋은 점 • **deal with:** 다루다 • **focus on:** ～에 주력하다, 초점을 맞추다
• **produce:** 생산하다

햇빛의 좋은 점

1. 햇빛은 여러분이 스트레스
를 다루고 더 행복하게 느
끼도록 돕는다.

2. 햇빛은 여러분이 하는 일
에 더 잘 집중할 수 있도록
도와준다.

3. 햇빛을 충분히 쬐면 밤에
잠을 더 잘 잘 것이다.

4. 해가 여러분의 피부에 비
칠 때, 여러분의 피부는 비
타민 D를 만드는데, 그것
은 튼튼한 뼈를 만드는 데
필요하다.

Writing Workshop

Health Comes First!

1. Wash your hands after going out. You will not catch a cold easily if you
명령문   동명사(전치사 뒤)   조건의 접속사

wash your hands well.

2. Get direct sunlight for 10 to 20 minutes every day. The more sunlight you
～ 동안

get, the happier and stronger you feel.
the 비교급+주어+동사 ～, the 비교급+주어+동사 …: ～할수록 …하다

3. It is a good breakfast that helps the brain work properly. When you eat a
It is[was] ～ that …' 강조 구문   = which   = to work   ～하면(= If)

good breakfast, you can focus more clearly on your work and remember

things better.

구문해설 • **direct sunlight:** 직사광선 • **focus on:** ～에 집중하다

건강이 먼저야!

1. 외출 후에는 손을 씻어라.
손을 잘 씻으면 쉽게 감기
에 걸리지 않을 것이다.

2. 매일 직사광선을 10～20분
간 받아라. 햇빛을 더 많이
받을수록 더 행복하고 더
강하게 느낄 것이다.

3. 두뇌가 적절히 작동하도록
돕는 것은 좋은 아침식사
이다. 좋은 아침을 먹으면,
일에 분명히 집중하고 더
잘 기억할 수 있다.

Words & Expressions

01 다음 빈칸에 들어가기에 적절한 단어를 고르시오.

> It was the most difficult _____ of her life.

① decision   ② decide   ③ decided
④ decisive   ⑤ deciding

02 다음 영영풀이에 해당하는 단어를 고르시오.

> the outer layer of a person's or animal's body

① knee   ② mood
③ cloth   ④ skin
⑤ production

03 다음 두 문장에 공통으로 알맞은 것을 고르시오.

> • The bus came right _____ time.
> • You'd better put _____ your coat in this cold weather.

① about   ② by   ③ for
④ with   ⑤ on

04 다음 밑줄 친 부분과 같은 뜻으로 쓰인 것은?

> What do you do to <u>stay</u> healthy?

① Where will you <u>stay</u> tomorrow?
② He will <u>stay</u> here for a month.
③ Will you <u>stay</u> there till he comes?
④ Remember to <u>stay</u> calm.
⑤ We enjoyed every minute of our <u>stay</u>.

Conversation

[05~06] 다음 우리말과 일치하도록 빈칸에 알맞은 말을 쓰시오.

05
> M: John, you are late again.
> B: I'm sorry. I took the wrong bus.
> M: I think you need to leave home a little earlier.
> B: I think so, too. Next time I won't be late.
> M: _____.
> (학교에 제 시간에 도착하는 것이 중요하다.)
> (arrive, on time) (8 words)

➡ _____

06
> B: Mina, how was the movie?
> G: I didn't enjoy it. It was boring.
> B: What was bad about it?
> G: I already knew the ending. _____
> _____ before seeing it. (나는 영화를 보기 전에 그것에 관하여 읽지 말았어야 했는데.) (should) (6 words)
> B: Oh, I'm sorry you didn't like it.

➡ _____

07 다음 대화의 빈칸에 들어가기에 적절하지 <u>않은</u> 것은?

> B: We missed our flight.
> G: Oh, no. _____

① We ought to have come earlier.
② We should have come earlier.
③ I am sorry that we didn't come earlier.
④ I regret that we didn't come earlier.
⑤ We have to come earlier.

[08~10] 다음 대화를 읽고 물음에 답하시오.

B: Mina, ⓐhow was the movie?
G: I didn't ⓑenjoy it. It was ___(A)___.
B: ⓒWhat was bad about it?
G: I already knew the ending. I ⓓshouldn't have read about it before ⓔseen it.
B: Oh, I'm sorry you didn't ___(B)___ it.

08 빈칸 (A), (B)에 들어가기에 알맞은 것을 〈보기〉에서 골라 쓰시오.

┌─ 보기 ─┐
exciting   boring   like   see   read
└──────┘

➡ (A) _____ (B) _____

09 위 대화의 밑줄 친 ⓐ~ⓔ 중에서 어법상 어색한 것을 고르시오.

① ⓐ   ② ⓑ   ③ ⓒ   ④ ⓓ   ⑤ ⓔ

10 위 대화를 통해서 알 수 있는 것은?

① Mina likes watching movies in her free time.
② The boy enjoyed the movie.
③ Mina has already read about the movie.
④ Mina thought the movie would be exciting.
⑤ The boy wants to read about the movie.

Grammar

11 다음 밑줄 친 부분과 바꿔 쓸 수 있는 것은?

It was last week that Mr. Miller asked me to attend the meeting.

① what   ② when   ③ who
④ where   ⑤ which

12 주어진 단어가 알맞은 형태로 바르게 짝지어진 것은?

• _____ we got to the fire, the warmer we felt. (close)
• _____ you ride a mountain bike, the more you will enjoy it. (much)

① Close – Much
② Closer – Much
③ Closer – The more
④ The close – The much
⑤ The closer – The more

13 다음 중 어법상 올바른 것은?

① Which one is the bigger of the two?
② The high the top of a mountain, the good the view.
③ More I got to know her, more I liked her.
④ The more angrier she got, the more loudly she yelled.
⑤ The older David gets, the wiser becomes.

14 다음 문장을 각각의 주어진 단어를 강조하는 문장으로 바꿔 쓰시오.

Tina bought a camera at the shop yesterday.

(1) Tina
➡ _____
_____

(2) bought
➡ _____
_____

(3) a camera

➡ _____

_____

(4) at the shop

➡ _____

_____

(5) yesterday

➡ _____

_____

15 다음 중 어법상 올바른 문장을 고르시오.

① It was my uncle what bought this smartphone for me on my birthday.

② It is Brian where broke the door.

③ It was his room which Kevin cleaned this morning.

④ It is the new car that my son wants to buy it.

⑤ It was on the day where I met her.

16 다음 밑줄 친 부분의 쓰임이 적절한 것은?

① More we exercise, the healthier we will get.

② More you study, better scores you will get in the test.

③ Much she gets to know him, the more she will like him.

④ The higher the bird flied up, the more it could see.

⑤ The old Ronald grew, the wise he became.

17 다음 괄호 안에서 어법상 알맞은 것을 고르시오.

(1) (The healthier / Healthier) one's mind is, (the healthier / healthier) one's body will be.

(2) I think (the much / the more) time I spend without her, (the sad / the sadder) I will become.

(3) It was getting (the darker and the darker / darker and darker), so we hurried to the shore.

(4) It was in the park (which / where) he left his car.

(5) It is the phone (which / when) I am looking for.

18 밑줄 친 말을 강조할 때, 빈칸에 알맞은 말을 쓰시오.

He had to reserve many seats <u>at the restaurant</u>.

→ _____ _____ at the restaurant _____ he had to reserve many seats.

Reading

[19~20] 다음 글을 읽고 물음에 답하시오.

Everyone feels happier when the sun shines. This is because of serotonin, the body's happy hormone. The more sun you get, the more "happy hormone" the brain produces. When your serotonin level goes up, you feel happier and stronger. This helps you fight everyday stress. Serotonin also has a calming effect, helping you focus better on what you are doing. _____ⓐ_____, serotonin helps you get a good night's sleep because it helps the brain produce a sleep hormone.

19 위 글의 빈칸 ⓐ에 들어갈 알맞은 말을 고르시오.

① For example
② That is
③ Therefore
④ Moreover
⑤ However

20 According to the passage, which is NOT true about serotonin?

① Because of it, everyone feels happier when the sun shines.
② You can feel happier and stronger by raising your serotonin level.
③ Raising your serotonin level can help you fight everyday stress.
④ Its calming effect helps us focus better on what we are doing.
⑤ Serotonin has nothing to do with a good night's sleep.

[21~22] 다음 글을 읽고 물음에 답하시오.

Sunshine does not just make you feel and sleep better. It also helps build strong bones. As you all know, it is calcium that builds strong bones and teeth. However, for the body to use calcium properly, it needs vitamin D. Interestingly, the skin creates vitamin D when sunlight shines on it. The easiest way to make strong bones is ⓐto go outside and enjoy the sun.

21 위 글의 밑줄 친 ⓐto go와 to부정사의 용법이 같은 것을 모두 고르시오.

① Why do you want to go outside?
② He likes to go outside.
③ She was pleased to go outside.
④ It's time for you to go outside.
⑤ You must be joking to go outside in this weather.

22 위 글의 제목으로 알맞은 것을 고르시오.

① Enjoying the Sun, the Easiest Way to Make Strong Bones!
② Various Usages of Vitamin D
③ How to Use Calcium Properly for Your Teeth
④ The Nutritional Value of Calcium
⑤ Too Much Sunshine and Your Skin Health

[23~25] 다음 글을 읽고 물음에 답하시오.

As you can see, sunshine has many benefits, but how can you enjoy its benefits safely? Fortunately, getting direct sunlight on your skin ⓐ하루에 10분에서 20분 동안 is enough to benefit from it. Try to go out into the sun between classes or during lunch breaks and get sunshine on your arms and hands. A walk in the sun, for just a few minutes every day, is good for both your mind and your body. However, avoid the sun during peak summer hours, _____ⓑ_____ 11 and 3, and use sunscreen to protect your face and neck. Enjoy the sun safely and see how a little sunshine can make a world of difference in your health and your mood.

23 위 글의 밑줄 친 ⓐ의 우리말에 맞게 7 단어로 영작하시오.

➡ _____

24 위 글의 빈칸 ⓑ에 알맞은 말을 쓰시오.

➡ _____

25 Which question CANNOT be answered after reading the passage?

① Is there any way to enjoy the benefits of sunshine safely?

② On what ground is getting direct sunlight on your skin for 10 to 20 minutes a day enough to benefit from it?

③ When is it that the writer advises you to go out into the sun?

④ When is it that you need to avoid the sun?

⑤ How can you protect your face and neck during peak summer hours?

[26~29] 다음 글을 읽고 물음에 답하시오.

Health Comes First!

1. Wash your hands after going out. You will not catch a cold easily if you wash your hands well.

2. Get direct sunlight for 10 to 20 minutes every day. ⓐThe more sunlight you get, the happier and stronger you feel.

3. It is a good breakfast that helps the brain work properly. When you eat a good breakfast, you can focus more clearly on your work and remember things better.

26 위 글의 밑줄 친 ⓐ를 접속사 As를 사용하여, 고쳐 쓰시오.

➡ _____

_____

27 According to the passage above, in order not to have a cold easily, what will be helpful? Fill in the blanks with suitable words.

> If you _____ _____ _____ well after going out, you won't have a cold easily.

28 위 건강 홍보물의 내용과 일치하지 않는 것은?

① 외출한 다음에는 손을 씻어야 한다.

② 매일 10분에서 20분 동안 피부에 직사광선을 쬐는 것이 좋다.

③ 햇빛을 쬘수록 여러분은 더 행복하고 더 건강하게 느낀다.

④ 좋은 아침 식사는 뇌가 올바르게 작동하는 데 도움이 된다.

⑤ 아침 식사를 거르면 당신의 일에 더 잘 집중할 수 있고 사물들을 더 잘 기억할 수 있다.

29 본문의 내용과 일치하도록 다음 빈칸에 알맞은 단어를 쓰시오.

> A _____ _____ helps you focus more clearly on your work and remember things better.

출제율 95%

01 짝지어진 단어의 관계가 같도록 빈칸에 알맞은 말을 쓰시오.

> wet : dry = regularly : _____

출제율 90%

02 다음 빈칸에 들어갈 말로 적절한 것은?

> Enjoy the sun safely and see how a little sunshine can make a _____ of difference in your health and your mood.

① word   ② sky   ③ world

④ light   ⑤ sunshine

출제율 95%

03 다음 빈칸에 들어가기에 적절한 것은?

> • When I have spare time, I usually _____ the Internet.
> • The sun _____ an important role in your health.

① play – tries   ② play – grows

③ surf – relaxes   ④ surf – plays

⑤ keep – gets

출제율 100%

04 다음 제시된 단어로 자연스러운 문장을 만들 수 없는 것은?

> ┤ 보기 ├
> flight   effect   journal   grade

① You will see the positive _____ of the advice.

② My _____ was an hour late because of bad weather.

③ He got the best _____ on the midterm exam.

④ He kept a _____ of his travels across Asia.

⑤ I came to _____ my rude remarks.

[05~07] 다음 대화를 읽고 물음에 답하시오.

> B: We still have 30 minutes to go before we _____(A)_____ the top of the mountain. Let's sit down over there and have a snack.
> G: Oh, I brought only water. (B)내가 간식을 좀 가지고 왔어야 했는데.
> B: That's okay. I brought a lot. We can share.
> G: I'll keep it in mind to bring some snacks next time.

출제율 90%

05 빈칸 (A)에 들어가기에 알맞은 것은?

① go   ② work   ③ reach

④ arrive   ⑤ walk

출제율 90%

06 밑줄 친 (B)에 우리말을 바르게 영작한 것은?

① I will have to bring some snacks.

② I should have brought some snacks.

③ I ought to have some snacks to bring.

④ I must have brought some snacks.

⑤ I should have to bring some snacks.

출제율 95%

07 Which one of the following is NOT true according to the dialogue above?

① They have been climbing the mountain for 30 minutes.

② They will reach the top of the mountain in half an hour.

③ The girl has brought no snacks.

④ The boy has brought enough snacks for the two.

⑤ The girl will bring enough snacks next time.

G: Ben, you look full of energy today!

B: Do I? Maybe that's because I finally got a good night's sleep last night.

G: Why? Don't you usually get enough sleep?

B: No, I know it's really important to get a good night's sleep, but I always stay ___(A)___ late surfing the Internet or playing with my phone.

G: That sometimes happens to me too.

B: After I do that, I regret it the next morning and say, "I ___(B)___ to bed earlier last night."

G: How was yesterday different?

B: Well, yesterday afternoon I climbed the mountain with my dad. I was really tired when I got home. I went to sleep right after I went to bed.

G: Outdoor activities are a great way to help you get a good night's sleep.

08 위 대화의 빈칸 (A)에 알맞은 것은? 출제율 90%

① up ② on ③ to
④ with ⑤ from

09 빈칸 (B)에 알맞은 것은? 출제율 95%

① must go ② will go
③ should go ④ must have gone
⑤ should have gone

10 밑줄 친 부분을 강조하는 문장으로 고쳐 쓰시오. 출제율 90%

(1) We are pretty much unsure about <u>the whole thing</u>.

➡ _____

_____

(2) She went to the movies <u>with her friends</u> last Sunday.

➡ _____

_____

(3) A friend of mine bought a luxurious car <u>yesterday</u>.

➡ _____

_____

11 다음 중 어법상 어색한 것은? 출제율 95%

① The more things I have to do, the more tired I feel.

② The smarter the journalists are, the better off our society is.

③ I think the more you know a musical, the more you will enjoy it.

④ The red the apples are, the sweet they taste.

⑤ The more, the merrier.

12 다음 중 어법상 올바른 문장을 모두 고르시오. (정답 2개) 출제율 100%

① The high I went up, the foggy it became.

② Of the two boys, Simon is taller.

③ The lower the grade is, the worse Noah feels.

④ It is too costly that buying new furniture may prove.

⑤ It was my dad that suggested I do mountain biking.

⑥ It was played that he basketball at the playground.

⑦ It was last Friday where Bill lost his smartphone.

13 괄호 안에 주어진 어휘를 활용하여 글자 수에 맞게 다음 우리말을 영작하시오.

(1) 우리는 주의할수록, 실수를 더 적게 한다. (few, much, make, careful, mistakes, 10단어)

➡ _____

_____

(2) 외출 전에 네가 발라야 하는 것은 자외선 차단제이다. (put on, should, that, go out, sunscreen, 12단어)

➡ _____

_____

[14~16] 다음 글을 읽고 물음에 답하시오.

Everyone feels happier when the sun shines. @This is because of serotonin, the body's happy hormone. (①) The more sun you get, the more "happy hormone" the brain produces. (②) This helps you fight everyday stress. (③) Serotonin also has a calming effect, helping you focus better on what you are doing. (④) Moreover, serotonin helps you get a good night's sleep because it helps the brain produce a sleep hormone. (⑤)

14 위 글의 흐름으로 보아, 주어진 문장이 들어가기에 가장 적절한 곳은?

When your serotonin level goes up, you feel happier and stronger.

① ② ③ ④ ⑤

15 위 글의 밑줄 친 @This가 가리키는 것을 본문에서 찾아 쓰시오.

➡ _____

16 위 글의 주제로 알맞은 것을 고르시오.

① the kinds of happy hormones in our body
② the influence of sunlight on our stress
③ the roles of the beneficial hormone, serotonin
④ the way to focus on what you're doing
⑤ the happy hormone versus the sleep hormone

[17~18] 다음 글을 읽고 물음에 답하시오.

Sunshine does not just make you feel and sleep better. It also helps build strong bones. @As you all know, it is calcium that builds strong bones and teeth. However, for the body to use calcium properly, it needs vitamin D. Interestingly, the skin creates vitamin D when sunlight shines on it. The easiest way to make strong bones is to go outside and enjoy the sun.

17 위 글의 밑줄 친 @As와 같은 의미로 쓰인 것을 고르시오.

① Sumi is not as pretty as Mary.
② As spring comes, the birds move northward.
③ As rust eats iron, so care eats the heart.
④ As she was tired, she didn't go there.
⑤ His anger grew as he talked.

18 According to the passage, which is NOT true?

① Sunshine makes you feel and sleep better.
② Sunshine helps build strong bones.
③ Calcium builds strong bones and teeth.

④ The body needs calcium to use vitamin D properly.

⑤ When sunlight shines on the skin, it creates vitamin D.

[19~21] 다음 글을 읽고 물음에 답하시오.

ⓐAs you can see, sunshine has many benefits, but how can you enjoy its benefits safe? Fortunately, getting direct sunlight on your skin for 10 to 20 minutes a day is enough to benefit from it. Try to go out into the sun between classes or during lunch breaks and get sunshine on your arms and hands. A walk in the sun, for just a few minutes every day, is good for both your mind and your body. However, avoid the sun during peak summer hours, between 11 and 3, and use sunscreen to protect your face and neck. Enjoy the sun safely and see how a little sunshine can make a world of difference in your health and your mood.

출제율 95%

19 위 글의 밑줄 친 ⓐ에서 어법상 틀린 부분을 찾아 고치시오.

_____ ➡ _____

출제율 90%

20 When do you need to avoid the sun? Fill in the blanks with suitable words.

> We need to avoid the sun during (A)_____ _____ _____ between 11 and 3.

출제율 100%

21 다음 중 본문에 소개된 '햇빛의 많은 이점을 즐길 수 있는 방법'에 해당하지 <u>않는</u> 것을 고르시오.

① 하루에 10분에서 20분 동안 피부에 직사광선을 쬔다.

② 수업 시간 사이나 점심시간에 햇빛을 쬐러 밖으로 나가서 팔과 손에 햇빛을 쬔다.

③ 매일 단 몇 분 동안 햇살을 쬐며 걷는다.

④ 얼굴과 목을 보호하기 위해 자외선 차단제를 사용한다.

⑤ 매일 많은 양의 햇빛을 쬐어 자신의 건강과 기분에 큰 차이를 만들어 낸다.

[22~24] 다음 글을 읽고 물음에 답하시오.

Good morning. Welcome to the ___ⓐ___ . I'm Hana Kim. Here's today's weather for three cities in different parts of the world. The sun is shining and it's warm in Seoul. In the afternoon, there may be a shower. In New York, the rain stopped early this morning. It's cloudy now. In Paris, it'll be cloudy today with a chance of showers. ⓑIf you're in Seoul or Paris, take your sunscreen. Have a wonderful day.

출제율 95%

22 위 글의 빈칸 ⓐ에 들어갈 알맞은 말을 고르시오.

① Book Report ② Today's Article

③ Weather Report ④ Movie Review

⑤ Cool Travel Essay

출제율 90%

23 위 글의 밑줄 친 ⓑ에서 흐름상 어색한 부분을 찾아 고치시오.

_____ ➡ _____

출제율 100%

24 위 글의 내용과 일치하지 <u>않는</u> 것은?

① 서울은 현재 화창하고 따뜻하다.

② 오후에 서울에는 비가 내릴 수 있다.

③ 뉴욕은 오늘 아침 일찍 비가 그쳤다.

④ 뉴욕은 현재 날씨가 화창하다.

⑤ 파리는 오후에 흐리고 비가 내릴 가능성이 있다.

[01~03] 다음 대화를 읽고 물음에 답하시오.

G: Ben, ①you look full of energy today!

B: Do I? Maybe that's because (A)마침내 나는 지난밤에 잠을 잘 잤다. (got, good)

G: Why? ②Don't you usually get enough sleep?

B: No, I know it's really important to get a good night's sleep, but I always stay up late surfing the Internet or playing with my phone.

G: ③That sometimes happens to me too.

B: After I do that, I regret it the next morning and say, "I should have gone to bed earlier last night."

G: ④How was yesterday the same?

B: Well, yesterday afternoon I climbed the mountain with my dad. ⑤I was really tired when I got home. I went to sleep right after I went to bed.

G: ___(B)___ activities are a great way to help you get a good night's sleep.

01 밑줄 친 ①~⑤ 중에서 내용상 어색한 문장을 찾아 번호를 쓰고 적절한 내용으로 바꾸어 다시 쓰시오.

➡ _____ , _____

02 밑줄 친 (A)의 우리말에 해당하는 영어 문장을 쓰시오. (9 words)

➡ _____

03 빈칸 (B)에 적절한 한 단어를 쓰시오.

➡ _____

04 어법상 어색한 것을 찾아 바르게 고쳐 문장을 다시 쓰시오.

(1) I think the old Sue gets, the wise she becomes.

➡ _____
_____

(2) Few the words, the good the prayer.

➡ _____
_____

(3) It was the library that he lent me the book yesterday.

➡ _____
_____

(4) It was last year where my family traveled to Busan.

➡ _____
_____

(5) It was because she lost her mother who the girl was confused.

➡ _____
_____

05 다음 그림을 보고, 'It ~ that …' 강조 구문과 주어진 어휘를 활용하여 빈칸에 알맞게 쓰시오.

➡ _____ is the bus that _____ _____ to go to the theater. (be, wait, in the rain)

Everyone feels happier when the sun shines. This is because of serotonin, the body's happy hormone. The more sun you get, the more "happy hormone" the brain produces. When your serotonin level goes (A)[down / up], you feel happier and stronger. This helps you fight everyday stress. Serotonin also has a (B)[calming / calmed] effect, (C)[helps / helping] you focus better on what you are doing. Moreover, serotonin helps you get a good night's sleep because it helps the brain produce a sleep hormone.

06 위 글의 괄호 (A)~(C)에서 문맥이나 어법상 알맞은 낱말을 골라 쓰시오.

➡ (A) _____ (B) _____ (C) _____

07 본문의 내용과 일치하도록 다음 빈칸 (A)와 (B)에 알맞은 단어를 쓰시오.

> If you need to fight (A)_____ _____, you may as well raise your (B)_____ _____, because it can help you feel happier and stronger.

[08~10] 다음 글을 읽고 물음에 답하시오.

As you can see, sunshine has many benefits, but how can you enjoy its benefits safely? Fortunately, getting direct sunlight on your skin for 10 to 20 minutes a day is enough to benefit from ⓐit. Try to go out into the sun between classes or during lunch breaks and get sunshine on your arms and hands. A walk in the sun, for just a few minutes every day, is good for both your mind and your body. However, avoid the sun during peak summer hours, between 11 and 3, and use sunscreen to protect your face and neck. Enjoy the sun safely and ⓑ적은 양의 햇빛이 여러분의 건강과 기분에 얼마나 큰 차이를 만들어 내는지 보세요.

08 위 글의 밑줄 친 ⓐit이 가리키는 것을 본문에서 찾아 쓰시오. (1 word)

➡ _____

09 위 글의 밑줄 친 ⓑ의 우리말에 맞게 주어진 어휘를 알맞게 배열하시오.

> your mood / your health / how / difference / can / see / and / in / a little sunshine / a world of / make

➡ _____

_____

10 본문의 내용과 일치하도록 다음 빈칸 (A)~(C)에 알맞은 단어를 쓰시오.

> You can enjoy (A)_____ _____ of sunshine in a (B)_____ way by getting direct sunlight on your skin for 10 to 20 minutes a day. You must also avoid the sun during peak summer hours, between 11 and 3, and use (C)_____ to protect your face and neck.

01 빈칸에 알맞은 낱말을 골라 햇빛의 좋은 점을 완성해 봅시다.

The Benefits of Sunshine

1. Sunshine helps you deal with _____ and feel _____.
2. Sunshine helps you _____ better on what you are doing.
3. If you get enough sunshine, you will _____ better at night.
4. When the sun shines on your skin, your skin produces _____, which is needed for strong _____.

stress   vitamin D   focus   bones   happier   sleep

02 다음 그림을 보고, 'It ~ that ...' 강조 구문을 활용하여 자유롭게 영작하시오.

(1) _____
(2) _____
(3) _____
(4) _____

03 다음 내용을 바탕으로 나만의 건강 홍보물을 만드시오.

건강을 위한 습관 중 실천하지 못하고 있는 것
- Washing your hands after going out
- Getting direct sunlight for 10 to 20 minutes a day
- Eating a good breakfast

Health Comes First!

1. Wash your hands (A)_____. You will not catch a cold easily if you (B)_____ well.
2. Get (C)_____ for (D)_____ every day. The more sunlight you get, the happier and stronger you feel.
3. It is a good breakfast that helps the brain work properly. When you eat (E) _____, you can focus more clearly on your work and remember things better.

단원별 모의고사

01 다음 짝지어진 두 단어의 관계가 같도록 빈칸에 알맞은 말을 쓰시오.

> wide : narrow = healthy : _____

02 다음 영영풀이에 해당하는 단어로 적절한 것은?

> a book in which people regularly write about what has happened to them

① novel ② comic book
③ journal ④ poem
⑤ newspaper

03 다음 빈칸에 들어갈 말로 적절한 것은?

> Layla always applies _____ before she goes outside.

① sunlight ② sunshine
③ sunset ④ sunrise
⑤ sunscreen

04 다음 문장의 빈칸에 알맞은 것을 〈보기〉에서 찾아 쓰시오.

> ┌─ 보기 ─┐
> properly   outdoors   mood   peak

(1) He's always in a bad _____ .
(2) The rain prevented them from eating _____ .
(3) The hotels are always full during the _____ season.
(4) The television isn't working _____ .

[05~07] 다음 대화를 읽고 물음에 답하시오.

> W: Oh, your blanket is wet from the rain! I should _____ (가) _____ .
> B: Did you wash it? (A)
> W: No. I just put it out in the sun this morning. (B)
> B: Why didn't you wash it? (C)
> W: Hanging a blanket in the sun is a nature-friendly way to keep the blanket clean.
> B: Oh, I didn't know that. (D)
> W: And it's also important to remember to do it regularly. (E)

05 빈칸 (가)에 들어가기에 적절한 것은?

① watch weather report
② have checked the weather
③ call the weather reporter
④ have known about the blanket
⑤ expect the sun

06 (A)~(E) 중에서 다음 문장이 들어가기에 적절한 곳은?

> I'll remember that.

① (A)   ② (B)   ③ (C)   ④ (D)   ⑤ (E)

07 Which one is NOT true according to the dialogue?

① The boy's blanket is wet from the rain.
② The woman didn't check the weather.
③ The woman washed the blanket this morning.
④ The woman hung the blanket in the sun.
⑤ The boy didn't know the nature-friendly way to keep the blanket clean.

[08~10] 다음 대화를 읽고 물음에 답하시오.

G: Ben, you look full of energy today!

B: Do I? Maybe that's ⓐbecause I finally got _____(A)_____ last night.

G: Why? Don't you usually get enough sleep?

B: No, I know it's really important to get a good night's sleep, but I always stay up late surfing the Internet or ⓑplay with my phone.

G: That sometimes happens to me too.

B: After I do that, I regret it the next morning and say, "I ⓒshould have gone to bed earlier last night."

G: How was yesterday different?

B: Well, yesterday afternoon I ⓓclimbed the mountain with my dad. I was really tired when I ⓔgot home. I went to sleep right after I went to bed.

G: Outdoor activities are a great way to help you get a good night's sleep.

08 빈칸 (A)에 적절한 것은?

① a good night's sleep
② a long sleeping
③ a poor sleeping condition
④ a quiet room
⑤ a full stomach

09 밑줄 친 ⓐ~ⓔ 중에서 어법상 어색한 것은?

① ⓐ　　② ⓑ　　③ ⓒ　　④ ⓓ　　⑤ ⓔ

10 Which one of the following CANNOT be answered according to the dialogue above?

① Does Ben look full of energy today?
② What does Ben usually do before going to bed?
③ Does Ben usually get enough sleep?
④ With whom did Ben climb the mountain yesterday?
⑤ What outdoor activities does Ben like most?

11 빈칸을 채워 주어진 문장과 같은 의미의 문장을 쓰시오.

(1) I do not think that the richer I become, the happier I am.
= I do not think that as _____ _____.

(2) The bigger the magnet is, the stronger it is.
= As _____.

(3) The more you practice, the better your English speaking skills are.
= As _____ _____.

12 다음 문장의 밑줄 친 부분을 강조하는 문장으로 바꿔 쓰시오.

(1) You should put away your smartphone.
➡ _____
_____

(2) I did not learn Hangeul until I came to Korea.
➡ _____
_____

(3) Jina had a chocolate cake for dessert.
➡ _____
_____

(4) Minji and Jian want to join the art club.
➡ _____

13 다음 문장의 빈칸에 들어갈 수 없는 말을 고르시오.

> The _____, the better.

① sooner　　② faster　　③ less

④ bitter　　⑤ more

14 다음 중 어법상 어색한 것을 모두 고르시오.

① The more Dan practices, the more skillful he is.

② The fast you go, the early you will reach your grandma's house.

③ It is on Sundays when Daniel and I meet.

④ It was the window what John broke.

⑤ The more Jay read this book, the more interested he is in it.

⑥ It was played that Harry the violin yesterday.

⑦ It was thoughtfully that I walked towards the train.

15 다음 우리말을 주어진 어휘를 이용하여 영작하시오.

(1) 국물을 오래 끓일수록 맛이 좋아진다. (I, taste, boil, long, good, it)

　➡ _____

(2) 날씨가 좋을수록, 나는 기분이 더 좋다. (good, the weather, feel)

　➡ _____

(3) Layla가 Jinho를 만난 곳은 바로 학교였다. (at)

　➡ _____

(4) Ella가 가장 존경하는 사람은 바로 그녀의 아버지이다. (respect, the most)

　➡ _____

[16~18] 다음 글을 읽고 물음에 답하시오.

Everyone feels happier when the sun shines. This is because of serotonin, the body's happy hormone. (A)여러분이 햇빛을 쬘수록 뇌는 행복 호르몬을 더 만들어 냅니다. When your serotonin level goes up, you feel happier and stronger. (B)This helps you fight everyday stress. Serotonin also has a calming effect, helping you focus better on ___ⓐ___ you are doing. Moreover, serotonin helps you get a good night's sleep because it helps the brain produce a sleep hormone.

16 위 글의 빈칸 ⓐ에 들어갈 알맞은 말을 고르시오.

① that　　② what　　③ when

④ which　　⑤ where

17 위 글의 밑줄 친 (A)의 우리말에 맞게 주어진 어휘를 이용하여 12 단어로 영작하시오.

> sun, get, happy, produce

➡ _____

_____

18 위 글의 밑줄 친 (B)가 가리키는 것을 본문에서 찾아 쓰시오.

➡ _____

_____

[19~21] 다음 글을 읽고 물음에 답하시오.

As you can see, sunshine has many benefits, but how can you enjoy its benefits safely? Fortunately, ⓐgetting direct sunlight on your skin for 10 to 20 minutes a day is enough to benefit from it. Try to go out into the sun between classes or during lunch breaks and get sunshine on your arms and hands. A walk in the sun, for just a few minutes every day, is good for both your mind and your body. However, avoid the sun during peak summer hours, between 11 and 3, and use sunscreen to protect your face and neck. Enjoy the sun safely and see how a little sunshine can make a world of difference in your health and your mood.

19 위 글의 밑줄 친 ⓐgetting과 문법적 쓰임이 같은 것을 모두 고르시오.

① My dream is getting ahead of him.
② Did she give up getting the job?
③ It's getting warmer and warmer.
④ Is there any advantage in getting there early?
⑤ The nights are getting longer.

20 위 글의 주제로 알맞은 것을 고르시오.

① many benefits of walking
② the proper amount of getting direct sunlight on your skin
③ the way to enjoy many benefits of sunshine safely
④ the time to avoid the sun
⑤ the right way to use sunscreen to protect your face and neck

21 According to the passage, which is NOT true?

① Sunshine has many benefits.
② To get direct sunlight on your skin for 10 to 20 minutes a day isn't enough to benefit from it.
③ A walk in the sun, for just a few minutes every day, is good for both your mind and your body.

④ It's necessary to avoid the sun during peak summer hours, between 11 and 3.
⑤ It's possible to enjoy the sun safely and see how a little sunshine can make lots of difference in your health and your mood.

[22~23] 다음 글을 읽고 물음에 답하시오.

The ⓐ of Sunshine
1. Sunshine helps you deal with stress and feel happier.
2. Sunshine helps you focus better on what you are doing.
3. If you get enough sunshine, you will sleep better at night.
4. When the sun shines on your skin, your skin produces vitamin D, which is needed for strong bones.

22 주어진 영영풀이를 참고하여 빈칸 ⓐ에 철자 B로 시작하는 단어를 쓰시오.

the helps that you get from something or the advantages that results from something

➡ _____

23 다음 중 햇빛의 좋은 점에 해당하지 않는 것을 고르시오.

① 여러분이 스트레스를 다루고 더 행복하게 느끼도록 돕는다.
② 여러분이 하는 일에 더 잘 집중할 수 있도록 도와준다.
③ 햇빛을 충분히 쬐면 밤에 잠을 잘 잘 수 없다.
④ 해가 여러분의 피부에 비칠 때, 여러분의 피부는 비타민 D를 만든다.
⑤ 비타민 D는 튼튼한 뼈를 만드는 데 필요하다.

INSIGHT
on the textbook

교과서 파헤치기

※ 다음 영어를 우리말로 쓰시오.

01	athlete	_____
02	celebrate	_____
03	whenever	_____
04	competition	_____
05	respect	_____
06	decide	_____
07	famous	_____
08	happen	_____
09	passion	_____
10	injure	_____
11	accident	_____
12	represent	_____
13	public	_____
14	realize	_____
15	admire	_____
16	injury	_____
17	accept	_____
18	hurt	_____
19	lie	_____
20	practice	_____
21	suddenly	_____

22	nearby	_____
23	official	_____
24	ceremony	_____
25	developer	_____
26	especially	_____
27	training	_____
28	experiment	_____
29	preparation	_____
30	author	_____
31	cheer	_____
32	remove	_____
33	shout	_____
34	toward	_____
35	be into	_____
36	give up	_____
37	teach oneself	_____
38	be proud of	_____
39	as a result	_____
40	be done with	_____
41	stand for	_____
42	come up to	_____
43	far behind	_____

※ 다음 우리말을 영어로 쓰시오.

01 깨닫다 _____

02 시합 _____

03 결정하다 _____

04 연습 _____

05 개발자 _____

06 제거하다 _____

07 다치다 _____

08 사고 _____

09 식, 의식 _____

10 대표하다 _____

11 환호성을 지르다, 환호하다 _____

12 결승선 _____

13 존중하다 _____

14 부상 _____

15 운동선수 _____

16 작가 _____

17 부상을 입히다 _____

18 축하 _____

19 실험하다 _____

20 대중 _____

21 일어나다 _____

22 부근의; 부근에 _____

23 두드리다 _____

24 갑자기 _____

25 ~쪽으로, ~을 향하여 _____

26 관료, 공무원, 경기 임원 _____

27 열정 _____

28 받다 _____

29 준비 _____

30 ~할 때마다 _____

31 준비하다 _____

32 특별히 _____

33 우승자, 수상자 _____

34 훈련 _____

35 나타내다, 상징하다 _____

36 포기하다 _____

37 멀리 뒤쳐진 _____

38 ~에 관심이 많다 _____

39 ~을 끝내다 _____

40 ~에 다가가다 _____

41 독학하다 _____

42 결과적으로 _____

43 ~을 자랑스러워하다 _____

※ 다음 영영풀이에 알맞은 단어를 <보기>에서 골라 쓴 후, 우리말 뜻을 쓰시오.

1 _____ : the writer of a book: _____

2 _____ : used to talk about a great distance: _____

3 _____ : to take something that someone offers: _____

4 _____ : a person who plays sports well: _____

5 _____ : a strong emotion or feeling: _____

6 _____ : to become aware of something: _____

7 _____ : to take something away: _____

8 _____ : in the direction of someone or something: _____

9 _____ : stop doing something that you have tried hard to do: _____

10 _____ : harm or damage to a person's or an animal's body: _____

11 _____ : the process of learning the skills that you need to do a job: _____

12 _____ : a race where people run a distance of 42.195 kilometers: _____

13 _____ : to officially speak or take action for people in a group: _____

14 _____ : a large sports ground surrounded by rows of seats and usually other buildings: _____

15 _____ : a person who collects and reports news for newspapers, radio or television: _____

16 _____ : to tell someone that you are happy when something pleasant has happened to them: _____

보기			
marathon	stadium	far	author
reporter	training	toward	passion
give up	injury	athlete	realize
represent	remove	congratulate	accept

대화문 Test

※ 다음 우리말과 일치하도록 빈칸에 알맞은 말을 쓰시오.

Listen & Speak 1 Listen

1. **B:** _____ was she _____ _____ become a great _____?
   G: She _____ 3 kilometers _____ _____.
2. **G:** How was he _____ to become a _____ player?
   B: He was _____, but he _____ _____ _____ shots a lot.
3. **B:** _____ was she _____ to _____ English so _____?
   G: She _____ English by _____ many Hollywood movies.
4. **G:** _____ was he able to _____ a famous _____?
   B: He _____ _____ with people in _____.

Listen & Speak 1-A

1. **B:** _____ was Thomas Edison _____ to invent so many things?
   G: Many people _____ that he _____ things on his _____ _____, but that's not _____.
   B: Oh, _____?
   G: Yes. _____ he invented something, he _____ many times.
   B: Maybe that's _____ so many people _____ him.
2. **G:** _____ was Hyeon Chung able to be one of the _____ four _____ in the tennis _____?
   B: He _____ do it _____ _____ years of hard _____.
   G: I see. When did he start _____ _____?
   B: He _____ _____ _____ tennis when he was _____.

Listen & Speak 2 Listen

1. **B:** _____ you _____ of the _____ of the singing _____?
   G: No, I _____. Who _____?
   B: The _____ is Vintop, who wrote all of his _____ songs.
2. **G:** _____ you _____ of Mia, the _____?
   B: Yes, I have. I heard that she _____ _____ to play.
3. **B:** Have you _____ about BTG, the _____ _____ _____ group?
   G: Yes, I have. I have _____ their video _____ _____ on the Internet.
4. **G:** Have you _____ of Jiho, the _____?
   B: No, I _____. What _____ does he _____?
   G: He usually _____ pictures _____ _____ artists.

해석

1. **B:** 어떻게 그녀는 훌륭한 달리기 선수가 될 수 있었니?
   G: 그녀는 매일 3킬로미터를 달렸어.
2. **G:** 어떻게 그는 농구 선수가 될 수 있었니?
   B: 그는 작았지만 3점 슛을 많이 연습했어.
3. **B:** 어떻게 그녀는 영어를 잘할 수 있었니?
   G: 그는 많은 할리우드 영화를 보면서 영어를 배웠어.
4. **G:** 어떻게 그는 유명한 기자가 될 수 있었니?
   B: 그는 대중 앞에서 사람들과 말하는 것을 연습했어.

---

1. **B:** 어떻게 토머스 에디슨을 그렇게 많은 것들을 발명할 수 있었을까?
   G: 많은 사람들은 그가 그것들을 첫 시도에 발명했다고 생각하지만 그것은 사실이 아니야.
   B: 오, 진짜?
   G: 응. 그는 무언가를 발명할 때마다 여러 번 실험했어.
   B: 아마 그것이 그렇게 많은 사람들이 그를 존경하는 이유일 거야.
2. **G:** 정현이 어떻게 테니스 경기에서 마지막 네 선수 중 한 명이 될 수 있었을까?
   B: 그는 혹독한 훈련을 몇 년 거친 뒤에야 그것을 할 수 있었어.
   G: 그렇구나. 그는 언제 테니스 치는 것을 시작했니?
   B: 그는 일곱 살 때 테니스 치는 것을 시작했어.

---

1. **B:** 노래 대회 우승자에 대해 들어 본 적 있니?
   G: 아니, 못 들어 봤어. 누가 이겼어?
   B: 우승자는 빈탑인데, 그는 자신의 모든 노래를 작곡했어.
2. **G:** 미아라는 기타 연주자에 대해 들어 본 적 있니?
   B: 응, 들어 봤어. 나는 그녀가 연주를 독학했다고 들었어.
3. **B:** BTG라는 세계적으로 유명한 댄스 그룹에 대해 들어 본 적 있니?
   G: 응, 들어 봤어. 나는 인터넷에서 그들의 영상을 여러 번 본 적이 있어.
4. **G:** 지호라는 사진작가에 대해 들어 본 적 있니?
   B: 아니, 못 들어 봤어. 그는 어떤 종류의 사진을 찍니?
   G: 그는 보통 거리 예술가들의 사진을 찍어.

Listen & Speak 2-A

1. **B:** _____ you _____ about the _____ club, Edutoon?

   G: Yes, I have. Are you _____ _____ _____ _____?

   B: Yes, I _____ _____ _____ a famous cartoon writer, so I want to _____ that club.

   G: Oh, I didn't _____ that you're _____ in _____ cartoons.

2. **G:** _____ you _____ of D.I.Y.?

   B: No, _____ is D.I.Y.?

   G: D.I.Y. _____ for 'do-it-yourself.' I'm really _____ it. Right now, I'm _____ a _____ _____.

   B: _____ are you going to make _____ you _____ that?

   G: When I'm _____ with the _____ case, I'm _____ _____ _____ my own _____.

Real-Life Zone

G: _____ you _____ _____ Eui Hyun Sin, the _____?

B: No. _____ is _____?

G: He's a Paralympian _____. He _____ the first gold _____ for Korea in the 2018 Winter Paralympics.

B: Wow! That's _____.

G: He _____ in a car _____ in his _____ _____ and _____ his legs.

B: How was he _____ _____ _____ a skier?

G: After his _____, he tried _____ different sports to _____ better. Then he became _____ interested _____ _____.

B: _____ is not easy. Not many people _____ _____ at skiing.

G: That's _____ he's so _____.

Wrap Up

B: Sora, have you _____ about the _____ last night?

G: Yes, I _____ that there _____ a big fire in a building _____. Was anybody _____?

B: No, _____ man _____ ten people who _____ in the building.

G: Oh, really? _____ was he _____ _____ _____ so many people?

B: He _____ on _____ _____ to _____ people to _____ the building.

G: Wow, that's _____!

1. **B:** 에듀툰이라는 만화 동아리에 대해 들어 본 적 있니?
   G: 응, 있어. 만화 그리는 것에 관심이 있니?
   B: 나는 유명한 만화 작가가 되고 싶어서 그 동아리에 가입하고 싶어.
   G: 오, 나는 네가 만화 그리기에 관심이 있는 줄 몰랐어.
2. **G:** D.I.Y에 대해 들어 본 적 있니?
   B: 아니, D.I.Y가 뭐야?
   G: D.I.Y는 '너 스스로 해라'를 의미해. 나는 그것에 푹 빠졌어. 지금 나는 필통을 만들고 있어.
   B: 그것을 완성하고 나면 무엇을 만들 거니?
   G: 필통을 완성하면, 나는 내 책상을 만들 계획이야.

G: 신의현이라는 스키 선수에 대해 들어 본 적 있니?
B: 아니, 그가 누구야?
G: 그는 페럴림픽의 스키 선수야. 그는 2018 동계 페럴림픽에서 한국의 첫 금메달을 땄어.
B: 와! 훌륭하다.
G: 그는 20대 초반에 차 사고를 당하고 다리를 다쳤어.
B: 어떻게 그가 스키 선수가 될 수 있었니?
G: 사고 후에 그는 회복하기 위해 여러 가지 운동들을 시도했어. 그때 그는 특히 스키 타는 것에 관심을 가지게 됐어.
B: 스키를 타는 것은 쉽지 않잖아. 스키를 잘 타는 사람들은 많지 않아.
G: 그것이 그가 그렇게 존경받는 이유야.

B: 소라야, 지난밤 화재에 대해 들었니?
G: 응, 이 근처 건물에서 큰 화재가 있었다고 들었어. 다친 사람이 있어?
B: 아니, 한 남자가 건물 안에 있던 열 명의 사람들을 구했어.
G: 오, 진짜? 어떻게 그는 그 많은 사람들을 구할 수 있었니?
B: 그는 사람들에게 건물을 떠나라고 말하기 위해서 모든 문을 두드렸어.
G: 와, 정말 놀랍구나!

※ 다음 우리말에 맞도록 대화를 영어로 쓰시오.

Listen & Speak 1 Listen

1. B: _____
   G: _____
2. G: _____
   B: _____
3. B: _____
   G: _____
4. G: _____
   B: _____

Listen & Speak 1-A

1. B: _____
   G: _____
   B: _____
   G: _____
   B: _____
2. G: _____
   _____
   B: _____
   G: _____
   B: _____

Listen & Speak 2 Listen

1. B: _____
   G: _____
   B: _____
2. G: _____
   B: _____
3. B: _____
   G: _____
4. G: _____
   B: _____
   G: _____

1. B: 어떻게 그녀는 훌륭한 달리기 선수가 될 수 있었니?
   G: 그녀는 매일 3킬로미터를 달렸어.
2. G: 어떻게 그는 농구 선수가 될 수 있었니?
   B: 그는 작았지만 3점 슛을 많이 연습했어.
3. B: 어떻게 그녀는 영어를 잘할 수 있었니?
   G: 그는 많은 할리우드 영화를 보면서 영어를 배웠어.
4. G: 어떻게 그는 유명한 기자가 될 수 있었니?
   B: 그는 대중 앞에서 사람들과 말하는 것을 연습했어.

1. B: 어떻게 토머스 에디슨을 그렇게 많은 것들을 발명할 수 있었을까?
   G: 많은 사람들은 그가 그것들을 첫 시도에 발명했다고 생각하지만 그것은 사실이 아니야.
   B: 오, 진짜?
   G: 응. 그는 무언가를 발명할 때마다 여러 번 실험했어.
   B: 아마 그것이 그렇게 많은 사람들이 그를 존경하는 이유일 거야.
2. G: 정현이 어떻게 테니스 경기에서 마지막 네 선수 중 한 명이 될 수 있었을까?
   B: 그는 혹독한 훈련을 몇 년 거친 뒤에야 그것을 할 수 있었어.
   G: 그렇구나. 그는 언제 테니스 치는 것을 시작했니?
   B: 그는 일곱 살 때 테니스 치는 것을 시작했어.

1. B: 노래 대회 우승자에 대해 들어 본 적 있니?
   G: 아니, 못 들어 봤어. 누가 이겼어?
   B: 우승자는 빈탑인데, 그는 자신의 모든 노래를 작곡했어.
2. G: 미아라는 기타 연주자에 대해 들어 본 적 있니?
   B: 응, 들어 봤어. 나는 그녀가 연주를 독학했다고 들었어.
3. B: BTG라는 세계적으로 유명한 댄스 그룹에 대해 들어 본 적 있니?
   G: 응, 들어 봤어. 나는 인터넷에서 그들의 영상을 여러 번 본 적이 있어.
4. G: 지호라는 사진작가에 대해 들어 본 적 있니?
   B: 아니, 못 들어 봤어. 그는 어떤 종류의 사진을 찍니?
   G: 그는 보통 거리 예술가들의 사진을 찍어.

Listen & Speak 2-A

1. B: _____

   G: _____

   B: _____

   G: _____

2. G: _____

   B: _____

   G: _____

   _____

   B: _____

   G: _____

---

1. B: 에듀툰이라는 만화 동아리에 대해 들어 본 적 있니?
   G: 응, 있어. 만화 그리는 것에 관심이 있니?
   B: 나는 유명한 만화 작가가 되고 싶어서 그 동아리에 가입하고 싶어.
   G: 오, 나는 네가 만화 그리기에 관심이 있는 줄 몰랐어.
2. G: D.I.Y에 대해 들어 본 적 있니?
   B: 아니, D.I.Y가 뭐야?
   G: D.I.Y는 '너 스스로 해라'를 의미해. 나는 그것에 푹 빠졌어. 지금 나는 필통을 만들고 있어.
   B: 그것을 완성하고 나면 무엇을 만들 거니?
   G: 필통을 완성하면, 나는 내 책상을 만들 계획이야.

Real-Life Zone

G: _____

B: _____

G: _____

   _____

B: _____

G: _____

B: _____

G: _____

B: _____

G: _____

G: 신의현이라는 스키 선수에 대해 들어 본 적 있니?
B: 아니, 그가 누구야?
G: 그는 패럴림픽의 스키 선수야. 그는 2018 동계 패럴림픽에서 한국의 첫 금메달을 땄어.
B: 와! 훌륭하다.
G: 그는 20대 초반에 차 사고를 당하고 다리를 다쳤어.
B: 어떻게 그가 스키 선수가 될 수 있었니?
G: 사고 후에 그는 회복하기 위해 여러 가지 운동들을 시도했어. 그때 그는 특히 스키 타는 것에 관심을 가지게 됐어.
B: 스키를 타는 것은 쉽지 않잖아. 스키를 잘 타는 사람들은 많지 않아.
G: 그것이 그가 그렇게 존경받는 이유야.

Wrap Up

B: _____

G: _____

B: _____

G: _____

B: _____

G: _____

B: 소라야, 지난밤 화재에 대해 들었니?
G: 응, 이 근처 건물에서 큰 화재가 있었다고 들었어. 다친 사람이 있어?
B: 아니, 한 남자가 건물 안에 있던 열 명의 사람들을 구했어.
G: 오, 진짜? 어떻게 그는 그 많은 사람들을 구할 수 있었니?
B: 그는 사람들에게 건물을 떠나라고 말하기 위해서 모든 문을 두드렸어.
G: 와, 정말 놀랍구나!

※ 다음 우리말과 일치하도록 빈칸에 알맞은 것을 골라 쓰시오.

1 The _____ _____
    A. Runner   B. Last

2 The last runner _____ the race _____ an hour _____ .
    A. before   B. finished   C. than   D. more

3 "There will be _____ _____ runners _____," the _____ decided.
    A. more   B. officials   C. coming   D. no

4 They _____ the tape at the finish line and started to _____ for the _____ _____ for the 1996 Atlanta Summer Olympics in the United States.
    A. prepare   B. ceremony   C. removed   D. closing

5 Someone _____, "Look! _____ comes _____ _____!"
    A. there   B. runner   C. shouted   D. another

6 A runner was just _____ the stadium, but there was _____ _____ _____ his legs.
    A. something   B. with   C. entering   D. wrong

7 Still, he _____ _____ _____ the finish line.
    A. going   B. kept   C. toward

8 The band and the _____ _____ their _____ for the closing _____ .
    A. stopped   B. ceremony   C. volunteers   D. preparations

9 _____ _____ were _____ the _____ .
    A. runner   B. eyes   C. all   D. on

10 _____, the band started playing _____ _____, and the volunteers _____ .
    A. cheered   B. celebration   C. suddenly   D. music

11 "Go! Go! _____ _____ _____!"
    A. for   B. it   C. go

12 Two volunteers _____ to the _____ _____ _____ a tape.
    A. line   B. ran   C. with   D. finish

13 _____, the runner _____ the tape and then _____ to the ground.
    A. through   B. finally   C. fell   D. ran

14 _____ _____ _____ Abdul Baser Wasiqi.
    A. name   B. his   C. was

15 He _____ _____ Afghanistan.
    A. from   B. was

16 Reporters _____ _____ _____ Wasiqi and started _____ him questions.
    A. to   B. came   C. asking   D. up

17 **Reporter:** What _____ _____ you?
    A. to   B. happened

18 **Wasiqi:** I _____ my leg _____ a _____ _____ .
    A. practice   B. injured   C. run   D. during

---

1 마지막 주자

2 마지막 주자가 한 시간도 더 전에 경주를 끝냈다.

3 "더 들어오는 선수는 없을 겁니다."라고 경기 임원들은 결론을 내렸다.

4 그들은 결승선에서 테이프를 걷어내고 1996년 미국 애틀랜타 하계 올림픽의 폐막식을 준비하기 시작했다.

5 누군가가 외쳤다. "봐! 저기 또 다른 선수가 온다!"

6 한 선수가 경기장으로 막 들어오고 있었는데, 그의 다리에 이상이 있었다.

7 그러나 그는 계속 결승선을 향해 움직였다.

8 밴드와 자원봉사자들이 폐막식을 위한 준비를 멈추었다.

9 모든 눈들이 그 선수에게 머물렀다.

10 갑자기 밴드가 축하 음악을 연주하기 시작했고, 자원봉사자들이 환호했다.

11 "달려! 달려! 잘해라!"

12 두 명의 자원봉사자가 테이프를 가지고 결승선으로 달려갔다.

13 결국, 그 주자는 테이프를 통과해 달렸고, 바닥에 쓰러졌다.

14 그의 이름은 압둘 베사르 와시키였다.

15 그는 아프가니스탄 출신이었다.

16 기자들은 와시키에게 가서 그에게 질문을 하기 시작했다.

17 리포터: 당신에게 무슨 일이 있었나요?

18 와시키: 저는 연습 경기를 하던 중 다리를 다쳤습니다.

19 The injury _____ _____ during the race, but I couldn't _____ _____.
A. worse   B. up   C. got   D. give

20 **Reporter:** _____ _____ ?
A. not   B. why

21 You knew _____ you were too _____ _____ to _____ a medal.
A. far   B. win   C. that   D. behind

22 **Wasiqi:** I am the _____ _____ here _____ _____.
A. representing   B. only   C. Afghanistan   D. athlete

23 There was _____ _____ I could _____ _____.
A. give   B. way   C. no   D. up

24 **Reporter:** Afghanistan is still _____ _____, _____ _____?
A. war   B. it   C. isn't   D. at

25 **Wasiqi:** Yes, we _____ _____ at war _____ 16 years.
A. been   B. for   C. have

26 _____ we were not _____ to send _____ to the Barcelona Olympics four years ago.
A. why   B. athletes   C. that's   D. able

27 I was _____ _____ my country _____ _____ when I could see no Afghan athletes in the opening ceremony.
A. back   B. for   C. sad   D. then

28 **Reporter:** _____ you _____ marathons _____ ?
A. running   B. then   C. were

29 **Wasiqi:** No. I _____ _____ _____ Barcelona.
A. running   B. started   C. after

30 I ran in _____ _____ _____.
A. of   B. lots   C. races

31 Finally I _____ _____ _____ in Germany.
A. a   B. won   C. marathon

32 _____ a _____, I was _____ _____ come to Atlanta.
A. to   B. able   C. result   D. as

33 **Reporter:** _____ do you _____ now?
A. feel   B. how

34 **Wasiqi:** I am _____ _____ _____ and proud to be _____ Afghanistan.
A. myself   B. proud   C. from   D. of

35 For me and my country, it was important _____ _____ _____ _____.
A. to   B. up   C. give   D. not

36 I _____ _____ here _____ _____.
A. come   B. win   C. didn't   D. to

37 For me, it was _____ _____ be here and to _____ the _____.
A. to   B. race   C. finish   D. enough

19 경기 중에 제 상처는 점점 더 심각졌지만, 저는 포기할 수 없었습니다.

20 리포터: 왜 포기할 수 없었죠?

21 당신은 메달을 얻기에 너무도 크게 뒤떨어져 있었다는 것을 알고 있었잖아요.

22 와시키: 저는 아프가니스탄을 대표하는 유일한 선수입니다.

23 제가 포기할 수 있는 방법은 없었습니다.

24 리포터: 아프가니스탄은 여전히 전쟁 중입니다. 맞나요?

25 와시키: 네, 우리나라는 16년째 전쟁 중입니다.

26 그것이 우리가 4년 전 바르셀로나 올림픽에 선수들을 보낼 수 없었던 이유입니다.

27 저는 개회식에서 아프가니스탄 선수를 볼 수 없었던 그 당시, 제 나라에 대해 매우 슬펐습니다.

28 리포터: 그 당시 마라톤을 뛰고 있었나요?

29 와시키: 아니요. 저는 바르셀로나 올림픽 이후에 달리기를 시작했습니다.

30 저는 많은 경주에서 뛰었어요.

31 마침내 독일 마라톤에서 우승했지요.

32 그 결과 애틀랜타에 올 수 있었어요.

33 리포터: 지금은 기분이 어떠신가요?

34 와시키: 저는 제 자신이, 그리고 제가 아프가니스탄 출신인 것이 자랑스러워요.

35 저와 제 조국을 위해서는, 포기하지 않는 것이 중요했어요.

36 저는 이곳에 이기러 온 것이 아닙니다.

37 제가 여기에 있고 경주를 끝마친 것으로 충분합니다.

※ 다음 우리말과 일치하도록 빈칸에 알맞은 말을 쓰시오.

1 The _____ _____

2 The last runner _____ the race _____ _____ an hour before.

3 "There will be _____ _____ runners _____," the _____ decided.

4 They _____ the tape at the _____ _____ and started to _____ _____ the _____ _____ for the 1996 Atlanta Summer Olympics in the United States.

5 Someone _____, "Look! _____ _____ _____ runner!"

6 A runner was just entering the stadium, but there was _____ _____ _____ his legs.

7 _____, he _____ _____ _____ the finish line.

8 The band and the volunteers _____ _____ _____ for the _____ _____.

9 _____ _____ _____ _____ the runner.

10 _____, the band started playing _____ _____, and the _____ _____.

11 "Go! Go! _____ _____ _____!"

12 Two volunteers ran to the finish line _____ _____.

13 _____, the runner _____ _____ the tape and then _____ _____ the ground.

14 _____ _____ was Abdul Baser Wasiqi.

15 He _____ _____ Afghanistan.

16 Reporters _____ _____ _____ Wasiqi and _____ _____ him questions.

17 **Reporter:** What _____ _____ you?

18 **Wasiqi:** I _____ my leg _____ _____ _____ _____.

1	마지막 주자
2	마지막 주자가 한 시간도 더 전에 경주를 끝냈다.
3	"더 들어오는 선수는 없을 겁니다."라고 경기 임원들은 결론을 내렸다.
4	그들은 결승선에서 테이프를 걷어내고 1996년 미국 애틀랜타 하계 올림픽의 폐막식을 준비하기 시작했다.
5	누군가 외쳤다. "봐! 저기 또 다른 선수가 온다!"
6	한 선수가 경기장으로 막 들어오고 있었는데, 그의 다리에 이상이 있었다.
7	그러나 그는 계속 결승선을 향해 움직였다.
8	밴드와 자원봉사자들이 폐막식을 위한 준비를 멈추었다.
9	모든 눈들이 그 선수에게 머물렀다.
10	갑자기 밴드가 축하 음악을 연주하기 시작했고, 자원봉사자들이 환호했다.
11	"달려! 달려! 잘해라!"
12	두 명의 자원봉사자가 테이프를 가지고 결승선으로 달려갔다.
13	결국, 그 주자는 테이프를 통과해 달렸고, 바닥에 쓰러졌다.
14	그의 이름은 압둘 베사르 와시키였다.
15	그는 아프가니스탄 출신이었다.
16	기자들은 와시키에게 가서 그에게 질문을 하기 시작했다.
17	리포터: 당신에게 무슨 일이 있었나요?
18	와시키: 저는 연습 경기를 하던 중 다리를 다쳤습니다.

19 The injury _____ _____ _____ the race, but I couldn't _____ _____.

20 **Reporter:** _____ _____?

21 You knew that you were too _____ _____ to win a medal.

22 **Wasiqi:** I am the _____ _____ here _____ _____.

23 There was _____ _____ I could _____ _____.

24 **Reporter:** Afghanistan is still _____ _____, _____ _____?

25 **Wasiqi:** Yes, we _____ _____ at war _____ 16 years.

26 _____ _____ we were not _____ _____ send athletes to the Barcelona Olympics four years ago.

27 I _____ _____ _____ my country _____ _____ when I could see no Afghan athletes in the _____ _____.

28 **Reporter:** _____ you _____ marathons then?

29 **Wasiqi:** No. I _____ _____ after Barcelona.

30 I ran in _____ _____ _____.

31 Finally I _____ _____ _____ in Germany.

32 _____ _____ _____, I was able to come to Atlanta.

33 **Reporter:** _____ do you _____ now?

34 **Wasiqi:** I am _____ _____ _____ and proud _____ _____ _____ Afghanistan.

35 For me and my country, it was important _____ _____ _____ _____.

36 I didn't come here _____ _____.

37 For me, _____ _____ _____ to be here and _____ _____ the race.

19 경기 중에 제 상처는 점점 더 심각해졌지만, 저는 포기할 수 없었습니다.

20 리포터: 왜 포기할 수 없었죠?

21 당신은 메달을 얻기에 너무도 크게 뒤떨어져 있었다는 것을 알고 있었잖아요.

22 와시키: 저는 아프가니스탄을 대표하는 유일한 선수입니다.

23 제가 포기할 수 있는 방법은 없었습니다.

24 리포터: 아프가니스탄은 여전히 전쟁 중입니다. 맞나요?

25 와시키: 네, 우리나라는 16년째 전쟁 중입니다.

26 그것이 우리가 4년 전 바르셀로나 올림픽에 선수들을 보낼 수 없었던 이유입니다.

27 저는 개회식에서 아프가니스탄 선수를 볼 수 없었던 그 당시, 제 나라에 대해 매우 슬펐습니다.

28 리포터: 그 당시 마라톤을 뛰고 있었나요?

29 와시키: 아니요. 저는 바르셀로나 올림픽 이후에 달리기를 시작했습니다.

30 저는 많은 경주에서 뛰었어요.

31 마침내 독일 마라톤에서 우승했지요.

32 그 결과 애틀랜타에 올 수 있었어요.

33 리포터: 지금은 기분이 어떠신가요?

34 와시키: 저는 제 자신이, 그리고 제가 아프가니스탄 출신인 것이 자랑스러워요.

35 저와 제 조국을 위해서는, 포기하지 않는 것이 중요했어요.

36 저는 이곳에 이기러 온 것이 아닙니다.

37 제가 여기에 있고 경주를 끝마친 것으로 충분합니다.

※ 다음 문장을 우리말로 쓰시오.

1 The Last Runner
➡ _____

2 The last runner finished the race more than an hour before.
➡ _____

3 "There will be no more runners coming," the officials decided.
➡ _____

4 They removed the tape at the finish line and started to prepare for the closing ceremony for the 1996 Atlanta Summer Olympics in the United States.
➡ _____

5 Someone shouted, "Look! There comes another runner!"
➡ _____

6 A runner was just entering the stadium, but there was something wrong with his legs.
➡ _____

7 Still, he kept going toward the finish line.
➡ _____

8 The band and the volunteers stopped their preparations for the closing ceremony.
➡ _____

9 All eyes were on the runner.
➡ _____

10 Suddenly, the band started playing celebration music, and the volunteers cheered.
➡ _____

11 "Go! Go! Go for it!"
➡ _____

12 Two volunteers ran to the finish line with a tape.
➡ _____

13 Finally, the runner ran through the tape and then fell to the ground.
➡ _____

14 His name was Abdul Baser Wasiqi.
➡ _____

15 He was from Afghanistan.
➡ _____

16 Reporters came up to Wasiqi and started asking him questions.
➡ _____

17 Reporter: What happened to you?
➡ _____

18 Wasiqi: I injured my leg during a practice run.
➡ _____

19 The injury got worse during the race, but I couldn't give up.
➡ _____

20 Reporter: Why not?
➡ _____

21 You knew that you were too far behind to win a medal.
➡ _____

22 Wasiqi: I am the only athlete here representing Afghanistan.
➡ _____

23 There was no way I could give up.
➡ _____

24 Reporter: Afghanistan is still at war, isn't it?
➡ _____

25 Wasiqi: Yes, we have been at war for 16 years.
➡ _____

26 That's why we were not able to send athletes to the Barcelona Olympics four years ago.
➡ _____

27 I was sad for my country back then when I could see no Afghan athletes in the opening ceremony.
➡ _____

28 Reporter: Were you running marathons then?
➡ _____

29 Wasiqi: No. I started running after Barcelona.
➡ _____

30 I ran in lots of races.
➡ _____

31 Finally I won a marathon in Germany.
➡ _____

32 As a result, I was able to come to Atlanta.
➡ _____

33 Reporter: How do you feel now?
➡ _____

34 Wasiqi: I am proud of myself and proud to be from Afghanistan.
➡ _____

35 For me and my country, it was important not to give up.
➡ _____

36 I didn't come here to win.
➡ _____

37 For me, it was enough to be here and to finish the race.
➡ _____

※ 다음 괄호 안의 단어들을 우리말에 맞도록 바르게 배열하시오.

1 (Last / The / Runner)
➡ _____

2 (last / the / finished / runner / race / the / than / more / an / before. / hour)
➡ _____

3 (will / "there / no / be / runners / more / coming," / the / decided. / officials)
➡ _____

4 (removed / they / tape / the / at / finish / the / line / and / to / started / for / prepare / the / ceremony / closing / the / for / Atlanta / 1996 / Olympics / Summer / the / in / States. / United)
➡ _____

5 (shouted, / someone / "look! / comes / there / runner!" / another)
➡ _____

6 (runner / a / just / was / the / entering / stadium, / there / but / something / was / with / wrong / legs. / his)
➡ _____

7 (he / still, / kept / toward / going / finish / the / line.)
➡ _____

8 (band / the / and / volunteers / the / their / stopped / preparations / the / for / ceremony. / closing)
➡ _____

9 (eyes / all / on / were / runner. / the)
➡ _____

10 (the / suddenly, / band / playing / started / music, / celebration / and / volunteers / the / cheered.)
➡ _____

11 ("go! / go / go! / it!" / for)
➡ _____

12 (volunteers / two / to / ran / finish / the / with / line / tape. / a)
➡ _____

13 (the / finally, / runner / through / ran / tape / the / and / fell / then / to / ground. / the)
➡ _____

14 (name / his / was / Baser / Abdul / Wasiqi.)
➡ _____

15 (was / he / Afghanistan. / from)
➡ _____

16 (came / reporters / to / up / and / Wasiqi / asking / started / questions. / him)
➡ _____

17 (Reporter: / happened / what / you? / to)
➡ _____

18 (Wasiqi: / injured / I / leg / my / a / during / run. / practice.)
➡ _____

1 마지막 주자

2 마지막 주자가 한 시간도 더 전에 경주를 끝냈다.

3 "더 들어오는 선수는 없을 겁니다."라고 경기 임원들은 결론을 내렸다.

4 그들은 결승선에서 테이프를 걷어내고 1996년 미국 애틀랜타 하계 올림픽의 폐막식을 준비하기 시작했다.

5 누군가가 외쳤다. "봐! 저기 또 다른 선수가 온다!"

6 한 선수가 경기장으로 막 들어오고 있었는데, 그의 다리에 이상이 있었다.

7 그러나 그는 계속 결승선을 향해 움직였다.

8 밴드와 자원봉사자들이 폐막식을 위한 준비를 멈추었다.

9 모든 눈들이 그 선수에게 머물렀다.

10 갑자기 밴드가 축하 음악을 연주하기 시작했고, 자원봉사자들이 환호했다.

11 "달려! 달려! 잘해라!"

12 두 명의 자원봉사자가 테이프를 가지고 결승선으로 달려갔다.

13 결국. 그 주자는 테이프를 통과해 달렸고, 바닥에 쓰러졌다.

14 그의 이름은 압둘 베사르 와시키였다.

15 그는 아프가니스탄 출신이었다.

16 기자들은 와시키에게 가서 그에게 질문을 하기 시작했다.

17 리포터: 당신에게 무슨 일이 있었나요?

18 와시키: 저는 연습 경기를 하던 중 다리를 다쳤습니다.

19 (injury / the / worse / got / the / during / race, / I / but / give / couldn't / up.)
➡ _____

20 (Reporter: / not? / why)
➡ _____

21 (knew / you / that / were / you / far / too / behind / win / to / medal. / a)
➡ _____

22 (Wasiqi: / am / I / the / athlete / only / here / Afghanistan. / representing)
➡ _____

23 (was / there / way / no / could / I / up. / give)
➡ _____

24 (Reporter: / is / Afghanistan / at / still / war, / it? / isn't)
➡ _____

25 (Wasiqi: / we / yes, / been / have / war / at / 16 / years. / for)
➡ _____

26 (why / that's / were / we / able / not / send / to / athletes / the / to / Olympics / Barcelona / four / ago. / years)
➡ _____

27 (was / I / sad / my / for / back / country / then / I / when / see / could / Afghan / no / athletes / the / in / ceremony. / opening)
➡ _____

28 (Reporter: / you / were / marathons / running / then?)
➡ _____

29 (Wasiqi: / no. // started / I / after / running / Barcelona.)
➡ _____

30 (ran / I / lots / in / races. / of)
➡ _____

31 (I / finally / won / marathon / a / Germany. / in)
➡ _____

32 (a / as / result, / was / I / to / able / to / come / Atlanta.)
➡ _____

33 (Reporter: / do / how / feel / you / now?)
➡ _____

34 (Wasiqi: / am / I / of / proud / and / myself / to / proud / be / Afghanistan. / from)
➡ _____

35 (me / for / and / country, / my / was / it / not / important / to / up. / give)
➡ _____

36 (didn't / I / here / come / win. / to)
➡ _____

37 (me, / for / was / it / to / enough / be / and / here / to / the / finish / race.)
➡ _____

19 경기 중에 제 상처는 점점 더 심각해졌지만, 저는 포기할 수 없었습니다.

20 리포터: 왜 포기할 수 없었죠?

21 당신은 메달을 얻기에 너무도 크게 뒤떨어져 있었다는 것을 알고 있었잖아요.

22 와시키: 저는 아프가니스탄을 대표하는 유일한 선수입니다.

23 제가 포기할 수 있는 방법은 없었습니다.

24 리포터: 아프가니스탄은 여전히 전쟁 중입니다. 맞나요?

25 와시키: 네, 우리나라는 16년째 전쟁 중입니다.

26 그것이 우리가 4년 전 바르셀로나 올림픽에 선수들을 보낼 수 없었던 이유입니다.

27 저는 개회식에서 아프가니스탄 선수를 볼 수 없었던 그 당시, 제 나라에 대해 매우 슬펐습니다.

28 리포터: 그 당시 마라톤을 뛰고 있었나요?

29 와시키: 아니요. 저는 바르셀로나 올림픽 이후에 달리기를 시작했습니다.

30 저는 많은 경주에서 뛰었어요.

31 마침내 독일 마라톤에서 우승했지요.

32 그 결과 애틀랜타에 올 수 있었어요.

33 리포터: 지금은 기분이 어떠신가요?

34 와시키: 저는 제 자신이, 그리고 제가 아프가니스탄 출신인 것이 자랑스러워요.

35 저와 제 조국을 위해서는, 포기하지 않는 것이 중요했어요.

36 저는 이곳에 이기러 온 것이 아닙니다.

37 제가 여기에 있고 경주를 끝마친 것으로 충분합니다.

※ 다음 우리말을 영어로 쓰시오.

1 마지막 주자

➡ _____

2 마지막 주자가 한 시간도 더 전에 경주를 끝냈다.

➡ _____

3 "더 들어오는 선수는 없을 겁니다."라고 경기 임원들은 결론을 내렸다.

➡ _____

4 그들은 결승선에서 테이프를 걷어내고 1996년 미국 애틀랜타 하계 올림픽의 폐막식을 준비하기 시작했다.

➡ _____

➡ _____

5 누군가가 외쳤다. "봐! 저기 또 다른 선수가 온다!"

➡ _____

6 한 선수가 경기장으로 막 들어오고 있었는데, 그의 다리에 이상이 있었다.

➡ _____

7 그러나 그는 계속 결승선을 향해 움직였다.

➡ _____

8 밴드와 자원봉사자들이 폐막식을 위한 준비를 멈추었다.

➡ _____

9 모든 눈들이 그 선수에게 머물렀다.

➡ _____

10 갑자기 밴드가 축하 음악을 연주하기 시작했고, 자원봉사자들이 환호했다.

➡ _____

11 "달려! 달려! 잘해라!"

➡ _____

12 두 명의 자원봉사자가 테이프를 가지고 결승선으로 달려갔다.

➡ _____

13 결국, 그 주자는 테이프를 통과해 달렸고, 바닥에 쓰러졌다.

➡ _____

14 그의 이름은 압둘 베사르 와시키였다.

➡ _____

15 그는 아프가니스탄 출신이었다.

➡ _____

16 기자들은 와시키에게 가서 그에게 질문을 하기 시작했다.

➡ _____

17 리포터: 당신에게 무슨 일이 있었나요?

➡ _____

18 와시키: 저는 연습 경기를 하던 중 다리를 다쳤습니다.

➡ _____

19 경기 중에 제 상처는 점점 더 심각해졌지만, 저는 포기할 수 없었습니다.
➡ _____

20 리포터: 왜 포기할 수 없었죠?
➡ _____

21 당신은 메달을 얻기에 너무도 크게 뒤떨어져 있었다는 것을 알고 있었잖아요.
➡ _____

22 와시키: 저는 아프가니스탄을 대표하는 유일한 선수입니다.
➡ _____

23 제가 포기할 수 있는 방법은 없었습니다.
➡ _____

24 리포터: 아프가니스탄은 여전히 전쟁 중입니다. 맞나요?
➡ _____

25 와시키: 네, 우리나라는 16년째 전쟁 중입니다.
➡ _____

26 그것이 우리가 4년 전 바르셀로나 올림픽에 선수들을 보낼 수 없었던 이유입니다.
➡ _____

27 저는 개회식에서 아프가니스탄 선수를 볼 수 없었던 그 당시, 제 나라에 대해 매우 슬펐습니다.
➡ _____

28 리포터: 그 당시 마라톤을 뛰고 있었나요?
➡ _____

29 와시키: 아니요. 저는 바르셀로나 올림픽 이후에 달리기를 시작했습니다.
➡ _____

30 저는 많은 경주에서 뛰었어요.
➡ _____

31 마침내 독일 마라톤에서 우승했지요.
➡ _____

32 그 결과 애틀랜타에 올 수 있었어요.
➡ _____

33 리포터: 지금은 기분이 어떠신가요?
➡ _____

34 와시키: 저는 제 자신이, 그리고 제가 아프가니스탄 출신인 것이 자랑스러워요.
➡ _____

35 저와 제 조국을 위해서는, 포기하지 않는 것이 중요했어요.
➡ _____

36 저는 이곳에 이기러 온 것이 아닙니다.
➡ _____

37 제가 여기에 있고 경주를 끝마친 것으로 충분합니다.
➡ _____

※ 다음 우리말과 일치하도록 빈칸에 알맞은 말을 쓰시오.

Communication Task

1. A: _____ you _____ _____ Jain Kim?

2. B: Yes, I have. She's _____ _____ _____ _____.

3. A: How _____ she _____ _____ _____ a famous rock climber?

4. B: She trained hard _____ _____ _____ _____ _____.

1. A: 너는 김자인에 대하여 들어본 적이 있니?
2. B: 그래. 그녀는 유명한 암벽 등반가야.
3. A: 어떻게 그녀가 유명한 암벽 등반가가 될 수 있었지?
4. B: 그녀는 5년 동안 매일 열심히 훈련했어.

Language in Use B

1. Last night, I _____ _____ _____ for 8 o'lock _____ _____ _____ _____ school today.

2. _____ it is _____ _____ _____ _____ my school, _____ is important _____ _____ _____ the bus.

3. _____ _____ _____, I quickly _____ the house and _____ _____ the bus stop.

4. _____, there _____ _____.

5. _____, I _____ _____ today was Saturday.

6. _____ _____ _____, not to _____ it _____ again, I will always check _____ _____ _____ _____.

1. 어젯밤에 나는 오늘 학교에 늦지 않으려고 시계를 8시에 맞춰 놓았다.
2. 학교까지는 길이 멀기 때문에, 버스를 놓치지 않는 것이 중요하다.
3. 아침도 먹지 않고 나는 빠르게 집을 떠나 버스 정거장으로 갔다.
4. 놀랍게도 아무도 없었다.
5. 그때, 나는 오늘이 토요일임을 기억했다.
6. 이제부터 그런 일이 다시 일어나지 않도록, 나는 항상 무슨 요일인지 확인하겠다.

Writing Workshop Step 3

1. I _____ _____ _____ _____ _____ the Singing Contest

2. I _____ _____ _____ the school _____ _____.

3. I love singing, and _____ _____ I _____ _____ _____ _____.

4. _____, I am _____ _____ _____ _____ _____ _____ many people.

5. _____ _____ _____ _____ during the contest, I will _____ _____ _____ _____ _____ my class first.

1. 나는 노래 대회에서 이기려는 목표를 가지고 있다
2. 나는 학교 노래 대회에서 이기고 싶다.
3. 나는 노래 부르는 것을 좋아하고 목소리가 좋다고 생각한다.
4. 그러나, 나는 너무 수줍어해서 많은 사람들 앞에서 노래를 부를 수 없다.
5. 대회 도중에 불안해하지 않기 위해서 먼저 학급 친구들 앞에서 노래 부르기를 연습할 것이다.

※ 다음 우리말을 영어로 쓰시오.

Communication Task

1. A: 너는 김자인에 대하여 들어본 적이 있니?

➡ _____

2. B: 그래. 그녀는 유명한 암벽 등반가야.

➡ _____

3. A: 어떻게 그녀가 유명한 암벽 등반가가 될 수 있었지?

➡ _____

4. B: 그녀는 5년 동안 매일 열심히 훈련했어.

➡ _____

Language in Use B

1. 어젯밤에 나는 오늘 학교에 늦지 않으려고 시계를 8시에 맞춰 놓았다.

➡ _____

2. 학교까지는 길이 멀기 때문에, 버스를 놓치지 않는 것이 중요하다.

➡ _____

3. 아침도 먹지 않고 나는 빠르게 집을 떠나 버스 정거장으로 갔다.

➡ _____

4. 놀랍게도 아무도 없었다.

➡ _____

5. 그때, 나는 오늘이 토요일임을 기억했다.

➡ _____

6. 이제부터 그런 일이 다시 일어나지 않도록, 나는 항상 무슨 요일인지 확인하겠다.

➡ _____

Writing Workshop Step 3

1. 나는 노래 대회에서 이기려는 목표를 가지고 있다

➡ _____

2. 나는 학교 노래 대회에서 이기고 싶다.

➡ _____

3. 나는 노래 부르는 것을 좋아하고 목소리가 좋다고 생각한다.

➡ _____

4. 그러나, 나는 너무 수줍어서 많은 사람들 앞에서 노래를 부를 수 없다.

➡ _____

5. 대회 도중에 불안해하지 않기 위해서 먼저 학급 친구들 앞에서 노래 부르기를 연습할 것이다.

➡ _____

※ 다음 영어를 우리말로 쓰시오.

01 avoid _____

02 counselor _____

03 recently _____

04 prove _____

05 relax _____

06 experiment _____

07 still _____

08 popular _____

09 vocabulary _____

10 latest _____

11 management _____

12 afraid _____

13 final _____

14 matter _____

15 hurt _____

16 match _____

17 upset _____

18 part _____

19 protein _____

20 helpful _____

21 disagree _____

22 sneakers _____

23 misunderstand _____

24 strict _____

25 teenager _____

26 decide _____

27 hate _____

28 worry _____

29 mistake _____

30 number _____

31 speech contest _____

32 P.E. teacher _____

33 advise _____

34 project _____

35 in style _____

36 for now _____

37 ask somebody out _____

38 without -ing _____

39 focus on _____

40 end up -ing _____

41 for a long time _____

42 have a hard time -ing _____

43 not ~ anymore _____

※ 다음 우리말을 영어로 쓰시오.

01 기분이 상한	22 관리
02 카운슬러, 상담역	23 부분, 배역, 역할
03 결정하다	24 다치다
04 시합	25 과제
05 실험	26 충고하다
06 엄격한	27 체육 교사
07 피하다	28 번호를 매기다
08 문제	29 쉬다
09 인기 있는	30 실수
10 증명하다, 입증하다	31 청소년
11 매우 싫어하다	32 걱정; 걱정하다
12 웅변대회	33 최근에
13 오해하다	34 시도하다
14 아직도	35 더 이상 ~가 아닌
15 동의하지 않다	36 유행하는, 유행되는
16 단백질	37 집중하다
17 도움이 되는	38 당분간은, 현재로는
18 운동화	39 결국 ~하게 되다
19 결승, 기말고사; 마지막의	40 오랫동안
20 어휘	41 ~의 역할을 하다
21 최신의	42 ~하는 데 어려움이 있다
	43 ~에 준비가 되다

※ 다음 영영풀이에 알맞은 단어를 <보기>에서 골라 쓴 후, 우리말 뜻을 쓰시오.

1 _____ : not long ago: _____

2 _____ : most recent and newest: _____

3 _____ : soft sided sports shoes: _____

4 _____ : to prevent something bad from happening: _____

5 _____ : to dislike something strongly: _____

6 _____ : words that are used in a language: _____

7 _____ : to have a different opinion: _____

8 _____ : the state or condition of worrying about something: _____

9 _____ : liked or enjoyed by a large number of people: _____

10 _____ : something that you do wrong without wanting to: _____

11 _____ : to show that something is true: _____

12 _____ : a person who is between the ages of 13 and 19: _____

13 _____ : to have same opinion as someone about a topic: _____

14 _____ : someone whose job it is to provide help and advice to people with problems:
      _____

15 _____ : a scientific test that is done in order to study what happens and to gain
      new knowledge: _____

16 _____ : to spend time resting or doing something enjoyable especially after you
      have been doing work: _____

보기			
prove	mistake	avoid	latest
relax	experiment	worry	hate
popular	teenager	recently	vocabulary
counselor	agree	disagree	sneakers

※ 다음 우리말과 일치하도록 빈칸에 알맞은 말을 쓰시오.

Listen & Speak 1 A Listen

1. **B:** I think _____ _____ music _____ you _____.
   G: I _____.
2. **G:** I think _____ history _____ _____ is _____.
   B: I agree. I _____ a lot _____ them.
3. **G:** Our school _____ is going to be a _____ of _____.
   B: I agree.
4. **B:** Our P.E. _____ is too _____. _____ you _____?
   G: No, I _____ agree. I don't think he's too _____.

Listen & Speak 1 A

1. **G:** Mom _____ me I could _____ the computer _____ _____ _____ _____ a _____. She thinks that's _____ time.
   M: I _____ _____ her.
   G: Sometimes, when _____ my homework, I _____ to use it _____ _____ _____ _____.
   M: Hmm. Then maybe we should all _____ _____ and _____ about it.
   G: Thanks _____ your _____, Dad.
2. **B:** I _____ talked _____ the science _____ with Jinho and Mina.
   G: Has your team _____ _____ you will _____?
   B: No, _____ yet. Jinho wants to _____ a science museum, but Mina _____ _____ do an _____.
   G: Who do you _____ _____, Jinho or Mina?
   B: I agree _____ Mina _____ I think the _____ would be more _____.

Listen & Speak 2 A Listen

1. **B:** I _____ a big soccer _____ tomorrow. I'm _____.
   G: _____ _____. I'm _____ you'll _____ very well.
2. **G:** I'm _____ about tomorrow's _____ _____.
   B: I'm _____ you'll _____ fine. Don't _____.
3. **G:** I'm _____ about making _____ at my new _____.
   M: _____ worry. I'm _____ you'll _____ a lot of _____ there.

해석

1. **B:** 나는 음악을 듣는 것이 긴장을 푸는 데 도움이 된다고 생각해.
   G: 나도 동의해.
2. **G:** 나는 역사 만화책을 읽는 것이 도움이 된다고 생각해.
   B: 나도 동의해. 나는 그것들로부터 많은 것을 배워.
3. **G:** 우리 학교 축제는 아주 재미있을 거야.
   B: 나도 동의해.
4. **B:** 우리 체육 선생님은 너무 엄격하셔. 너도 동의하지 않니?
   G: 응, 난 동의하지 않아. 나는 그가 너무 엄격하다고 생각하지 않아.

1. **G:** 엄마는 제가 하루에 한 시간만 컴퓨터를 사용할 수 있다고 말씀하셨어요. 그녀는 그게 충분한 시간이라고 생각하세요.
   M: 나도 그녀의 말에 동의한단다.
   G: 숙제를 할 때 그것을 오래 사용할 필요가 있어요.
   M: 음. 그러면 아마 우리는 다 같이 모여 그것에 대해 이야기를 해야 할 것 같구나.
   G: 이해해 줘서 고마워요. 아빠.
2. **B:** 나는 진호랑 미나랑 과학 프로젝트에 대해 방금 이야기했어.
   G: 너희 팀은 무엇을 할지 결정했니?
   B: 아니, 아직. 진호는 과학 박물관을 방문하고 싶어하지만, 미나는 실험을 하고 싶어해.
   G: 너는 진호나 미나 중에 누구에게 동의해?
   B: 나는 실험이 더 흥미로울 거라고 생각해서 미나의 말에 동의해.

1. **B:** 내일 큰 축구 경기가 있어. 긴장돼.
   G: 걱정하지 마. 난 네가 아주 잘 경기할 거라고 확신해.
2. **G:** 내일 있을 말하기 대회 때문에 긴장돼.
   B: 난 네가 잘할 거라고 확신해. 걱정하지 마.
3. **G:** 새 학교에서 친구를 사귀는 게 걱정돼요.
   M: 걱정하지 마. 난 네가 그곳에서 많은 친구들을 사귈 거라고 확신해.

Listen & Speak 2 A

1. B: You look _____. Is _____ _____?
   G: Yes, my sister is _____ _____ me.
   B: _____? What did you _____?
   G: I _____ _____ _____ her shirts _____ asking.
   B: Tell her you're _____. I'm sure she'll _____.

2. B: I'm _____ a hard time _____ new English words.
   G: I _____ the same problem, so I _____ my English _____
      _____ _____.
   B: _____ did he say?
   G: He _____ me to _____ an English _____ app. It has helped
      me a lot. I'm _____ it would _____ _____ you, too.

Real-Life Zone

B: The team _____ for English class is _____ a lot of time.
G: I _____. I have a problem. _____ _____ the _____ on
   our team isn't _____ his _____.
B: _____ not good. Everybody on the _____ has to do their job.
G: I _____, but I don't _____ _____ _____ _____ him
   _____ do his part.
B: Maybe he _____ know how to _____ _____ or doesn't
   _____ his _____.
G: Then _____ should I _____?
B: Talk _____ him. Ask him _____ he's not _____ his part.
   _____ tell him _____ help him _____ he _____.
G: Okay. I'll _____ that.
B: I'm _____ he'll do _____ _____ you _____ to him.
   Good luck _____ your _____.
G: Thanks.

Wrap Up

G: What's the _____, Dongha? You _____ _____.
B: I'm not _____ for the _____. I sit at my _____ to _____
   but end _____ doing _____ _____.
G: Well, time _____ is not _____.
B: I _____. What _____ I do?
G: _____ the things you _____ to do. _____ write
   how _____ time _____ _____ _____ each one.
B: Thank you, Emily. I'll _____ your idea.
G: I'm sure _____ will be _____ for you. Good _____
   your finals.

---

1. B: 걱정스러워 보여. 무슨 일 있니?
   G: 응, 우리 언니가 나한테 화가 났어.
   B: 왜? 무엇을 했니?
   G: 내가 묻지도 않고 언니의 셔츠 중에 하나를 입었어.
   B: 그녀에게 미안하다고 말해. 나는 그녀가 이해해 줄 거라고 확신해.

2. B: 나는 새로운 영어 단어를 배우는 데 어려움을 겪고 있어.
   G: 나도 같은 문제가 있어서 영어 선생님께 조언을 구했어.
   B: 그가 뭐라고 하셨어?
   G: 그는 나에게 영어 어휘 앱을 사용하라고 조언해 주셨어. 그것은 나에게 큰 도움이 됐어. 나는 그것이 너에게도 효과가 있을 거라고 확신해.

B: 영어 수업의 팀 프로젝트는 시간이 많이 걸려.
G: 나도 동의해. 나 문제가 있어. 우리 팀의 한 사람이 자기 역할을 다하지 않아.
B: 좋지 않네. 팀의 모든 사람들은 자신들의 일을 해야 해.
G: 알아. 하지만 어떻게 그가 그의 역할을 하게 할지 모르겠어.
B: 어쩌면 그는 시작하는 법을 모르거나 자기 역할을 좋아하지 않을 수도 있어.
G: 그러면 나는 무엇을 해야 할까?
B: 그에게 말해. 그에게 왜 자신의 역할을 안 하는지 물어봐. 그러고 나서 원한다면 네가 도와주겠다고 말해.
G: 그래. 한번 해 볼게.
B: 나는 네가 말하고 나면 그가 더 잘할 거라고 확신해. 네 프로젝트가 잘 되길 바랄게.
G: 고마워.

G: 동하야, 무슨 일이야? 걱정스러워 보여.
B: 기말고사 준비가 안 됐어. 나는 공부하기 위해 책상에 앉지만 결국 다른 것을 하게 돼.
G: 음, 시간 관리가 쉽지 않지.
B: 나도 동의해. 내가 어떻게 해야 할까?
G: 해야 할 일에 번호를 매겨. 그러고 나서 각 항목을 끝내는 데 필요한 시간을 적어 봐.
B: 고마워, 에밀리. 네 방안을 한번 해 볼게.
G: 나는 그것이 너에게 도움이 될 거라고 확신해. 기말고사 잘 보길 바랄게.

※ 다음 우리말에 맞도록 대화를 영어로 쓰시오.

Listen & Speak 1 A Listen

1. B: _____
   G: _____
2. G: _____
   B: _____
3. G: _____
   B: _____
4. B: _____
   G: _____

1. B: 나는 음악을 듣는 것이 긴장을 푸는 데 도움이 된다고 생각해.
   G: 나도 동의해.
2. G: 나는 역사 만화책을 읽는 것이 도움이 된다고 생각해.
   B: 나도 동의해. 나는 그것들로부터 많은 것을 배워.
3. G: 우리 학교 축제는 아주 재미있을 거야.
   B: 나도 동의해.
4. B: 우리 체육 선생님은 너무 엄격하셔. 너도 동의하지 않니?
   G: 응, 난 동의하지 않아. 나는 그가 너무 엄격하다고 생각하지 않아.

Listen & Speak 1 A

1. G: _____
   M: _____
   G: _____
   M: _____
   G: _____
2. B: _____
   G: _____
   B: _____
   _____
   G: _____
   B: _____

1. G: 엄마는 제가 하루에 한 시간만 컴퓨터를 사용할 수 있다고 말씀하셨어요. 그녀는 그게 충분한 시간이라고 생각하세요.
   M: 나도 그녀의 말에 동의한단다.
   G: 숙제를 할 때 그것을 오래 사용할 필요가 있어요.
   M: 음. 그러면 아마 우리는 다 같이 모여 그것에 대해 이야기를 해야 할 것 같구나.
   G: 이해해 줘서 고마워요. 아빠.
2. B: 나는 진호랑 미나랑 과학 프로젝트에 대해 방금 이야기했어.
   G: 너희 팀은 무엇을 할지 결정했니?
   B: 아니, 아직. 진호는 과학 박물관을 방문하고 싶어하지만, 미나는 실험을 하고 싶어해.
   G: 너는 진호나 미나 중에 누구에게 동의해?
   B: 나는 실험이 더 흥미로울 거라고 생각해서 미나의 말에 동의해.

Listen & Speak 2 A Listen

1. B: _____
   G: _____
2. G: _____
   B: _____
3. G: _____
   M: _____

1. B: 내일 큰 축구 경기가 있어. 긴장돼.
   G: 걱정하지 마. 난 네가 아주 잘 경기할 거라고 확신해.
2. G: 내일 있을 말하기 대회 때문에 긴장돼.
   B: 난 네가 잘할 거라고 확신해. 걱정하지 마.
3. G: 새 학교에서 친구를 사귀는 게 걱정돼요.
   M: 걱정하지 마. 난 네가 그곳에서 많은 친구들을 사귈 거라고 확신해.

Listen & Speak 2 A

1. B: _____
   G: _____
   B: _____
   G: _____
   B: _____

2. B: _____
   G: _____
   B: _____
   G: _____
   _____

Real-Life Zone

B: _____
G: _____
_____
B: _____
G: _____
B: _____
G: _____
B: _____
G: _____
B: _____
G: _____

Wrap Up

G: _____
B: _____
_____
G: _____
B: _____
G: _____
_____
B: _____
G: _____

1. B: 걱정스러워 보여. 무슨 일 있니?
   G: 응, 우리 언니가 나한테 화가 났어.
   B: 왜? 무엇을 했니?
   G: 내가 묻지도 않고 언니의 셔츠 중에 하나를 입었어.
   B: 그녀에게 미안하다고 말해. 나는 그녀가 이해해 줄 거라고 확신해.
2. B: 나는 새로운 영어 단어를 배우는 데 어려움을 겪고 있어.
   G: 나도 같은 문제가 있어서 영어 선생님께 조언을 구했어.
   B: 그가 뭐라고 하셨어?
   G: 그는 나에게 영어 어휘 앱을 사용하라고 조언해 주셨어. 그것은 나에게 큰 도움이 됐어. 나는 그것이 너에게도 효과가 있을 거라고 확신해.

B: 영어 수업의 팀 프로젝트는 시간이 많이 걸려.
G: 나도 동의해. 나 문제가 있어. 우리 팀의 한 사람이 자기 역할을 다하지 않아.
B: 좋지 않네. 팀의 모든 사람들은 자신들의 일을 해야 해.
G: 알아. 하지만 어떻게 그가 그의 역할을 하게 할지 모르겠어.
B: 어쩌면 그는 시작하는 법을 모르거나 자기 역할을 좋아하지 않을 수도 있어.
G: 그러면 나는 무엇을 해야 할까?
B: 그에게 말해. 그에게 왜 자신의 역할을 안 하는지 물어봐. 그러고 나서 원한다면 네가 도와주겠다고 말해.
G: 그래. 한번 해 볼게.
B: 나는 네가 말하고 나면 그가 더 잘할 거라고 확신해. 네 프로젝트가 잘 되길 바랄게.
G: 고마워.

G: 동하야, 무슨 일이야? 걱정스러워 보여.
B: 기말고사 준비가 안 됐어. 나는 공부하기 위해 책상에 앉지만 결국 다른 것을 하게 돼.
G: 음, 시간 관리가 쉽지 않지.
B: 나도 동의해. 내가 어떻게 해야 할까?
G: 해야 할 일에 번호를 매겨. 그러고 나서 각 항목을 끝내는 데 필요한 시간을 적어 봐.
B: 고마워, 에밀리. 네 방안을 한번 해 볼게.
G: 나는 그것이 너에게 도움이 될 거라고 확신해. 기말고사 잘 보길 바랄게.

※ 다음 우리말과 일치하도록 빈칸에 알맞은 것을 골라 쓰시오.

1 What _____ I _____?
A. Do   B. Should

2 _____ has _____.
A. worries   B. everyone

3 _____ you have _____ you _____ about, what do you do?
A. worry   B. things   C. when

4 _____ are some _____ that three _____ worry _____.
A. teenagers   B. here   C. about   D. things

5 Sohui thought Hayeon was her best friend, but now, Sohui feels that Hayeon _____ _____ and she _____ _____ her.
A. avoiding   B. has   C. is   D. changed

6 **Sohui:** (To her _____ sister) You know my friend Hayeon, _____ _____?
A. you   B. don't   C. older

7 **Sister:** Yeah. Why? _____ _____ her?
A. about   B. what

8 **Sohui:** I _____ she's _____ me.
A. avoiding   B. feel

9 When I see her at school, she _____ _____ and _____ _____ from me.
A. around   B. away   C. turns   D. walks

10 **Sister:** I'm _____ _____ _____ that.
A. to   B. hear   C. sorry

11 Do you have any idea _____ _____ _____ _____?
A. she   B. why   C. that   D. does

12 **Sohui:** No. I don't think I've _____ _____ _____.
A. anything   B. done   C. wrong

13 It just _____ _____ she _____ like me _____.
A. anymore   B. like   C. feels   D. doesn't

14 **Sister:** Maybe you _____ just ask her _____ there is _____.
A. if   B. wrong   C. something   D. should

15 **Sohui:** _____ I _____. I _____ want to be friends _____ her.
A. still   B. maybe   C. with   D. should

16 Daeho, _____ that new things will make him more _____, often wants new things _____ _____ his friends have them.
A. just   B. thinking   C. popular   D. because

17 **Daeho:** Seongjin, look _____ my _____ _____.
A. sneakers   B. at   C. new

18 _____ do you _____?
A. think   B. what

---

1 제가 어떻게 해야 할까요?

2 누구나 고민은 있습니다.

3 여러분은 걱정되는 것이 있을 때 무엇을 하나요?

4 여기 세 명의 청소년이 걱정하는 것들이 있습니다.

5 소희는 하연이가 그녀의 가장 친한 친구라고 생각했지만, 지금은 하연이가 변했고 그녀를 피한다고 느낍니다.

6 소희: (그녀의 언니에게) 내 친구 하연이 알지, 그렇지?

7 언니: 응. 왜? 그녀가 어떤데?

8 소희: 나는 그녀가 나를 피하고 있다고 느껴.

9 학교에서 내가 그녀를 볼 때 그녀는 돌아서서 나로부터 멀리 걸어가.

10 언니: 그거 참 안타깝구나.

11 너는 그녀가 왜 그렇게 하는지 아니?

12 소희: 아니. 나는 내가 잘못한 것이 있다고 생각하지 않아.

13 단지 그녀가 더 이상 나를 좋아하지 않는다고 느껴져.

14 언니: 혹시 모르니 뭔가 잘못된 것이 있는지 그녀에게 물어봐.

15 소희: 아마 그래야겠어. 나는 여전히 그녀와 친구로 지내고 싶거든.

16 대호는 새 물건이 그를 더 인기 있게 만들어 줄 것이라고 생각해서 단지 친구들이 그것을 가지고 있다는 이유로 종종 새 물건을 사기를 원합니다.

17 대호: 성진아, 내 새 운동화 봐.

18 어떠니?

19 **Seongjin:** They're nice, but _____ _____ just buy new sneakers a _____ _____ months ago?

    A. couple   B. you   C. of   D. didn't

20 **Daeho:** Yeah, but they're _____ _____ _____ _____ .

    A. style   B. no   C. in   D. longer

21 I _____ _____ in these, _____ ?

    A. look   B. right   C. cooler

22 **Seongjin:** Daeho, _____ the _____ fashion doesn't make you _____ or more _____ .

    A. latest   B. popular   C. wearing   D. cooler

23 People like you _____ _____ _____ , not because of your _____ .

    A. you're   B. clothes   C. you   D. because

24 **Daeho:** Yeah?

25 **Seongjin:** Listen, you're _____ _____ _____ .

    A. guy   B. great   C. a

26 You don't _____ new sneakers _____ it.

    A. prove   B. need   C. to

27 _____ , Minkyeong was _____ _____ by a boy in her _____ .

    A. class   B. asked   C. recently   D. out

28 She wants to _____ no _____ does not want to _____ his _____ .

    A. hurt   B. but   C. feelings   D. say

29 **Minkyeong:** I _____ your _____ .

    A. advice   B. need

30 A boy in my class _____ _____ _____ .

    A. me   B. asked   C. out

31 I like him, but _____ _____ I don't want to _____ _____ with him.

    A. now   B. out   C. for   D. go

32 I _____ _____ _____ _____ my studies.

    A. focus   B. need   C. on   D. to

33 What _____ I _____ ?

    A. do   B. should

34 **Counselor:** _____ _____ _____ tell him why you _____ go?

    A. don't   B. can't   C. why   D. you

35 **Minkyeong:** I'm _____ I might _____ his _____ .

    A. hurt   B. afraid   C. feelings

36 **Counselor:** If you don't tell him soon, he will _____ your feelings, and you may _____ _____ _____ him even more.

    A. end   B. misunderstand   C. hurting   D. up

37 **Minkyeong:** _____ you're _____ .

    A. right   B. maybe

38 _____ _____ the _____ .

    A. advice   B. thanks   C. for

---

19 성진: 멋지다. 그런데 너 겨우 몇 달 전에 새 운동화 사지 않았니?

20 대호: 응, 하지만 그건 더 이상 유행이 아니야.

21 이걸 신으니까 더 멋져 보이지, 그렇지?

22 성진: 대호야, 최신 유행하는 것을 입는 것이 너를 더 멋지고 더 인기 있게 만들어 주지는 않아.

23 사람들은 네가 너이기 때문에 너를 좋아하는 것이지, 네 옷 때문이 아니야.

24 대호: 그래?

25 성진: 들어봐. 너는 멋진 사람이야.

26 그것을 증명하기 위해 새 운동화가 필요하지 않아.

27 최근에 민경이는 그녀의 반 남자아이에게 데이트 신청을 받았습니다.

28 그녀는 거절하고 싶지만 그의 감정을 상하게 하고 싶지는 않습니다.

29 민경: 저는 선생님의 조언이 필요해요.

30 같은 반 남자아이가 저에게 데이트 신청을 했어요.

31 저는 그를 좋아하지만 당분간은 그와 데이트하고 싶지 않아요.

32 저는 공부에 집중해야 해요.

33 제가 어떻게 해야 할까요?

34 상담 선생님: 왜 네가 데이트를 할 수 없는지 그에게 말하는 것은 어떨까?

35 민경: 제가 그의 감정을 상하게 할까 봐 걱정돼요.

36 상담 선생님: 네가 그에게 빨리 말하지 않으면, 그는 네 감정을 오해할 것이고, 너는 그를 더 아프게 할 수도 있단다.

37 민경: 선생님 말씀이 맞는 것 같아요.

38 조언 감사합니다.

※ 다음 우리말과 일치하도록 빈칸에 알맞은 말을 쓰시오.

1 _____ _____ I Do?

2 Everyone _____ _____.

3 When you have things you _____ about, _____ _____ _____ _____?

4 _____ _____ _____ _____ _____ _____ that three teenagers _____ _____.

5 Sohui thought Hayeon was _____ _____ _____, but now, Sohui feels that Hayeon _____ _____ and she _____ _____ her.

6 Sohui: (To her _____ sister) You know my friend Hayeon, _____ _____?

7 Sister: Yeah. Why? _____ _____ her?

8 Sohui: _____ _____ she's _____ me.

9 When I see her at school, she _____ _____ and _____ _____ _____ me.

10 Sister: I'm sorry _____ _____ _____.

11 Do you have any idea _____ _____ _____ _____ _____?

12 Sohui: No. I don't think _____ _____ _____ _____.

13 It just _____ _____ she _____ like me _____.

14 Sister: _____ you _____ just ask her _____ there is _____ _____.

15 Sohui: Maybe I should. I _____ want to be friends _____ her.

16 Daeho, _____ that new things will _____ him more _____, often wants new things _____ _____ his friends have them.

17 Daeho: Seongjin, _____ _____ my _____ _____.

18 _____ do you _____?

---

1 제가 어떻게 해야 할까요?

2 누구나 고민은 있습니다.

3 여러분은 걱정되는 것이 있을 때 무엇을 하나요?

4 여기 세 명의 청소년이 걱정하는 것들이 있습니다.

5 소희는 하연이가 그녀의 가장 친한 친구라고 생각했지만, 지금은 하연이가 변했고 그녀를 피한다고 느낍니다.

6 소희: (그녀의 언니에게) 내 친구 하연이 알지, 그렇지?

7 언니: 응. 왜? 그녀가 어떤데?

8 소희: 나는 그녀가 나를 피하고 있다고 느껴.

9 학교에서 내가 그녀를 볼 때 그녀는 돌아서서 나로부터 멀리 걸어가.

10 언니: 그거 참 안타깝구나.

11 너는 그녀가 왜 그렇게 하는지 아니?

12 소희: 아니. 나는 내가 잘못한 것이 있다고 생각하지 않아.

13 단지 그녀가 더 이상 나를 좋아하지 않는다고 느껴져.

14 언니: 혹시 모르니 뭔가 잘못된 것이 있는지 그녀에게 물어봐.

15 소희: 아마 그래야겠어. 나는 여전히 그녀와 친구로 지내고 싶거든.

16 대호는 새 물건이 그를 더 인기 있게 만들어 줄 것이라고 생각해서 단지 친구들이 그것을 가지고 있다는 이유로 종종 새 물건을 사기를 원합니다.

17 대호: 성진아, 내 새 운동화 봐.

18 어떠니?

19 **Seongjin:** They're nice, but _____ _____ just buy new sneakers a _____ _____ _____ _____?

20 **Daeho:** Yeah, but they're _____ _____ _____ _____.

21 I look _____ _____ _____, right?

22 **Seongjin:** Daeho, _____ the _____ _____ doesn't make you _____ or _____ _____.

23 People like you _____ _____ _____, not _____ _____ your clothes.

24 **Daeho:** Yeah?

25 **Seongjin:** Listen, you're _____ _____ _____.

26 You don't need new sneakers _____ _____ _____.

27 Recently, Minkyeong _____ _____ _____ by a boy in her class.

28 She wants to say no but does not want _____ _____ _____ _____.

29 **Minkyeong:** I _____ your _____.

30 A boy in my class _____ _____ _____.

31 I like him, but _____ _____ I don't want to _____ _____ _____ him.

32 I need to _____ _____ my _____.

33 What _____ I do?

34 **Counselor:** _____ _____ _____ tell him why you _____ _____?

35 **Minkyeong:** _____ _____ I _____ _____ his feelings.

36 **Counselor:** _____ _____ _____ _____ him soon, he will _____ your feelings, and you may _____ _____ _____ him even more.

37 **Minkyeong:** Maybe _____ _____.

38 _____ _____ the _____.

---

19 성진: 멋지다. 그런데 너 겨우 몇 달 전에 새 운동화 사지 않았니?

20 대호: 응, 하지만 그건 더 이상 유행이 아니야.

21 이걸 신으니까 더 멋져 보이지, 그렇지?

22 성진: 대호야. 최신 유행하는 것을 입는 것이 너를 더 멋지고 더 인기 있게 만들어 주지는 않아.

23 사람들은 네가 너이기 때문에 너를 좋아하는 것이지, 네 옷 때문이 아니야.

24 대호: 그래?

25 성진: 들어봐. 너는 멋진 사람이야.

26 그것을 증명하기 위해 새 운동화가 필요하지 않아.

27 최근에 민경이는 그녀의 반 남자아이에게 데이트 신청을 받았습니다.

28 그녀는 거절하고 싶지만 그의 감정을 상하게 하고 싶지는 않습니다.

29 민경: 저는 선생님의 조언이 필요해요.

30 같은 반 남자아이가 저에게 데이트 신청을 했어요.

31 저는 그를 좋아하지만 당분간은 그와 데이트하고 싶지 않아요.

32 저는 공부에 집중해야 해요.

33 제가 어떻게 해야 할까요?

34 상담 선생님: 왜 네가 데이트를 할 수 없는지 그에게 말하는 것은 어떨까?

35 민경: 제가 그의 감정을 상하게 할까 봐 걱정돼요.

36 상담 선생님: 네가 그에게 빨리 말하지 않으면, 그는 네 감정을 오해할 것이고, 너는 그를 더 아프게 할 수도 있단다.

37 민경: 선생님 말씀이 맞는 것 같아요.

38 조언 감사합니다.

※ 다음 문장을 우리말로 쓰시오.

1 What Should I Do?
➡ _____

2 Everyone has worries.
➡ _____

3 When you have things you worry about, what do you do?
➡ _____

4 Here are some things that three teenagers worry about.
➡ _____

5 Sohui thought Hayeon was her best friend, but now, Sohui feels that Hayeon has changed and she is avoiding her.
➡ _____

6 Sohui: (To her older sister) You know my friend Hayeon, don't you?
➡ _____

7 Sister: Yeah. Why? What about her?
➡ _____

8 Sohui: I feel she's avoiding me.
➡ _____

9 When I see her at school, she turns around and walks away from me.
➡ _____

10 Sister: I'm sorry to hear that.
➡ _____

11 Do you have any idea why she does that?
➡ _____

12 Sohui: No. I don't think I've done anything wrong.
➡ _____

13 It just feels like she doesn't like me anymore.
➡ _____

14 Sister: Maybe you should just ask her if there is something wrong.
➡ _____

15 Sohui: Maybe I should. I still want to be friends with her.
➡ _____

16 Daeho, thinking that new things will make him more popular, often wants new things just because his friends have them.
➡ _____
_____

17 Daeho: Seongjin, look at my new sneakers.
➡ _____

18 What do you think?
➡ _____

19 Seongjin: They're nice, but didn't you just buy new sneakers a couple of months ago?

➡ _____

20 Daeho: Yeah, but they're no longer in style.

➡ _____

21 I look cooler in these, right?

➡ _____

22 Seongjin: Daeho, wearing the latest fashion doesn't make you cooler or more popular.

➡ _____

23 People like you because you're you, not because of your clothes.

➡ _____

24 Daeho: Yeah?

➡ _____

25 Seongjin: Listen, you're a great guy.

➡ _____

26 You don't need new sneakers to prove it.

➡ _____

27 Recently, Minkyeong was asked out by a boy in her class.

➡ _____

28 She wants to say no but does not want to hurt his feelings.

➡ _____

29 Minkyeong: I need your advice.

➡ _____

30 A boy in my class asked me out.

➡ _____

31 I like him, but for now I don't want to go out with him.

➡ _____

32 I need to focus on my studies.

➡ _____

33 What should I do?

➡ _____

34 Counselor: Why don't you tell him why you can't go?

➡ _____

35 Minkyeong: I'm afraid I might hurt his feelings.

➡ _____

36 Counselor: If you don't tell him soon, he will misunderstand your feelings, and you may end up hurting him even more.

➡ _____

37 Minkyeong: Maybe you're right.

➡ _____

38 Thanks for the advice.

➡ _____

※ 다음 괄호 안의 단어들을 우리말에 맞도록 바르게 배열하시오.

1 (Should / What / Do? / I)

➡ _____

2 (has / everyone / worries.)

➡ _____

3 (you / when / things / have / worry / you / about, / do / what / do? / you)

➡ _____

4 (are / here / things / some / three / that / teenagers / about. / worry)

➡ _____

5 (thought / Sohui / was / Hayeon / best / her / friend, / now, / but / feels / Sohui / that / has / Hayeon / changed / she / and / is / her. / avoiding)

➡ _____
_____

6 (Sohui: / her / (to / sister) / older // know / you / friend / my / Hayeon, / you? / don't)

➡ _____

7 (Sister: / yeah. // why? // about / her? / what)

➡ _____

8 (Sohui: / feel / I / avoiding / she's / me.)

➡ _____

9 (I / when / her / see / school, / at / turns / she / and / around / walks / from / away / me.)

➡ _____

10 (Sister: / sorry / I'm / hear / to / that.)

➡ _____

11 (you / do / have / idea / any / she / why / that? / does)

➡ _____

12 (Sohui: / no. // don't / I / I've / think / anything / done / wrong.)

➡ _____

13 (just / it / like / feels / doesn't / she / like / anymore. / me)

➡ _____

14 (Sister: / you / maybe / just / should / her / ask / there / if / something / is / wrong.)

➡ _____

15 (Sohui: / I / maybe / should. // still / I / to / want / friends / be / her. / with)

➡ _____

1 제가 어떻게 해야 할까요?

2 누구나 고민은 있습니다.

3 여러분은 걱정되는 것이 있을 때 무엇을 하나요?

4 여기 세 명의 청소년이 걱정하는 것들이 있습니다.

5 소희는 하연이가 그녀의 가장 친한 친구라고 생각했지만, 지금은 하연이가 변했고 그녀를 피한다고 느낍니다.

6 소희: (그녀의 언니에게) 내 친구 하연이 알지, 그렇지?

7 언니: 응. 왜? 그녀가 어떤데?

8 소희: 나는 그녀가 나를 피하고 있다고 느껴.

9 학교에서 내가 그녀를 볼 때 그녀는 돌아서서 나로부터 멀리 걸어가.

10 언니: 그거 참 안타깝구나.

11 너는 그녀가 왜 그렇게 하는지 아니?

12 소희: 아니. 나는 내가 잘못한 것이 있다고 생각하지 않아.

13 단지 그녀가 더 이상 나를 좋아하지 않는다고 느껴져.

14 언니: 혹시 모르니 뭔가 잘못된 것이 있는지 그녀에게 물어봐.

15 소희: 아마 그래야겠어. 나는 여전히 그녀와 친구로 지내고 싶거든.

16 (thinking / Daeho, / new / that / will / things / him / make / popular, / more / wants / often / things / new / because / just / friends / his / them. / have)

➡ _____

_____

17 (Daeho: / look / Seongjin, / my / at / sneakers. / new)

➡ _____

18 (do / what / think? / you)

➡ _____

19 (Seongjin: / nice, / they're / didn't / but / just / you / new / buy / a / sneakers / couple / months / of / ago?)

➡ _____

_____

20 (Daeho: / but / yeah, / they're / longer / no / stlye. / in)

➡ _____

21 (look / I / cooler / these, / in / right?)

➡ _____

22 (Seongjin: / wearing / Daeho, / the / fashion / latest / make / doesn't / cooler / you / more / or / popular.)

➡ _____

_____

23 (like / people / you / you're / because / you, / because / not / of / clothes. / your)

➡ _____

_____

24 (Yeah? / Daeho:)

➡ _____

25 (Seongjin: / you're / listen / guy. / great / a)

➡ _____

26 (don't / you / new / need / to / sneakers / it. / prove)

➡ _____

27 (Minkyeong / recently, / asked / was / by / out / boy / a / in / class. / her)

➡ _____

28 (wants / she / say / to / but / no / not / does / to / want / his / hurt / feelings.)

➡ _____

_____

29 (Minkyeong: / need / I / advice. / your)

➡ _____

16 대호는 새 물건이 그를 더 인기 있게 만들어 줄 것이라고 생각해서 단지 친구들이 그것을 가지고 있다는 이유로 종종 새 물건을 사기를 원합니다.

17 대호: 성진아, 내 새 운동화 봐.

18 어떠니?

19 성진: 멋지다. 그런데 너 겨우 몇 달 전에 새 운동화 사지 않았니?

20 대호: 응, 하지만 그건 더 이상 유행이 아니야.

21 이걸 신으니까 더 멋져 보이지. 그렇지?

22 성진: 대호야, 최신 유행하는 것을 입는 것이 너를 더 멋지고 더 인기 있게 만들어 주지는 않아.

23 사람들은 네가 너이기 때문에 너를 좋아하는 것이지, 네 옷 때문이 아니야.

24 대호: 그래?

25 성진: 들어봐. 너는 멋진 사람이야.

26 그것을 증명하기 위해 새 운동화가 필요하지 않아.

27 최근에 민경이는 그녀의 반 남자아이에게 데이트 신청을 받았습니다.

28 그녀는 거절하고 싶지만 그의 감정을 상하게 하고 싶지는 않습니다.

29 민경: 저는 선생님의 조언이 필요해요.

30 (boy / a / my / in / asked / class / out. / me)

➡ _____

31 (like / I / him, / for / but / I / now / want / don't / to / go / with / out / him.)

➡ _____

32 (need / I / focus / to / on / studies. / my)

➡ _____

33 (should / what / do? / I)

➡ _____

34 (Counselor: / don't / why / tell / you / why / him / can't / you / go?)

➡ _____

35 (Minkyeong: / afraid / I'm / might / I / his / hurt / feelings.)

➡ _____

36 (Counselor: / you / if / tell / don't / soon, / him / will / he / misunderstand / feelings, / your / and / may / you / up / end / him / hurting / more. / even)

➡ _____

➡ _____

37 (Minkyeong: / you're / maybe / right.)

➡ _____

38 (for / thanks / advice. / the)

➡ _____

30 같은 반 남자아이가 저에게 데이트 신청을 했어요.

31 저는 그를 좋아하지만 당분간은 그와 데이트하고 싶지 않아요.

32 저는 공부에 집중해야 해요.

33 제가 어떻게 해야 할까요?

34 상담 선생님: 왜 네가 데이트를 할 수 없는지 그에게 말하는 것은 어떨까?

35 민경: 제가 그의 감정을 상하게 할까 봐 걱정돼요.

36 상담 선생님: 네가 그에게 빨리 말하지 않으면, 그는 네 감정을 오해할 것이고, 너는 그를 더 아프게 할 수도 있단다.

37 민경: 선생님 말씀이 맞는 것 같아요.

38 조언 감사합니다.

※ 다음 우리말을 영어로 쓰시오.

1 제가 어떻게 해야 할까요?

➡ _____

2 누구나 고민은 있습니다.

➡ _____

3 여러분은 걱정되는 것이 있을 때 무엇을 하나요?

➡ _____

4 여기 세 명의 청소년이 걱정하는 것들이 있습니다.

➡ _____

5 소희는 하연이가 그녀의 가장 친한 친구라고 생각했지만, 지금은 하연이가 변했고 그녀를 피한다고 느낍니다.

➡ _____

➡ _____

6 소희: (그녀의 언니에게) 내 친구 하연이 알지, 그렇지?

➡ _____

7 언니: 응. 왜? 그녀가 어떤데?

➡ _____

8 소희: 나는 그녀가 나를 피하고 있다고 느껴.

➡ _____

9 학교에서 내가 그녀를 볼 때 그녀는 돌아서서 나로부터 멀리 걸어가.

➡ _____

10 언니: 그거 참 안타깝구나.

➡ _____

11 너는 그녀가 왜 그렇게 하는지 아니?

➡ _____

12 소희: 아니. 나는 내가 잘못한 것이 있다고 생각하지 않아.

➡ _____

13 단지 그녀가 더 이상 나를 좋아하지 않는다고 느껴져.

➡ _____

14 언니: 혹시 모르니 뭔가 잘못된 것이 있는지 그녀에게 물어봐.

➡ _____

15 소희: 아마 그래야겠어. 나는 여전히 그녀와 친구로 지내고 싶거든.

➡ _____

16 대호는 새 물건이 그를 더 인기 있게 만들어 줄 것이라고 생각해서 단지 친구들이 그것을 가지고 있다는 이유로 종종 새 물건을 사기를 원합니다.

➡ _____

➡ _____

17 대호: 성진아, 내 새 운동화 봐.

➡ _____

18 어떠니?

➡ _____

19 성진: 멋지다, 그런데 너 겨우 몇 달 전에 새 운동화 사지 않았니?
➡ _____

20 대호: 응, 하지만 그건 더 이상 유행이 아니야.
➡ _____

21 이걸 신으니까 더 멋져 보이지, 그렇지?
➡ _____

22 성진: 대호야, 최신 유행하는 것을 입는 것이 너를 더 멋지고 더 인기 있게 만들어 주지는 않아.
➡ _____

23 사람들은 네가 너이기 때문에 너를 좋아하는 것이지, 네 옷 때문이 아니야.
➡ _____

24 대호: 그래?
➡ _____

25 성진: 들어봐. 너는 멋진 사람이야.
➡ _____

26 그것을 증명하기 위해 새 운동화가 필요하지 않아.
➡ _____

27 최근에 민경이는 그녀의 반 남자아이에게 데이트 신청을 받았습니다.
➡ _____

28 그녀는 거절하고 싶지만 그의 감정을 상하게 하고 싶지는 않습니다.
➡ _____

29 민경: 저는 선생님의 조언이 필요해요.
➡ _____

30 같은 반 남자아이가 저에게 데이트 신청을 했어요.
➡ _____

31 저는 그를 좋아하지만 당분간은 그와 데이트하고 싶지 않아요.
➡ _____

32 저는 공부에 집중해야 해요.
➡ _____

33 제가 어떻게 해야 할까요?
➡ _____

34 상담 선생님: 왜 네가 데이트를 할 수 없는지 그에게 말하는 것은 어떨까?
➡ _____

35 민경: 제가 그의 감정을 상하게 할까 봐 걱정돼요
➡ _____

36 상담 선생님: 네가 그에게 빨리 말하지 않으면, 그는 네 감정을 오해할 것이고, 너는 그를 더 아프게 할 수도 있단다.
➡ _____
_____

37 민경: 선생님 말씀이 맞는 것 같아요.
➡ _____

38 조언 감사합니다.
➡ _____

※ 다음 우리말과 일치하도록 빈칸에 알맞은 말을 쓰시오.

Communication Task

1. A: _____ _____ school _____ _____ _____ in the morning.

2. B: I _____ _____ you. We can _____ _____ _____ _____ school starts _____.

3. A: I think school _____ _____ _____ in the morning.

4. B: I _____ _____ _____ you. School _____ _____ _____ if it starts later.

Writing Workshop

Hena's World

1. I want to _____ _____. I do not feel good _____ _____ _____ in the group.

2. I'd _____ _____ _____ _____ _____ I can _____ _____.

tallboy1201

3. I heard you _____ _____ if you _____ _____ _____ _____.

4. I _____ you eat _____ _____ _____ _____, milk, and beans.

5. These foods, _____ _____ _____ _____ _____ and _____, can _____ you _____ _____.

6. _____, you should sleep _____ _____ _____ _____ every night.

7. I hope these tips _____ _____ _____ _____ _____ you.

After You Read B

1. I _____ _____ my best friend _____ _____.

2. _____ _____ _____ ask her if there is _____ _____?

3. I need _____ _____. They'll _____ me _____ _____.

4. People like you _____ _____ _____ _____, not _____ _____ _____.

5. How can I say _____ _____ _____ _____ _____ _____?

6. _____ _____ you tell him _____ _____ _____ _____?

1. A: 나는 학교가 아침에 더 늦게 시작해야 한다고 생각해.
2. B: 나도 네 말에 동의해. 학교가 늦게 시작하면 우리는 더 많이 잠을 잘 수 있어.
3. A: 나는 학교가 아침에 더 늦게 시작해야 한다고 생각해.
4. B: 나는 동의하지 않아. 학교가 늦게 시작하면 더 늦게 끝날 거야.

Hena의 세계
1. 나는 키가 더 크고 싶어. 나는 그룹에서 키가 가장 작아서 기분이 안 좋아.
2. 나는 내가 키가 더 클 수 있는 방법을 알고 싶어.
tallboy1201
3. 나는 네가 키가 더 클 수 있는지 궁금해한다고 들었어.
4. 나는 네가 달걀, 우유, 콩 같은 음식을 먹을 것을 제안해.
5. 이 음식들은 많은 단백질과 칼슘을 갖고 있어서 네가 키가 더 크는 것을 도와줄 수 있어.
6. 또한 너는 매일 밤 적어도 8시간을 자야 해.
7. 이 조언들이 네게 도움이 되기를 바라.

1. 내 가장 친한 친구가 나를 피하고 있다고 느껴.
2. 뭔가 잘못된 것이 있는지 그녀에게 물어보는 게 어때?
3. 나는 새 옷이 필요해. 그것들은 나를 더 인기 있게 만들어 줄 거야.
4. 사람들은 네가 너이기 때문에 너를 좋아하는 것이지, 네 옷 때문이 아니야.
5. 어떻게 그의 감정을 상하게 하지 않으면서 거절할 수 있을까?
6. 왜 네가 데이트를 할 수 없는지 그에게 말하는 것은 어떨까?

※ 다음 우리말을 영어로 쓰시오.

Communication Task

1. A: 나는 학교가 아침에 더 늦게 시작해야 한다고 생각해.
   ➡ _____

2. B: 나도 네 말에 동의해. 학교가 늦게 시작하면 우리는 더 많이 잠을 잘 수 있어.
   ➡ _____

3. A: 나는 학교가 아침에 더 늦게 시작해야 한다고 생각해.
   ➡ _____

4. B: 나는 동의하지 않아. 학교가 늦게 시작하면 더 늦게 끝날 거야.
   ➡ _____

Writing Workshop

Hena의 세계
1. 나는 키가 더 크고 싶어. 나는 그룹에서 가장 키가 작아서 기분이 안 좋아.
   ➡ _____

2. 내가 키가 더 클 수 있는 방법을 알고 싶어.
   ➡ _____

tallboy1201
3. 나는 네가 키가 더 클 수 있는지 궁금해한다고 들었어.
   ➡ _____

4. 나는 네가 달걀, 우유, 콩 같은 음식을 먹을 것을 제안해.
   ➡ _____

5. 이 음식들은 많은 단백질과 칼슘을 갖고 있어서 네가 키가 더 크는 것을 도와줄 수 있어.
   ➡ _____

6. 또한 너는 매일 밤 적어도 8시간을 자야 해.
   ➡ _____

7. 이 조언들이 네게 도움이 되기를 바라.
   ➡ _____

After You Read B

1. 내 가장 친한 친구가 나를 피하고 있다고 느껴.
   ➡ _____

2. 뭔가 잘못된 것이 있는지 그녀에게 물어보는 게 어때?
   ➡ _____

3. 나는 새 옷이 필요해. 그것들은 나를 더 인기 있게 만들어 줄 거야.
   ➡ _____

4. 사람들은 네가 너이기 때문에 너를 좋아하는 것이지, 네 옷 때문이 아니야.
   ➡ _____

5. 어떻게 그의 감정을 상하게 하지 않으면서 거절할 수 있을까?
   ➡ _____

6. 왜 네가 데이트를 할 수 없는지 그에게 말하는 것은 어떨까?
   ➡ _____

※ 다음 영어를 우리말로 쓰시오.

01 benefit _____

02 moreover _____

03 calming _____

04 nature-friendly _____

05 regret _____

06 produce _____

07 avoid _____

08 finally _____

09 blanket _____

10 flight _____

11 grade _____

12 regularly _____

13 brain _____

14 fortunately _____

15 calcium _____

16 journal _____

17 serotonin _____

18 wet _____

19 sunscreen _____

20 mood _____

21 properly _____

22 shine _____

23 protect _____

24 already _____

25 skin _____

26 weather _____

27 outdoors _____

28 peak _____

29 review _____

30 safely _____

31 direct _____

32 effect _____

33 bone _____

34 healthy _____

35 put on _____

36 keep ~ in mind _____

37 both A and B _____

38 full of _____

39 stay up _____

40 should have p.p. _____

41 put out _____

42 too ~ to ... _____

43 be good for _____

※ 다음 우리말을 영어로 쓰시오.

01	이미		22	날씨	
02	흥미롭게도		23	일지, 일기	
03	이득; 이득을 보다		24	뼈	
04	게다가		25	기분, 감정	
05	건강한		26	절정의, 최고조의	
06	진정시키는		27	만들어 내다	
07	햇살		28	후회하다	
08	자연친화적인		29	규칙적으로	
09	야외에서		30	역할	
10	피부		31	젖은	
11	피하다		32	제대로	
12	항공편, 비행		33	보호하다	
13	이불, 담요		34	안전하게	
14	다행스럽게도		35	~로 가득 찬	
15	점검하다		36	착용하다, 바르다	
16	걸다		37	~에 유익하다	
17	복습하다		38	제시간에	
18	뇌		39	A와 B 둘 다	
19	마침내		40	내놓다	
20	햇볕, 햇빛		41	깨어 있다	
21	효과		42	~을 명심하다	
			43	인터넷 검색을 하다	

※ 다음 영영풀이에 알맞은 단어를 <보기>에서 골라 쓴 후, 우리말 뜻을 쓰시오.

1 _____ : the highest point: _____

2 _____ : a temporary state of mind: _____

3 _____ : light and heat from the sun: _____

4 _____ : to take advantages from something: _____

5 _____ : to become higher or greater: _____

6 _____ : to study or look at something again: _____

7 _____ : the part assumed to be played by a person: _____

8 _____ : the outer layer of a person's or animal's body: _____

9 _____ : covered or touched with water or another liquid: _____

10 _____ : a large piece of cloth used as a covering for warmth: _____

11 _____ : to produce or reflect light: _____

12 _____ : at the same time every day, week, month, or year: _____

13 _____ : the organ inside the head that control movements and feelings: _____

14 _____ : the hard part of the body that forms a framework inside people or animals: _____

15 _____ : a book in which people regularly write about what has happened to them: _____

16 _____ : to make sure that someone or something is not harmed, injured, damaged, etc.: _____

<보기>

journal	peak	brain	go up
shine	blanket	mood	benefit
protect	regularly	review	skin
role	bone	sunshine	wet

※ 다음 우리말과 일치하도록 빈칸에 알맞은 말을 쓰시오.

Listen & Speak 1 Listen

1. **G:** How _____ we _____ _____?

   B: _____, it's _____ _____ _____ a good _____.

2. **B:** _____ can we _____ _____ _____ good _____?

   G: It's _____ to _____ every day.

3. **G:** I _____ it's important to _____ a _____ after reading.

   B: I agree.

4. **B:** It's important _____ _____ _____ what you _____ your money _____.

   G: I _____ so, _____.

Listen & Speak 1 A

1. **B:** _____ did you _____ on the _____?

   G: I _____ tennis. I have _____ _____ _____ on the weekend _____ my health.

   B: Good for _____. It's _____ to _____ _____.

   G: _____. How _____ _____ tennis _____ me?

   B: Why _____?

2. **M:** John, you are _____ again.

   B: I'm sorry. I _____ the _____ _____.

   M: I _____ you need to _____ home a little _____.

   B: I think so, _____. Next time I _____ _____ _____.

   M: It's important to _____ at school _____ _____.

Listen & Speak 2

1. **G:** Your bag is _____ small.

   B: Yes. I _____ _____ _____ a bigger _____.

2. **G:** Aren't you _____?

   B: Yes. I _____ _____ _____ a jacket.

3. **B:** We _____ our _____.

   G: Oh, no. We should _____ come _____.

4. **G:** _____ _____ my face. I _____ _____ _____ _____ some sunscreen.

   B: Yes. You're _____.

해석

1. **G:** 우리는 어떻게 건강을 유지할 수 있을까?
   B: 음, 든든한 아침 식사를 하는 것이 중요해.
2. **B:** 좋은 점수를 받기 위해 우리는 무엇을 할 수 있을까?
   G: 매일 복습하는 것이 중요해.
3. **G:** 나는 독서 후에 일기를 쓰는 것이 중요하다고 생각해.
   B: 나도 동의해.
4. **B:** 네가 돈을 어디에 썼는지 적는 것은 중요해.
   G: 나도 그렇게 생각해.

1. **B:** 주말에 뭐 했니?
   G: 나는 테니스를 쳤어. 나는 건강을 위해 주말에 운동을 하기로 결정했어.
   B: 잘했어. 규칙적으로 운동하는 것은 중요해.
   G: 맞아. 나와 테니스 치는 것은 어때?
   B: 왜 안 되겠어?
2. **M:** 존, 또 지각이구나!
   B: 죄송해요. 버스를 잘못 탔어요.
   M: 나는 네가 집에서 좀 더 빨리 출발할 필요가 있다고 생각한단다.
   B: 저도 그렇게 생각해요. 다음번에는 늦지 않을 게요.
   M: 학교에 제시간에 오는 것은 중요하단다.

1. **G:** 네 가방은 정말 작아.
   B: 응. 난 더 큰 것을 가져왔어야 했어.
2. **G:** 춥지 않니?
   B: 응. 나는 재킷을 입었어야 했어.
3. **B:** 우리 비행기를 놓쳤어.
   G: 오, 안 돼. 우리는 더 빨리 왔어야 했어.
4. **G:** 내 얼굴 좀 봐. 나는 자외선 차단제를 발랐어야 했어.
   B: 그래. 네 말이 맞아.

Listen & Speak 2 A

1. **B:** Mina, _____ was the _____?
   G: I didn't _____ it. It _____ _____.
   B: _____ was bad _____ it?
   G: I already _____ the _____. I shouldn't _____ read about it _____ _____ it.
   B: Oh, I'm _____ you didn't _____ it.

2. **B:** We _____ have 30 _____ to go _____ we reach the _____ of the mountain. Let's _____ _____ over there _____ have a _____.
   G: Oh, I _____ only water. I should have _____ some snacks.
   B: That's _____. I _____ a lot. We can _____.
   G: I'll _____ it in _____ to bring _____ snacks next _____.

Real-Life Zone

G: Ben, you _____ full of _____ today!
B: Do I? Maybe that's _____ I finally _____ a good night's sleep _____ night.
G: Why? Don't you _____ get _____ _____?
B: No, I _____ it's really _____ to get a good _____ sleep, but I _____ _____ _____ late _____ the Internet or _____ _____ my _____.
G: That _____ _____ to _____ too.
B: _____ I do that, I _____ it the next _____ and say, "I should _____ gone to bed _____ last night."
G: How was yesterday _____?
B: Well, yesterday afternoon I _____ the mountain with my _____. I was really _____ when I got _____. I went to _____ right _____ I _____ _____ _____.
G: _____ activities _____ a great _____ _____ _____ you _____ a good night's sleep.

Wrap Up 1

W: Oh, your _____ is _____ from the rain! I _____ _____ _____ the weather.
B: Did you _____ it?
W: No. I just _____ it _____ in the _____ this morning.
B: _____ didn't you _____ it?
W: Hanging a _____ in the sun is a nature-friendly _____ to _____ the blanket _____.
B: Oh, I didn't _____ that. I'll _____ that.
W: And it's also _____ to _____ to do it _____.

※ 다음 우리말에 맞도록 대화를 영어로 쓰시오.

Listen & Speak 1 Listen

1. G: _____

   B: _____

2. B: _____

   G: _____

3. G: _____

   B: _____

4. B: _____

   G: _____

Listen & Speak 1 A

1. B: _____

   G: _____

   B: _____

   G: _____

   B: _____

2. M: _____

   B: _____

   M: _____

   B: _____

   M: _____

Listen & Speak 2

1. G: _____

   B: _____

2. G: _____

   B: _____

3. B: _____

   G: _____

4. G: _____

   B: _____

 해석

1. G: 우리는 어떻게 건강을 유지할 수 있을까?
   B: 음, 든든한 아침 식사를 하는 것이 중요해.
2. B: 좋은 점수를 받기 위해 우리는 무엇을 할 수 있을까?
   G: 매일 복습하는 것이 중요해.
3. G: 나는 독서 후에 일기를 쓰는 것이 중요하다고 생각해.
   B: 나도 동의해.
4. B: 네가 돈을 어디에 썼는지 적는 것은 중요해.
   G: 나도 그렇게 생각해.

1. B: 주말에 뭐 했니?
   G: 나는 테니스를 쳤어. 나는 건강을 위해 주말에 운동을 하기로 결정했어.
   B: 잘했어. 규칙적으로 운동하는 것은 중요해.
   G: 맞아. 나와 테니스 치는 것은 어때?
   B: 왜 안 되겠어?
2. M: 존, 또 지각이구나!
   B: 죄송해요. 버스를 잘못 탔어요.
   M: 나는 네가 집에서 좀 더 빨리 출발할 필요가 있다고 생각한단다.
   B: 저도 그렇게 생각해요. 다음번에는 늦지 않을 게요.
   M: 학교에 제시간에 오는 것은 중요하단다.

1. G: 네 가방은 정말 작아.
   B: 응. 난 더 큰 것을 가져왔어야 했어.
2. G: 춥지 않니?
   B: 응. 나는 재킷을 입었어야 했어.
3. B: 우리 비행기를 놓쳤어.
   G: 오, 안 돼. 우리는 더 빨리 왔어야 했어.
4. G: 내 얼굴 좀 봐. 나는 자외선 차단제를 발랐어야 했어.
   B: 그래. 네 말이 맞아.

Listen & Speak 2 A

1. B: _____
   G: _____
   B: _____
   G: _____
   B: _____
2. B: _____
   _____
   G: _____
   B: _____
   G: _____

Real-Life Zone

G: _____
B: _____
G: _____
B: _____
_____
G: _____
B: _____
_____
G: _____
B: _____
_____
G: _____

Wrap Up 1

W: _____
B: _____
W: _____
B: _____
W: _____
B: _____
W: _____

---

1. B: 미나야, 영화 어땠니?
   G: 나는 그것을 즐기지 못했어. 지루했어.
   B: 무엇이 별로였니?
   G: 나는 이미 결말을 알고 있었어. 보기 전에 그것에 대해 읽지 말았어야 했는데.
   B: 오, 네가 좋아하지 않다니 유감이야.
2. B: 우리는 산 정상에 도착하기까지 아직 30분은 더 가야 해. 저기서 앉아서 간식 먹고 가자.
   G: 오, 난 물만 가져왔어. 간식을 가져왔어야 했는데.
   B: 괜찮아. 내가 많이 가져왔어. 우리는 같이 먹을 수 있어.
   G: 다음번에는 간식을 가져올 것을 명심할게.

G: 벤, 너 오늘 기운 차 보여!
B: 내가 그래? 그건 아마 내가 지난밤 마침내 잠을 잘 잤기 때문일 거야.
G: 왜? 평소에 충분한 잠을 자지 못하니?
B: 응, 잠을 잘 자는 것이 정말 중요하다는 것은 알지만 나는 언제나 인터넷 검색을 하거나 휴대폰을 가지고 놀면서 늦게까지 깨어 있어.
G: 그건 나에게도 가끔 일어나는 일이야.
B: 그러고 난 뒤에, 나는 다음 날 아침 후회하고 "지난밤에 더 일찍 잠들었어야 했는데."라고 말해.
G: 어제는 어떻게 달랐니?
B: 음, 어제 오후에 나는 아빠와 등산을 했어. 집에 왔을 때 나는 매우 피곤했어. 나는 침대에 가자마자 바로 잠들었어.
G: 야외 활동은 네가 잠을 잘 자도록 돕는 훌륭한 방법이구나.

W: 오, 네 이불이 비에 젖었어! 내가 날씨를 확인했어야 했는데.
B: 그것을 빨았어요?
W: 아니. 오늘 아침에 그냥 햇볕에 널어놓았어.
B: 왜 빨지 않았어요?
W: 햇볕에 이불을 널어놓는 것은 이불을 깨끗하게 유지하는 친환경적인 방법이야.
B: 오, 저는 그것을 몰랐어요. 기억해 둘게요.
W: 그리고 정기적으로 그렇게 하는 것을 기억하는 것 또한 중요해.

※ 다음 우리말과 일치하도록 빈칸에 알맞은 것을 골라 쓰시오.

1 _____ the _____
  A. Sunshine   B. Enjoy

2 How _____ time do you _____ every day _____ _____ the sun?
  A. out   B. much   C. in   D. spend

3 _____ _____, right?
  A. much   B. not

4 Most people are _____ _____ at school or at work to _____ much time _____.
  A. outdoors   B. busy   C. spend   D. too

5 _____, the sun _____ an important _____ in your _____.
  A. role   B. plays   C. health   D. however

6 It _____ you _____ _____.
  A. stay   B. helps   C. healthy

7 Everyone _____ _____ when the sun _____.
  A. happier   B. feels   C. shines

8 This is _____ of serotonin, the _____ _____ _____.
  A. hormone   B. because   C. body's   D. happy

9 The _____ sun you get, the more "happy _____" the _____ _____.
  A. brain   B. hormone   C. more   D. produces

10 _____ your serotonin level _____ _____, you feel happier and _____.
  A. up   B. stronger   C. goes   D. when

11 This helps you _____ _____ _____.
  A. stress   B. fight   C. everyday

12 Serotonin also has a _____ _____, helping you focus better on _____ you are _____.
  A. effect   B. what   C. calming   D. doing

13 _____, serotonin helps you get a good _____ _____ because it helps the brain _____ a sleep hormone.
  A. sleep   B. moreover   C. produce   D. night's

14 Sunshine does _____ _____ make you _____ and sleep _____.
  A. just   B. better   C. not   D. feel

---

1 햇빛을 즐기세요

2 여러분은 매일 햇빛 속에서 얼마나 많은 시간을 보내나요?

3 많지 않죠, 그렇죠?

4 대부분의 사람들은 학교와 직장에서 너무 바빠서 많은 시간을 야외에서 보내지 못합니다.

5 그러나 햇빛은 여러분의 건강에 중요한 역할을 합니다.

6 그것은 여러분이 건강을 유지하는 데 도움을 줍니다.

7 모든 사람들은 해가 비칠 때 더 행복하게 느낍니다.

8 이것은 몸의 행복 호르몬인 세로토닌 때문입니다.

9 여러분이 햇빛을 쬘수록 뇌는 행복 호르몬을 더 만들어 냅니다.

10 여러분의 세로토닌 수치가 높아지면, 여러분은 더 행복하고 더 건강하게 느낍니다.

11 이것은 여러분이 매일의 스트레스를 이겨 내는 데 도움을 줍니다.

12 세로토닌은 또한 진정 효과가 있고, 여러분이 하는 일에 더 잘 집중할 수 있도록 도와줍니다.

13 게다가, 세로토닌은 뇌가 수면 호르몬을 생성하도록 도와주기 때문에 여러분이 숙면을 취하도록 해 줍니다.

14 햇빛은 단지 여러분이 더 기분 좋게 느끼고 잠을 더 잘 자게 하는 것만은 아닙니다.

15 It _____ helps _____ _____ _____.

    A. strong   B. also   C. bones   D. build

16 _____ you all know, it is calcium that _____ strong _____ and _____.

    A. bones   B. as   C. teeth   D. builds

17 However, _____ the _____ to _____ calcium _____, it needs vitamin D.

    A. properly   B. body   C. use   D. for

18 Interestingly, the skin _____ vitamin D _____ _____ _____ on it.

    A. shines   B. creates   C. sunlight   D. when

19 The _____ way to make strong _____ is to _____ _____ and enjoy the sun.

    A. outside   B. easiest   C. go   D. bones

20 _____ you can _____, sunshine has many _____, but how can you enjoy its benefits _____?

    A. benefits   B. safely   C. as   D. see

21 Fortunately, getting _____ _____ on your _____ for 10 to 20 minutes a day is enough to _____ from it.

    A. direct   B. benefit   C. sunlight   D. skin

22 Try to go out into the sun between _____ or during lunch _____ and get _____ on your _____ and hands.

    A. arms   B. sunshine   C. breaks   D. classes

23 A _____ in the sun, for just a _____ _____ every day, is good for both your _____ and your body.

    A. few   B. mind   C. walk   D. minutes

24 However, avoid the sun during _____ summer hours, between 11 and 3, and use sunscreen to _____ your _____ and _____.

    A. protect   B. neck   C. peak   D. face

25 Enjoy the sun _____ and see how a _____ sunshine can make a world of _____ in your health and your _____.

    A. difference   B. little   C. safely   D. mood

---

15 그것은 또한 튼튼한 뼈를 만드는 것을 돕습니다.

16 여러분 모두가 알다시피, 튼튼한 뼈와 치아를 만드는 것은 칼슘입니다.

17 그러나 몸이 칼슘을 적절하게 사용하기 위해서는 비타민 D가 필요합니다.

18 흥미롭게도, 피부는 햇빛이 피부에 비칠 때 비타민 D를 만들어 냅니다.

19 튼튼한 뼈를 만드는 가장 쉬운 방법은 밖으로 나가서 햇빛을 즐기는 겁니다.

20 보시다시피, 햇빛은 많은 이점이 있지만, 어떻게 그것의 이점을 안전하게 즐길 수 있을까요?

21 다행히도, 하루에 10분에서 20분 동안 피부에 직사광선을 쪼이는 것은 햇빛으로부터 이점을 얻는 데 충분합니다.

22 수업 시간 사이나 점심시간에 햇빛을 쐬러 밖으로 나가서 팔과 손에 햇빛을 쐬어 보세요.

23 매일 단 몇 분 동안 햇살을 쐬며 걷는 것은 여러분의 마음과 몸 모두에 좋습니다.

24 그러나 여름 절정 시간인 11시에서 3시 사이에는 햇빛을 피하고, 얼굴과 목을 보호하기 위해 자외선 차단제를 사용하세요.

25 태양을 안전하게 즐기고 적은 양의 햇빛이 여러분의 건강과 기분에 얼마나 큰 차이를 만들어 내는지 보세요.

※ 다음 우리말과 일치하도록 빈칸에 알맞은 말을 쓰시오.

1 _____ the _____

2 How much time do you _____ every day _____ _____ _____ _____?

3 _____ _____, right?

4 Most people are _____ _____ at school or _____ _____ _____ _____ much time _____.

5 _____, the sun _____ _____ _____ _____ in your health.

6 It _____ you _____ _____.

7 Everyone _____ _____ when the sun _____.

8 This is _____ _____ serotonin, _____ _____ _____ _____.

9 _____ _____ _____ you get, _____ _____ " _____ _____ " the brain _____.

10 When your serotonin level _____ _____, you _____ _____ and _____.

11 This _____ you _____ _____ _____ _____.

12 Serotonin also has a _____ _____, helping you _____ better on _____ _____ _____ _____ _____.

13 _____, serotonin helps you get _____ _____ _____ _____ because it _____ the brain _____ a sleep hormone.

14 Sunshine does _____ _____ make you feel and _____ _____.

1	햇빛을 즐기세요
2	여러분은 매일 햇빛 속에서 얼마나 많은 시간을 보내나요?
3	많지 않죠, 그렇죠?
4	대부분의 사람들은 학교와 직장에서 너무 바빠서 많은 시간을 야외에서 보내지 못합니다.
5	그러나 햇빛은 여러분의 건강에 중요한 역할을 합니다.
6	그것은 여러분이 건강을 유지하는 데 도움을 줍니다.
7	모든 사람들은 해가 비칠 때 더 행복하게 느낍니다.
8	이것은 몸의 행복 호르몬인 세로토닌 때문입니다.
9	여러분이 햇빛을 쬘수록 뇌는 행복 호르몬을 더 만들어 냅니다.
10	여러분의 세로토닌 수치가 높아지면, 여러분은 더 행복하고 더 건강하게 느낍니다.
11	이것은 여러분이 매일의 스트레스를 이겨 내는 데 도움을 줍니다.
12	세로토닌은 또한 진정 효과가 있고, 여러분이 하는 일에 더 잘 집중할 수 있도록 도와줍니다.
13	게다가, 세로토닌은 뇌가 수면 호르몬을 생성하도록 도와주기 때문에 여러분이 숙면을 취하도록 해 줍니다.
14	햇빛은 단지 여러분이 더 기분 좋게 느끼고 잠을 더 잘 자게 하는 것만은 아닙니다.

Step2

15 It _____ helps _____ _____ _____.

16 _____ _____ _____, it is calcium that builds strong _____ and _____.

17 However, _____ _____ _____ _____ _____ calcium _____, it needs vitamin D.

18 _____, the skin _____ vitamin D _____ _____ _____ on it.

19 _____ _____ _____ to make strong bones is _____ _____ _____ and enjoy the sun.

20 _____ _____ _____ _____, sunshine has many benefits, but how can you _____ _____ _____ _____?

21 Fortunately, _____ _____ _____ on your skin for 10 to 20 minutes a day is enough _____ _____ _____ _____.

22 _____ _____ _____ _____ the sun _____ classes or _____ lunch breaks and _____ your arms and hands.

23 A walk in the sun, _____ _____ _____ _____ _____ _____, is good for _____ your mind _____ your body.

24 However, _____ the sun during _____ summer hours, between 11 and 3, and use sunscreen _____ _____ _____ _____ _____.

25 Enjoy the sun safely and see how _____ _____ _____ can _____ in your _____ and your _____.

---

15 그것은 또한 튼튼한 뼈를 만드는 것을 돕습니다.

16 여러분 모두가 알다시피, 튼튼한 뼈와 치아를 만드는 것은 칼슘입니다.

17 그러나 몸이 칼슘을 적절하게 사용하기 위해서는 비타민 D가 필요합니다.

18 흥미롭게도, 피부는 햇빛이 피부에 비칠 때 비타민 D를 만들어 냅니다.

19 튼튼한 뼈를 만드는 가장 쉬운 방법은 밖으로 나가서 햇빛을 즐기는 겁니다.

20 보시다시피, 햇빛은 많은 이점이 있지만, 어떻게 그것의 이점을 안전하게 즐길 수 있을까요?

21 다행히도, 하루에 10분에서 20분 동안 피부에 직사광선을 쪼이는 것은 햇빛으로부터 이점을 얻는 데 충분합니다.

22 수업 시간 사이나 점심시간에 햇빛을 쬐러 밖으로 나가서 팔과 손에 햇빛을 쬐어 보세요.

23 매일 단 몇 분 동안 햇살을 쬐며 걷는 것은 여러분의 마음과 몸 모두에 좋습니다.

24 그러나 여름 절정 시간인 11시에서 3시 사이에는 햇빛을 피하고, 얼굴과 목을 보호하기 위해 자외선 차단제를 사용하세요.

25 태양을 안전하게 즐기고 적은 양의 햇빛이 여러분의 건강과 기분에 얼마나 큰 차이를 만들어 내는지 보세요.

※ 다음 문장을 우리말로 쓰시오.

1 Enjoy the Sunshine

➡ _____

2 How much time do you spend every day out in the sun?

➡ _____

3 Not much, right?

➡ _____

4 Most people are too busy at school or at work to spend much time outdoors.

➡ _____

5 However, the sun plays an important role in your health.

➡ _____

6 It helps you stay healthy.

➡ _____

7 Everyone feels happier when the sun shines.

➡ _____

8 This is because of serotonin, the body's happy hormone.

➡ _____

9 The more sun you get, the more "happy hormone" the brain produces.

➡ _____

10 When your serotonin level goes up, you feel happier and stronger.

➡ _____

11 This helps you fight everyday stress.

➡ _____

12 Serotonin also has a calming effect, helping you focus better on what you are doing.

➡ _____

13 Moreover, serotonin helps you get a good night's sleep because it helps the brain produce a sleep hormone.

➡ _____

14 Sunshine does not just make you feel and sleep better.

➡ _____

15 It also helps build strong bones.

➡ _____

16 As you all know, it is calcium that builds strong bones and teeth.

➡ _____

17 However, for the body to use calcium properly, it needs vitamin D.

➡ _____

18 Interestingly, the skin creates vitamin D when sunlight shines on it.

➡ _____

19 The easiest way to make strong bones is to go outside and enjoy the sun.

➡ _____

20 As you can see, sunshine has many benefits, but how can you enjoy its benefits safely?

➡ _____

21 Fortunately, getting direct sunlight on your skin for 10 to 20 minutes a day is enough to

benefit from it.

➡ _____

22 Try to go out into the sun between classes or during lunch breaks and get sunshine on your

arms and hands.

➡ _____

23 A walk in the sun, for just a few minutes every day, is good for both your mind and your body.

➡ _____

24 However, avoid the sun during peak summer hours, between 11 and 3, and use sunscreen to

protect your face and neck.

➡ _____

25 Enjoy the sun safely and see how a little sunshine can make a world of difference in your

health and your mood.

➡ _____

※ 다음 괄호 안의 단어들을 우리말에 맞도록 바르게 배열하시오.

1 (the / Enjoy / Sunshine)
➡ _____

2 (much / how / time / you / do / every / spend / out / day / in / sun? / the)
➡ _____

3 (much, / not / right?)
➡ _____

4 (people / most / too / are / at / busy / or / school / at / to / work / much / spend / outdoors. / time)
➡ _____
_____

5 (the / however, / sun / an / plays / role / important / your / in / health.)
➡ _____

6 (helps / it / you / healthy. / stay)
➡ _____

7 (feels / everyone / when / happier / the / shines. / sun)
➡ _____

8 (is / this / of / because / serotonin, / body's / the / hormone. / happy)
➡ _____

9 (more / the / you / sun / get, / more / the / hormone" / "happy / the / produces. / brain)
➡ _____

10 (your / when / level / serotonin / up, / goes / feel / you / stronger. / and / happier)
➡ _____

11 (helps / this / fight / you / stress. / everyday)
➡ _____

12 (also / serotonin / a / has / effect, / calming / you / helping / better / focus / what / on / are / you / doing.)
➡ _____
_____

13 (serotonin / moreover, / you / helps / a / get / night's / good / because / sleep / helps / it / brain / the / a / produce / hormone. / sleep)
➡ _____
_____

14 (does / sunshine / just / not / you / make / feel / and / better. / sleep)
➡ _____

1　햇빛을 즐기세요

2　여러분은 매일 햇빛 속에서 얼마나 많은 시간을 보내나요?

3　많지 않죠, 그렇죠?

4　대부분의 사람들은 학교와 직장에서 너무 바빠서 많은 시간을 야외에서 보내지 못합니다.

5　그러나 햇빛은 여러분의 건강에 중요한 역할을 합니다.

6　그것은 여러분이 건강을 유지하는 데 도움을 줍니다.

7　모든 사람들은 해가 비칠 때 더 행복하게 느낍니다.

8　이것은 몸의 행복 호르몬인 세로토닌 때문입니다.

9　여러분이 햇빛을 쬘수록 뇌는 행복 호르몬을 더 만들어 냅니다.

10　여러분의 세로토닌 수치가 높아지면, 여러분은 더 행복하고 더 건강하게 느낍니다.

11　이것은 여러분이 매일의 스트레스를 이겨 내는 데 도움을 줍니다.

12　세로토닌은 또한 진정 효과가 있고, 여러분이 하는 일에 더 잘 집중할 수 있도록 도와줍니다.

13　게다가, 세로토닌은 뇌가 수면 호르몬을 생성하도록 도와주기 때문에 여러분이 숙면을 취하도록 해 줍니다.

14　햇빛은 단지 여러분이 더 기분 좋게 느끼고 잠을 더 잘 자게 하는 것만은 아닙니다.

15 (also / it / build / helps / bones. / strong)

➡ _____

16 (you / as / know, / all / is / it / that / calcium / strong / builds / teeth. / and / bones)

➡ _____

17 (for / however, / body / the / use / to / properly, / calcium / it / vitamin / needs / D.)

➡ _____

18 (the / interestingly, / skin / vitamin / creates / when / D / sunlight / on / shines / it.)

➡ _____

19 (easiest / the / to / way / strong / make / is / bones / go / to / and / outside / the / enjoy / sun. / the)

➡ _____

20 (you / as / see, / can / has / sunshine / benefits, / many / how / but / you / can / its / enjoy / safely? / benefits)

➡ _____

21 (getting / fortunately, / sunlight / direct / your / on / for / skin / to / 10 / minutes / 20 / day / a / enough / is / benefit / to / it. / from)

➡ _____

22 (to / try / out / go / into / sun / the / classes / between / or / lunch / during / breaks / and / sunshine / get / your / on / arms / hands. / and)

➡ _____

23 (walk / a / in / sun, / the / just / for / a / minutes / few / day, / every / good / is / both / for / mind / your / and / body. / your)

➡ _____

24 (avoid / however, / sun / the / peak / during / hours, / summer / between / 3, / and / 11 / use / and / to / sunscreen / protect / face / your / fance / neck. / and)

➡ _____

25 (the / enjoy / sun / and / safely / see / a / how / little / can / sunshine / a / make / world / difference / of / your / in / health / and / mood. / your)

➡ _____

15 그것은 또한 튼튼한 뼈를 만드는 것을 돕습니다.

16 여러분 모두가 알다시피, 튼튼한 뼈와 치아를 만드는 것은 칼슘입니다.

17 그러나 몸이 칼슘을 적절하게 사용하기 위해서는 비타민 D가 필요합니다.

18 흥미롭게도, 피부는 햇빛이 피부에 비칠 때 비타민 D를 만들어 냅니다.

19 튼튼한 뼈를 만드는 가장 쉬운 방법은 밖으로 나가서 햇빛을 즐기는 겁니다.

20 보시다시피, 햇빛은 많은 이점이 있지만, 어떻게 그것의 이점을 안전하게 즐길 수 있을까요?

21 다행히도, 하루에 10분에서 20분 동안 피부에 직사광선을 쪼이는 것은 햇빛으로부터 이점을 얻는 데 충분합니다.

22 수업 시간 사이나 점심시간에 햇빛을 쪼러 밖으로 나가서 팔과 손에 햇빛을 쬐어 보세요.

23 매일 단 몇 분 동안 햇살을 쬐며 걷는 것은 여러분의 마음과 몸 모두에 좋습니다.

24 그러나 여름 절정 시간인 11시에서 3시 사이에는 햇빛을 피하고, 얼굴과 목을 보호하기 위해 자외선 차단제를 사용하세요.

25 태양을 안전하게 즐기고 적은 양의 햇빛이 여러분의 건강과 기분에 얼마나 큰 차이를 만들어 내는지 보세요.

※ 다음 우리말을 영어로 쓰시오.

1 ▶ 햇빛을 즐기세요

➡ _____

2 ▶ 여러분은 매일 햇빛 속에서 얼마나 많은 시간을 보내나요?

➡ _____

3 ▶ 많지 않죠, 그렇죠?

➡ _____

4 ▶ 대부분의 사람들은 학교와 직장에서 너무 바빠서 많은 시간을 야외에서 보내지 못합니다.

➡ _____

5 ▶ 그러나 햇빛은 여러분의 건강에 중요한 역할을 합니다.

➡ _____

6 ▶ 그것은 여러분이 건강을 유지하는 데 도움을 줍니다.

➡ _____

7 ▶ 모든 사람들은 해가 비칠 때 더 행복하게 느낍니다.

➡ _____

8 ▶ 이것은 몸의 행복 호르몬인 세로토닌 때문입니다.

➡ _____

9 ▶ 여러분이 햇빛을 쬘수록 뇌는 행복 호르몬을 더 만들어 냅니다.

➡ _____

10 ▶ 여러분의 세로토닌 수치가 높아지면, 여러분은 더 행복하고 더 건강하게 느낍니다.

➡ _____

11 ▶ 이것은 여러분이 매일의 스트레스를 이겨 내는 데 도움을 줍니다.

➡ _____

12 ▶ 세로토닌은 또한 진정 효과가 있고, 여러분이 하는 일에 더 잘 집중할 수 있도록 도와줍니다.

➡ _____

13 ▶ 게다가, 세로토닌은 뇌가 수면 호르몬을 생성하도록 도와주기 때문에 여러분이 숙면을 취하도록

해 줍니다.

➡ _____

_____

14 햇빛은 단지 여러분이 더 기분 좋게 느끼고 잠을 더 잘 자게 하는 것만은 아닙니다.

➡ _____

15 그것은 또한 튼튼한 뼈를 만드는 것을 돕습니다.

➡ _____

16 여러분 모두가 알다시피, 튼튼한 뼈와 치아를 만드는 것은 칼슘입니다.

➡ _____

17 그러나 몸이 칼슘을 적절하게 사용하기 위해서는 비타민 D가 필요합니다.

➡ _____

18 흥미롭게도, 피부는 햇빛이 피부에 비칠 때 비타민 D를 만들어 냅니다.

➡ _____

19 튼튼한 뼈를 만드는 가장 쉬운 방법은 밖으로 나가서 햇빛을 즐기는 겁니다.

➡ _____

20 보시다시피, 햇빛은 많은 이점이 있지만, 어떻게 그것의 이점을 안전하게 즐길 수 있을까요?

➡ _____

21 다행히도, 하루에 10분에서 20분 동안 피부에 직사광선을 쪼이는 것은 햇빛으로부터 이점을 얻는 데 충분합니다.

➡ _____

_____

22 수업 시간 사이나 점심시간에 햇빛을 쬐러 밖으로 나가서 팔과 손에 햇빛을 쬐어 보세요.

➡ _____

_____

23 매일 단 몇 분 동안 햇살을 쬐며 걷는 것은 여러분의 마음과 몸 모두에 좋습니다.

➡ _____

24 그러나 여름 절정 시간인 11시에서 3시 사이에는 햇빛을 피하고, 얼굴과 목을 보호하기 위해 자외선 차단제를 사용하세요.

➡ _____

_____

25 태양을 안전하게 즐기고 적은 양의 햇빛이 여러분의 건강과 기분에 얼마나 큰 차이를 만들어 내는지 보세요.

➡ _____

_____

※ 다음 우리말과 일치하도록 빈칸에 알맞은 말을 쓰시오.

Communication Task

1. A: I think _____ _____ _____ _____ every day. Do you _____ _____ _____?
2. B: _____, I _____. But I'll _____.
3. A: _____.

1. A: 나는 매일 운동하는 것이 중요하다고 생각해. 너는 매일 운동하니?
2. B: 아니, 하지만 노력할 거야.
3. A: 알았어.

After You Read A

1. The _____ of _____
2. Sunshine _____ you _____ _____ stress and _____ _____.
3. Sunshine _____ _____ _____ _____ _____ _____ you are doing.
4. If you _____ _____ _____, you _____ _____ _____ at night.
5. _____ the _____ _____ _____ _____ _____, your skin produces vitamin D, _____ _____ _____ for strong bones.

1. 햇빛의 좋은 점
2. 햇빛은 여러분이 스트레스를 다루고 더 행복하게 느끼도록 돕는다.
3. 햇빛은 여러분이 하는 일에 더 잘 집중할 수 있도록 도와준다.
4. 햇빛을 충분히 쬐면 밤에 잠을 더 잘 잘 것이다.
5. 해가 여러분의 피부에 비칠 때, 여러분의 피부는 비타민 D를 만드는데, 그것은 튼튼한 뼈를 만드는 데 필요하다.

Writing Workshop

1. _____ Comes _____!
2. _____ your hands _____ _____ _____. You _____ _____ _____ _____ _____ easily _____ you wash your hands well.
3. Get _____ _____ for 10 to 20 minutes _____ _____.
4. _____ _____ sunlight you get, the _____ and _____ _____ _____.
5. _____ is a good breakfast _____ helps the _____ _____ _____.
6. _____ you eat a good breakfast, you can _____ _____ _____ _____ _____ and _____ things _____.

1. 건강이 먼저야!
2. 외출 후에는 손을 씻어라. 손을 잘 씻으면 쉽게 감기에 걸리지 않을 것이다.
3. 매일 직사광선을 10~20분간 받아라.
4. 햇빛을 더 많이 받을수록 더 행복하고 더 강하게 느낄 것이다.
5. 두뇌가 적절히 작동하도록 돕는 것은 좋은 아침식사이다.
6. 좋은 아침을 먹으면, 일에 분명히 집중하고 더 잘 기억할 수 있다.

※ 다음 우리말을 영어로 쓰시오.

Communication Task

1. A: 나는 매일 운동하는 것이 중요하다고 생각해. 너는 매일 운동하니?
➡ _____

2. B: 아니, 하지만 노력할 거야.
➡ _____

3. A: 좋아.
➡ _____

After You Read A

1. 햇빛의 좋은 점
➡ _____

2. 햇빛은 여러분이 스트레스를 다루고 더 행복하게 느끼도록 돕는다.
➡ _____

3. 햇빛은 여러분이 하는 일에 더 잘 집중할 수 있도록 도와준다.
➡ _____

4. 햇빛을 충분히 쬐면 밤에 잠을 더 잘 잘 것이다.
➡ _____

5. 해가 여러분의 피부에 비칠 때, 여러분의 피부는 비타민 D를 만드는데, 그것은 튼튼한 뼈를 만드는 데 필요하다.
➡ _____

Writing Workshop

1. 건강이 먼저야!
➡ _____

2. 외출 후에는 손을 씻어라. 손을 잘 씻으면 쉽게 감기에 걸리지 않을 것이다.
➡ _____

3. 매일 직사광선을 10~20분간 받아라.
➡ _____

4. 햇빛을 더 많이 받을수록 더 행복하고 강하게 느낄 것이다.
➡ _____

5. 두뇌가 적절히 작동하도록 돕는 것은 좋은 아침식사이다.
➡ _____

6. 좋은 아침을 먹으면, 일에 분명히 집중하고 더 잘 기억할 수 있다.
➡ _____

MEMO

MEMO

MEMO

Passion for Life

시험대비 실력평가   p.08

01 (1) celebrate   (2) inform   02 officials / ③

03 ⑤   04 ④   05 ④   06 ②

01 invite 초대하다 invitation 초대, celebrate 축하하다 celebration 축하, inform 정보를 주다 informatrion 정보

02 주어진 문장의 빈칸에 들어가기에 적절한 것은 officials(공무원, 경기 임원)이다. ① Kelly가 퀴즈쇼에서 우리 반/학교…을 대표했다. ② 마라톤/달리기 시합에 달리는 것은 힘들다 ③ 이 구역은 임원 전용입니다. ④ 그는 아침/점심/행사 등을 준비한다. ⑤ 그 학생은 수학 시험에서 좋은 점수를 받았을 때 자신이 자랑스러웠다.

03 ⑤ "give up"은 "포기하다"의 뜻이다.

04 ① 졸업식 = graduation ceremony ② cheered 환호하다 ③ 마라톤 = marathon ④ 준비하고 있다 = are preparing ⑤ 제거하다 = remove

05 주어진 단어는 "저자"라는 뜻으로 "writer"에 해당한다.① competitor 경쟁자 ② athlete 운동선수 ③ creator 창조자 ④ writer 저자, 작가 ⑤ developer 개발자

06 be proud of = ~을 자랑스러워하다, one of ~ = ~ 중의 하나

서술형 시험대비   p.09

01 preparation   02 experimentation

03 get / get   04 why / Why

05 (e)nthusiasm

06 (1) good   (2) done   (3) up   (4) result

07 (1) interested   (2) give   (3) public   (4) toward

01 "세심한 시험 대비가 필수적이다." prepare 준비하다, preparation 준비

02 주어진 단어는 동사-명사의 관계이다. congratulate 축하하다, congratulation 축하, experiment 실험하다, experimentation 실험

03 • 그녀는 눈을 감고 그가 낫기를 빌었다. • 방치해 두면 문제가 더 악화될 수 있어요. get better 좋아지다, 낫다, get worse 악화되다

04 • 버스 편이 없다. 그래서 나는 보통 택시를 타는 거야. that's why = 그래서, 그런 이유로 • "우리 외식하자." "그거 좋지." Why not? = 왜 아니겠어?, 좋지.

05 그의 아버지는 축구를 향한 그의 열정을 알아챘다. passion 열정 = enthusiasm

06 (1) ~을 잘하다 = be good at (2) ~을 끝내다 = be done with (3) ~에 다가가다 = come up to (4) 결과적으로 = as a result

07 (1) ~에 관심이 있다 = be interested in (2) 포기하다 = give up (3) 공개적으로, 사람들이 있는 데서 = in public (4) ~을 향해서 = toward

교과서 Conversation

핵심 Check   p.10~11

1 How was she able to speak English so well

2 ②

01 "어떻게 ~할 수 있게 되었는가?"는 의문사 how를 사용하여 "How was she/he able to ~?"라고 물어본다.

02 알고 있는지 묻는 말은 "Have you heard of ~?" 또는 "Have you been told about ~?"이다.

교과서 대화문 익히기

Check(√) True or False   p.12

1 T   2 F   3 T   4 F   5 T

교과서 확인학습   p.14~15

Listen & Speak 1 Listen

1. How, able, runner / ran, every
2. able, basketball / short, practiced
3. How, able, speak, well / learned, watching
4. How, become, reporter / practiced, public

Listen & Speak 1-A

1. How, able / think, invented, first, true / really / Whenever, experimented / why, admire
2. How, final, players / could, only after / playing tennis / started, seven

Listen & Speak 2 Listen

1. Have, winner, contest / haven't / winner, own
2. heard, guitar player / taught

3. heard, dance / watched, times
4. heard, photographer / haven't, pictures, take / takes, street

Listen & Speak 2-A

1. Have, heard, cartoon / interested, drawing cartoons / want to be, join / know, interested, drawing
2. heard / what / stands, into, making, case / What, after, finish / done, pencil, planning, desk

Real-Life Zone

Have, skier / Who, he / skier, medal / great / was, accident, twenties / become / accident, several, get, especially, skiing / Skiing, are good / why, respected

Wrap Up

heard, fire / heard, was, nearby, hurt / one, saved, were / How, save / knocked, tell, leave / amazing

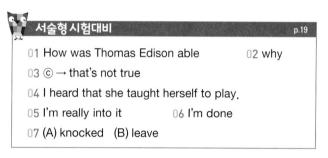

시험대비 기본평가   p.16

01 ①   02 ④   03 ③

01 주어진 질문에 대한 답을 보았을 때 (A)는 방법을 묻는 How, (B)는 시간을 묻는 When이 적절하다.
02 "No, what is D.I.Y.?"라는 대답에 이어서 D.I.Y.가 무엇인지 설명해주는 것으로 보아 빈칸에는 D.I.Y.를 아는지 물어보는 질문인 "Have you heard of D.I.Y.?"가 적절하다.
03 (B) 다친 사람이 있느냐는 질문에 없다는 대답이 와야 하고 (C) 한 사람이 열 명을 구했다는 말에 어떻게 구할 수 있었는지를 묻고 (A) 사람들에게 건물을 떠나도록 모든 문을 두드렸다는 대답을 하는 순서가 자연스러운 배열이다.

시험대비 실력평가   p.17~18

01 ②   02 ①   03 ②   04 ③
05 ③   06 ①   07 ③   08 ④
09 ④   10 ⑤   11 ③

01 주어진 질문은 그녀가 어떻게 훌륭한 달리기 선수가 되었는지를 묻는 것으로 적절한 대답은 ②이다.
02 주어진 빈칸은 시간의 부사절을 나타내기 때문에 적절한 접속사는 Whenever이다.
03 소년은 Edison에 대하여 모르는 것은 아니다. 소년이 알고 있는 것 중에서 부족한 부분에 대하여 소녀가 정보를 제공하는 대화이다.
04 "Have you heard about ~?"은 알고 있는지 묻는 표현이다.
05 cartoon writer가 되고 싶어서 cartoon club에 관심이 있는

것은 the boy이다.
06 이어지는 대화에서 우승자를 소개하는 것으로 보아 질문은 우승자가 누구인지를 묻는 말일 것이다.
07 이어지는 대답을 보았을 때 (가)는 사람을 묻는 Who, (나)는 방법을 묻는 How가 적절하다.
08 스키에 관심을 가지게 된 것은 다른 운동을 시도한 이후의 일이기 때문에 (D)가 적절한 위치이다.
09 교통사고를 당하여 다리를 다친 후에 여러 가지 운동을 시도해 보고 스키 선수가 된 과정은 소개되었지만 누가 그에게 스키 선수가 되라고 말했는지는 알 수 없다.
10 주어진 문장에 이어지는 대답의 내용을 보면 빈칸에는 화재에 관하여 들어보았는지를 묻는 ⑤가 적절하다.
11 빈칸에 들어가기에 적절한 말은 사람을 선행사로 하는 who/that이다. ① which/that ② which/that ③ who/that ④ why ⑤ where

서술형 시험대비   p.19

01 How was Thomas Edison able   02 why
03 ⓒ → that's not true
04 I heard that she taught herself to play.
05 I'm really into it   06 I'm done
07 (A) knocked   (B) leave

01 "어떻게 ~할 수 있었지?"에 해당하는 표현은 "How was+주어+able to ~?"이다.
02 결과를 유도하는 표현으로 "그것이 ~한 이유이다."에 해당하는 "That's why ~"가 되어야 한다.
03 소녀는 사람들이 Edison에 관하여 잘못 알고 있는 것을 설명하는 입장으로 사람들이 생각하고 있는 것은 사실이 아니라고 해야 자연스러운 연결이 된다.
04 "독학으로 ~을 배우다"는 "teach oneself to ~"이다.
05 "~에 대하여 관심을 가지다"는 'be into"이다.
06 "~을 끝내다"는 의미로 "be done with"가 적절하다.
07 "He knocked on every door to tell people to leave the building."을 보면 (A)는 "knocked", (B)는 "leave"가 적절하다는 것을 알 수 있다.

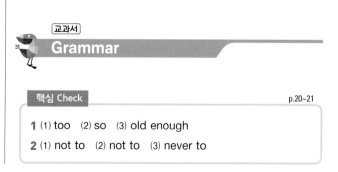

Grammar

핵심 Check   p.20~21

1 (1) too   (2) so   (3) old enough
2 (1) not to   (2) not to   (3) never to

3

01 ④   02 ②, ⑤

03 (1) to wear   (2) to object   (3) come

04 (1) She was disappointed not to be chosen.

    (2) It was so long ago that I can't remember.

    (3) She was always too busy to listen.

    (4) She was kind enough to buy us a meal.

01 too+형용사/부사+to부정사: 너무 ~해서 …할 수 없다[…하기에는 너무 ~하다] Is it too late to cancel my order?라고 쓰는 것이 적절하다.

02 to부정사의 부정은 to부정사 바로 앞에 'not'이나 'never'를 쓴다.

03 too ... to부정사 = so ... that+주어+can't[couldn't]+동사원형

04 (1) to부정사의 부정은 to부정사 바로 앞에 'not'이나 'never'를 쓴다. (2)~(4) too ... to부정사 = so ... that+주어+can't[couldn't]+동사원형: 너무 ~해서 …할 수 없다[…하기에는 너무 ~하다], enough to부정사 = so ... that+주어+can[could]+동사원형: ~하기에 충분하다

01 ⑤   02 ④   03 ③

04 (1) to go   (2) too   (3) not to   (4) never to

05 ①, ②   06 ④

07 (1) sailing → sail   (2) too → so

    (3) enough believe → enough to believe

    (4) to never → never to

    (5) to pursue not → not to pursue

08 I am so shy that I can't sing in front of many people.

09 ③   10 ②   11 ⑤

12 (1) The cellphone was so expensive that I couldn't buy it.

    (2) The ice is so thin that it can't bear your weight.

    (3) The rope was so long that it can reach the ground.

    (4) She is so healthy that she can travel.

13 ①   14 ④

15 (1) too fast to avoid colliding   (2) not to cause

16 ⑤   17 ②

18 My sister went to Japan to open a restaurant, not to study Japanese.

19 ③

01 'too ... to ~'는 '…하기에는 너무 ~하다', '너무 ~해서 …할 수 없다'는 뜻이다.

02 ① Anne asked me not to wait for her. ② She studied hard not to fail the math exam. ③ The teacher warned us not to use our cell phone in class. ⑤ The doctor told me not to smoke.

03 '~할 만큼 충분히 …한'이란 의미의 'so ... that 주어 can 동사원형'은 '... enough to부정사'와 같다

04 (1), (2) too ... to ~': …하기에는 너무 ~하다, 너무 ~해서 …할 수 없다 (3), (4) to부정사의 부정은 to부정사 바로 앞에 'not'이나 'never'를 쓴다.

05 too ... to부정사 = so ... that+주어+can't[couldn't]+동사원형: 너무 ~해서 …할 수 없다[…하기에는 너무 ~하다]

06 to부정사의 부정은 not이나 never를 부정하고자 하는 to부정사의 to 앞에 붙인다.

07 (1) too+형용사/부사+to부정사: 너무 ~해서 …할 수 없다[…하기에는 너무 ~하다] (2) too ... to부정사 = so ... that+주어+can't[couldn't]+동사원형 (3) enough+to부정사: ~하기에 충분하다 (4), (5) to부정사의 부정은 to부정사 바로 앞에 'not'이나 'never'를 쓴다.

08 'too ... to부정사'는 'so ... that+주어+can't[couldn't]+동사원형'으로 바꾸어 쓸 수 있다.

09 to부정사의 부정은 not이나 never를 부정하고자 하는 to부정사의 to 앞에 붙인다.

10 too+형용사/부사+to부정사: 너무 ~해서 …할 수 없다[…하기에는 너무 ~하다]

11 'not to부정사'가 부사적 용법의 '목적'으로 쓰인 경우 'so as not to'나 'in order not to'로 바꿔 쓸 수 있다.

12 too ... to부정사 = so ... that+주어+can't[couldn't]+동사원형: 너무 ~해서 …할 수 없다[…하기에는 너무 ~하다], enough to부정사 = so ... that+주어+can[could]+동사원형: ~하기에 충분하다 'too … to부정사'나 'enough to부정사'를 'so ... that'을 이용하여 바꿔 쓸 때 문장의 주어나 목적어이기 때문에 생략되어 있던 to부정사의 목적어를 써 주어야 함에 주의한다.

13 to부정사의 부정은 not이나 never를 부정하고자 하는 to부정사의 to 앞에 붙인다.

14 too ... to부정사: 너무 ~해서 …할 수 없다[…하기에는 너무 ~하다], to부정사의 부정은 not이나 never를 부정하고자 하는 to부정사의 to 앞에 붙인다.

15 (1) '너무 빨리 몰아서 충돌을 피할 수 없었다'라고 하는 것이 자연스러우므로 'too ... to부정사'를 이용하고, avoid는 동명사를 목적어로 받으므로 colliding으로 써야 한다. (2) '사고를 일으키지 않도록'이라고 하는 것이 자연스러우므로 'not to cause'로 쓴다.

16 asked의 목적격 보어로 to부정사가 적절하며 to부정사의 부정은 not이나 never를 부정사 앞에 붙인다.

17 주어진 우리말을 10 단어로 쓰면 'My brother is too young

to eat food by himself.'이다.

18 to부정사의 부정은 not이나 never를 부정하고자 하는 to부정사의 to 앞에 붙인다.

19 'too … to부정사'는 'so … that+주어+can't[couldn't]+동사원형'으로 바꾸어 쓸 수 있다.

서술형 시험대비
p.26~27

01 (1) This computer is so slow that I[we] can't surf the web.
 (2) Boris was so nervous that he couldn't give a speech.
 (3) The woman was so kind that she helped[could help] the old lady.
 (4) The cable is so long that it can reach the socket.
 (5) Your computer is so slow that I can't use it.

02 (1) This TV is too big to carry on my own.
 (2) Susie was too slow to catch up with Mike.
 (3) The bag is so small that I can't put the books in it.

03 해석: (1) 나는 그에게 가라고 말하지 않았다.
 (2) 나는 그에게 가지 말라고 말했다.
 차이: (1)번 문장은 동사 tell을 부정하는 문장이고
 (2)번 문장은 부정사 to go를 부정하는 문장이다.

04 (1) (a) The fried chicken is too spicy to eat.
 (b) The fried chicken is so spicy that I can't eat it
 (2) (a) The questions are too difficult to answer.
 (b) The questions are so difficult that I can't answer them.
 (3) (a) He is strong enough to lift a car.
 (b) He is so strong that he can lift a car.
 (4) (a) The print was clear enough to read.
 (b) The print was so clear that I could read it.

05 not to use

06 (1) I run too slowly to finish the race within the limited amount of time given.
 (2) This coat is too big to fit you.
 (3) The text is too long to read.
 (4) The man is strong enough to move the rock.
 (5) She is wise enough to make a good decision.
 (6) The dress is beautiful enough to wear at the party.

07 (1) not to make a noise (2) not to run

08 (1) too young to (2) too weak to
 (3) good enough to (4) smart enough

09 (1) Henry was so busy that he couldn't answer the phone.

 (2) The car is so old that I can't drive it.
 (3) A boy under 15 is so young that he can't watch the movie.
 (4) The film was so interesting that I could watch it again.

01 (1)~(5) too … to부정사 = so…… that+주어+can't[couldn't]+동사원형, enough to부정사 = so … that+주어+can[could]+동사원형. (5) 'too … to부정사'나 'enough to부정사'를 'so … that'을 이용하여 바꿔 쓸 때 문장의 주어나 목적어이기 때문에 생략되어 있던 to부정사의 목적어를 써 주어야 함에 주의한다.

02 too … to부정사 = so … that+주어+can't[couldn't]+동사원형: 너무 ~해서 …할 수 없다[…하기에는 너무 ~하다]

03 to부정사의 부정은 not이나 never를 to부정사 앞에 붙인다.

04 too … to부정사 = so … that+주어+can't[couldn't]+동사원형, enough to부정사 = so … that+주어+can[could]+동사원형. 'too … to부정사'나 'enough to부정사'를 'so … that'을 이용하여 바꿔 쓸 때 문장의 주어나 목적어이기 때문에 생략되어 있던 to부정사의 목적어를 써 주어야 함에 주의한다.

05 휴대폰을 사용하지 말라는 것이므로 'not to use'가 적절하다. to부정사의 부정은 not이나 never를 to부정사 앞에 붙인다.

06 too … to부정사 = so … that+주어+can't[couldn't]+동사원형: 너무 ~해서 …할 수 없다[…하기에는 너무 ~하다], enough to부정사 = so … that+주어+can[could]+동사원형: ~하기에 충분하다

07 각각의 목적격보어로 to부정사가 나와야 하는데 부정으로 써야 하므로 not을 to부정사 앞에 붙인다.

08 의미에 맞게 'too … to부정사'나 'enough to부정사'를 이용한다. not good enough to ~: ~할 자격[가치]이 없는

09 too … to부정사 = so … that+주어+can't[couldn't]+동사원형, enough to부정사 = so … that+주어+can[could]+동사원형. 'too … to부정사'나 'enough to부정사'를 'so … that'을 이용하여 바꿔 쓸 때 문장의 주어나 목적어이기 때문에 생략되어 있던 to부정사의 목적어를 써 주어야 함에 주의한다.

교과서
Reading

확인문제
p.28

1 T 2 F 3 T 4 F 5 T 6 F

확인문제
p.29

1 T 2 F 3 T 4 F 5 T 6 F

01 Last

02 more than

03 no more, coming

04 prepare for, closing ceremony

05 There comes another

06 something wrong

07 Still, kept going

08 stopped their preparations

09 All eyes were on

10 celebration musicm, cheered

11 Go for it

12 with a tape

13 Finally, ran through, fell to

14 His name

15 was from

16 came up to

17 happened to

18 during a practice run

19 got worse

20 Why not

21 far behind

22 representing Afghanistan

23 no way

24 at war, isn't it

25 have been

26 That's why

27 was sad for, back then

28 Were, running

29 started running

30 lots of

31 won a marathon

32 As a result

33 How

34 myself, to be from

35 not to give up

36 to win

37 it was enough

1 The Last Runner

2 The last runner finished the race more than an hour before.

3 "There will be no more runners coming," the officials decided.

4 They removed the tape at the finish line and started to prepare for the closing ceremony for the 1996 Atlanta Summer Olympics in the United States.

5 Someone shouted, "Look! There comes another runner!"

6 A runner was just entering the stadium, but there was something wrong with his legs.

7 Still, he kept going toward the finish line.

8 The band and the volunteers stopped their preparations for the closing ceremony.

9 All eyes were on the runner.

10 Suddenly, the band started playing celebration music, and the volunteers cheered.

11 "Go! Go! Go for it!"

12 Two volunteers ran to the finish line with a tape.

13 Finally, the runner ran through the tape and then fell to the ground.

14 His name was Abdul Baser Wasiqi.

15 He was from Afghanistan.

16 Reporters came up to Wasiqi and started asking him questions.

17 Reporter: What happened to you?

18 Wasiqi: I injured my leg during a practice run.

19 The injury got worse during the race, but I couldn't give up.

20 Reporter: Why not?

21 You knew that you were too far behind to win a medal.

22 Wasiqi: I am the onlya athlete here representing Afghanistan.

23 There was no way I could give up.

24 Reporter: Afghanistan is still at war, isn't it?

25 Wasiqi: Yes, we have been at war for 16 years.

26 That's why we were not able to send athletes to the Barcelona Olympics four years ago.

27 I was sad for my country back then when I could see no Afghan athletes in the opening ceremony.

28 Reporter: Were you running marathons then?

29 Wasiqi: No. I started running after Barcelona.

30 I ran in lots of races.

31 Finally I won a marathon in Germany.

32 As a result, I was able to come to Atlanta.

33 Reporter: How do you feel now?

34 Wasiqi: I am proud of myself and proud to be from Afghanistan.

35 For me and my country, it was important not to give up.

36 I didn't come here to win.

37 For me, it was enough to be here and to finish the race.

01 ④

02 who[that] are

03 Because the last runner finished the race more than an hour before.

04 ②, ⑤

05 because → why

06 the race → a practice run

또는 Wasiqi injured his leg → The injury got worse

07 ②, ③

08 All of a sudden / All at once / On a sudden

09 ④

10 representing

11 of

01 ⓐ prepare for: ~을 준비하다, ⓑ for: ~을 위한

02 coming 앞에는 '관계대명사+be동사(who[that] are)'가 생략되었다.

03 마지막 주자가 한 시간도 더 전에 경주를 끝냈기 때문이다.

04 ⓐ와 ②, ⑤: happen to ~(<일·사건 등이> 일어나다, 생기다), ①, ③, ④: happen to+동사원형(우연히 ~하다)

05 '그것이 우리가 4년 전 바르셀로나 올림픽에 선수들을 보낼 수 없었던 이유'라고 해야 하므로, why로 고치는 것이 적절하다. That's why ~: 그래서 ~하게 된 것이다, why 뒤에는 어떤 행동의 결과가 되는 내용이 온다. That's because ~: 그것은 ~ 때문이다.

06 Wasiqi가 다리를 다친 것은 '연습 경기를 하던 중'이었고, 경기 중에 상처가 점점 더 심해졌다.

07 Wasiqi가 다리에 이상이 있는데도 계속 결승선을 향해 움직여 결국 테이프를 통과해 달렸다는 내용이므로 '감동적인' 분위기라고 하는 것이 적절하다. ②, ③: 감동적인, ① 수치스러운, 창피한, ④ 난처한, 쑥스러운, ⑤ 실망스러운, 기대에 못 미치는

08 Suddenly = All of a sudden, All at once, On a sudden: 갑자기

09 Wasiqi는 결승선의 테이프를 '통과해' 달린 다음에 바닥에 쓰러졌다.

10 앞의 명사 athlete를 수식하는 현재분사형이 적절하다.

11 ask는 간접목적어를 직접목적어 뒤로 보낼 때 of를 붙인다.

12 (B)와 ②, ⑤: 계속 용법, ①, ④: 경험 용법, ③: 완료 용법

13 (A) interviewee: 인터뷰 받는 사람, (B) Wasiqi는 심각한 상처에도 불구하고 '포기하지' 않고 마라톤을 완주함으로써 올림픽 정신을 보여주었다고 말할 수 있다.

14 to부정사의 부정은 to부정사 앞에 not을 쓰는 것이 적절하다.

15 ⓑ와 ②: 명사적 용법(진주어), It: 가주어, ② = To be present at the party was good enough. ①, ③, ④, ⑤: 부사적 용법

16 ⓐ와 ④: 그런데도, 그럼에도 불구하고(부사), ①, ⑤: 아직(도)(계속해서)(부사), ② (비교급을 강조하여) 훨씬[더욱](부사), ③ 가만히 있는, 고요한(형용사)

17 이 글은 'Wasiqi가 다리에 이상이 있는데도 불구하고 폐막식 준비를 하고 있을 정도로 뒤늦은 시간까지 계속 달려 결국 결승선 테이프를 통과했다'는 내용의 글이므로, 제목으로는 ①번 '마지막 그러나 가장 감명 깊은 주자'가 적절하다. ③ consideration: 배려, ⑤ alas: 아아(슬픔·유감을 나타내는 소리)

18 Wasiqi가 얼마나 오래 달렸는지는 대답할 수 없다. ① There was something wrong with his legs. ② No. ③ The band started playing celebration music, and the volunteers cheered. "Go! Go! Go for it!" ④ He fell to the ground.

19 앞의 내용의 결과가 나오고 있으므로 As a result가 적절하다. ③ 그럼에도 불구하고, ④ ~임에 비하여[반하여]

20 Wasiqi가 독일 마라톤에서 우승하기 전에 얼마나 많은 경주에서 뛰었는지는 대답할 수 없다. ① After the Barcelona Olympics. ③ He was proud of himself and proud to be from Afghanistan. ④ It was important not to give up. ⑤ No.

21 ⓐ preparation for: ~을 위한 준비, ⓑ through: ~을 통해, ~을 관통하여

22 '또 다른 선수'라고 해야 하므로 another로 고치는 것이 적절하다. the other: 둘 중 나머지 하나

23 All eyes were on ~: 모든 눈이 ~를 주시했다(~에게 머물렀다)

🦉 서술형 시험대비　　　p.38~39

01 (A) last　(B) removed　(C) closing
02 over
03 There will be no more runners coming
04 going　　　05 Go for it 또는 Way to go
06 to prepare → preparing
07 isn't it
08 you were so far behind that you couldn't win a medal
09 at war
10 (A) give up　(B) representing Afghanistan
11 At last, In the end, Eventually 중에서 쓰면 된다.
12 pride, pride
13 (A) many　(B) Germany
14 (A) giving up　(B) to win

01 (A) '마지막 주자'라고 해야 하므로 last가 적절하다. last: 마지막의, latest: 최근의, (B) 테이프를 '걷어냈다'고 해야 하므로 removed가 적절하다. install: 설치하다, (C) '폐막식'이라고 해야 하므로 closing이 적절하다.

02 more than = over: ~ 이상

03 no more: 더 이상 ~ 아닌

04 keep ~ing: 계속해서 ~하다

05 Go for it!: 자, 해봐!, 어서!, 힘내!, Way to go!: 잘한다, 잘해! = Come on! = Go! = Stick it out!, 우울해 보이는 사람에게 격려할 때: Cheer up!(힘내!)

06 stop+to부정사: ~하기 위하여 멈추다, stop+~ing: ~을 그만두다[멈추다]. '밴드와 자원봉사자들이 폐막식을 위한 준비를 멈

7

추었다'고 했기 때문에, 'stop+동명사'로 고치는 것이 적절하다.

07 be동사가 있으므로, be동사를 사용하여 부가의문문을 만드는 것이 적절하다.

08 too ~ to부정사 = so ~ that 주어 can't: 너무 ~해서 …할 수 없다

09 인터뷰 당시 아프가니스탄이 16년째 전쟁 중이라고 했으므로, 4년 전인 바르셀로나 올림픽 경기가 열리던 무렵에는 12년째 '전쟁 중'이었음을 알 수 있다. at war: 전쟁 중인

10 Wasiqi는 '아프가니스탄을 대표하는' 유일한 선수였기 때문에, 자신이 메달을 따는 것이 불가능하다는 것을 알았지만 '포기할 수' 없었다.

11 finally = at last = in the end = eventually: 마침내

12 be proud of = take pride in: ~을 자랑스러워하다, proud의 명사형인 pride를 쓰는 것이 적절하다.

13 Wasiqi가 달리기를 시작한 이후 그는 '많은' 경주에서 뛰었고, 마침내 '독일' 마라톤에서 우승했다. 그리고 그것이 그를 애틀랜타로 오게 이끌었다.

14 Wasiqi는 자기 자신, 그리고 자신이 아프가니스탄 선수인 것이 자랑스러웠다. 그와 그의 조국을 위해서는, '포기하지' 않는 것이 중요했다. 그는 애틀랜타에 '이기러' 온 것이 아니었고 그가 애틀랜타 올림픽에 참가하여 경주를 끝마친 것으로 충분했다. sufficient: 충분한

영역별 핵심문제
p.41~45

01 ③　　02 ⑤　　03 ①　　04 ③

05 Have you heard of the winner of the singing contest?

06 How was she able to speak English so well?

07 ③　　08 ⑤　　09 ③

10 Many people are good at skiing.
　→ Not many people are good at skiing.

11 ①, ⑤　　12 ⑤　　13 ⑤　　14 ②

15 ⑤

16 I read a book quietly not to disturb my classmates.　　17 ③

18 They tried hard so as not to fail the entrance exam.　　19 ③

20 (1) We were too late to catch the last train.
　(2) We were so late that we couldn't catch the last train.　　21 ④

22 The man was so tired that he couldn't play tennis.　　23 ④

24 (1) I was too tired to focus on the test.
　(2) The presenter was too nervous to eat dinner.
　(3) The evidence is detailed enough to support his argument.

25 The cellphone was so expensive that I couldn't buy it.

26 Afghanistan is still at war　　27 ⑤

28 racing　　29 ②　　30 ③

31 I am so shy that I can't sing in front of many people.

32 (1) 강점: 노래 부르는 것을 좋아하고 목소리가 좋다.
　　약점: 수줍어하고 불안해한다.
　(2) 너무 수줍어해서 많은 사람들 앞에서 노래를 부를 수 없다.
　(3) 콘테스트 도중에 불안해하지 않기 위해서 먼저 학급 친구들 앞에서 노래 부르기를 연습할 것이다.

---

01 come up to ~ = ~로 오다, 다가오다, give up = 포기하다

02 문장의 주어이기 때문에 동사 prepare의 명사형인 preparation이 적절하다.

03 "운동을 잘하는 사람"이라는 설명에 해당하는 단어는 "운동선수"이다.

04 "join"은 "가입하다, 합류하다"의 뜻이다.

05 "~에 대하여 들어 본 적 있니?"라는 의미로 상대가 아는지 물어보는 말은 "Have you heard of ~?"이다.

06 "어떻게 그녀가 ~할 수 있었니?"는 "How was she able to ~?"로 나타낸다.

07 앞에 나온 문장에서 새로운 것을 발명할 때마다 여러 번 실험을 하는 수고를 마지않았다는 내용이 사람들이 존경하는 이유이므로 "that's why"가 적절하다.

08 그는 20대 초반에 차 사고를 당했다 = He was in a car accident in his early twenties, 그는 다리를 다쳤다 He hurt his legs.

09 여러 가지 운동을 했지만 스키 선수가 된 것으로 보아 스키 타는 것에 관심을 가지게 된 것을 알 수 있다.

10 "Skiing is not easy."라고 한 후에 "Many people are good at skiing."이라고 한 것은 흐름에 일관성이 없다.

11 상대에게 알고 있는지를 묻는 말은 "Have you heard ~?", "Have you been told ~?", "Do you know ~?", "Are you aware of/that ~?" 등이다.

12 한 사람이 열 명을 어떻게 구했는지를 설명하는 말이 되도록 구체적인 방법을 소개한다. 모든 사람이 건물을 떠나도록 하기 위하여 문을 두드렸다고 하는 것이 적절하다.

13 화재가 났을 때 한 사람이 열 명을 구했다는 사실을 소개하는 대화로, 열 명을 구한 사람이 소방관이었다는 언급은 없다.

14 ②번은 '매우 느렸지만 이길 수 있었다'라는 의미이고 나머지는 모두 '너무 느려서 이길 수 없었다'라는 의미이다.

15 ① Some people told her not to become a professional. ② I read the newspaper every morning in order not to get behind the times. ③ The teacher asked us not

to make any sound during the class. ④ I hurried so as not to be late for the meeting.

16 to부정사의 부정은 not이나 never를 to부정사 앞에 붙인다.

17 too ... to부정사 = so ... that+주어+can't[couldn't]+동사원형: 너무 ~해서 …할 수 없다[…하기에는 너무 ~하다], enough to부정사 = so ... that+주어+can[could]+동사원형: ~하기에 충분하다 'too ... to부정사'나 'enough to부정사'를 'so ... that'을 이용하여 바꿔 쓸 때 문장의 주어나 목적어이기 때문에 생략되어 있던 to부정사의 목적어를 써 주어야 함에 주의한다.

18 so as to ~의 부정은 not을 to부정사 앞에 붙인다.

19 too ... to부정사 = so ... that+주어+can't[couldn't]+동사원형: 너무 ~해서 …할 수 없다 […하기에는 너무 ~하다]

20 too ... to부정사 = so ... that+주어+can't[couldn't]+동사원형: 너무 ~해서 …할 수 없다[…하기에는 너무 ~하다]

21 ask는 목적격 보어로 to부정사가 나오며 부정사의 부정은 not이나 never를 부정사 앞에 붙인다.

22 so ... that+주어+can't[couldn't]+동사원형: 너무 ~해서 …할 수 없다[…하기에는 너무 ~하다]

23 주어진 우리말을 영작하면 'The students promised not to make any noise again.'이다.

24 too ... to부정사 = so ... that+주어+can't[couldn't]+동사원형: 너무 ~해서 …할 수 없다[…하기에는 너무 ~하다], enough to부정사 = so ... that+주어+can[could]+동사원형: ~하기에 충분하다

25 too ... to부정사 = so ... that+주어+can't[couldn't]+동사원형: 너무 ~해서 …할 수 없다[…하기에는 너무 ~하다]. 'too ... to부정사'나 'enough to부정사'를 'so ... that'을 이용하여 바꿔 쓸 때 문장의 주어나 목적어이기 때문에 생략되어 있던 to부정사의 목적어를 써 주어야 함에 주의한다.

26 at war: 전쟁 중인

27 Wasiqi는 '4년 전 바르셀로나 올림픽의 개회식에서 아프가니스탄 선수를 볼 수 없어서' 슬펐다고 했다.

28 finish는 목적어로 동명사를 취하므로 racing으로 쓰는 것이 적절하다.

29 위 글은 '(신문·잡지의) 글, 기사'이다. ③ 전기, ④ 독후감, ⑤ (책·연극·영화 등에 대한) 논평[비평], 감상문

30 앞에 나오는 내용과 상반되는 내용이 뒤에 이어지므로 However가 가장 적절하다. ② 그러므로, ④ 즉[말하자면], ⑤ 게다가, 더욱이

31 too ~ to부정사 = so ~ that 주어 can't: 너무 ~해서 …할 수 없다

32 (1) Strength: love singing, good voice, Weakness: shy, nervous, (2) I am too shy to sing in front of many people. (3) Not to be nervous during the contest, I will practice singing in front of my class first.

단원별 예상문제 p.46~49

01 (a)dmire 02 ① 03 ④ 04 ④
05 ③ 06 ④ 07 ⑤ 08 ④
09 ③ 10 ④ 11 ④ 12 ③
13 ① 14 ②

15 (1) I'm so sick that I can't go out to eat.
   (2) She is so old that she can do what she wants.

16 ① 17 ④

18 Why couldn't you give up?

19 That's why we were not able to send athletes to the Barcelona Olympics four years ago.

20 ④ 21 me → myself 22 ④

23 (A) kilometer (B) given (C) running

24 In order that I may not fall behind the other runners

01 주어진 단어는 유의어 관계이다. author 작가, writer 작가, admire 존경하다, respect 존경하다

02 이 그림은 무엇을 의미하고 있습니까? - represent 의미하다, 나타내다, 대표하다, reduce 줄이다, take 가지고 가다, realize 깨닫다

03 그녀는 틀림없이 자신이 아주 자랑스러울 것이다. be proud of = 자랑스러워하다 / 난 테니스를 별로 잘 치지는 못한다. be good at = 잘하다, 능숙하다

04 '① preparation 준비 ② removed 제거했다 ③ public 공적인 ④ famous 등의 형용사가 적절함. ⑤ officials 공무원

05 어떻게 될 수 있었는지를 묻는 말은 "How was he able to ~?"이다. "Could you tell me ~?"도 상대에게 궁금증을 물어보는 말이다.

06 (A) "~을 들어 본 적이 있니?"는 "Have you heard of ~?"이다. (B) "좋아지다, 회복하다"는 "get better"이다.

07 몇 가지 다른 운동을 시도한 것은 the boy가 아니라 Eui Hyun Sin이었다.

08 "be into"는 "~에 관심이 많다"는 뜻으로 "be interested in"에 해당한다.

09 D.I.Y.는 직접 만들어 보는 것을 나타낸다. D.I.Y.에 관심이 많다는 것은 직접 만드는 것을 좋아한다는 의미이므로 "buying"은 적절하지 않다. buying → making

10 소녀가 소년에게 D.I.Y.에 관하여 들어보았는지 묻는 것으로 보았을 때, 소녀는 D.I.Y.에 관하여 알고 있는 것을 알 수 있지만 어디에서 들었는지는 이 대화를 통해서 알 수 없다.

11 too ... to부정사 = so ... that+주어+can't[couldn't]+동사원형: 너무 ~해서 …할 수 없다[…하기에는 너무 ~하다]

12 위 글을 영어로 옮기면, 'The old man took a deep breath not to be upset.'이다.

13 주절의 시제가 과거이므로 that절에서도 과거형 couldn't로 쓰는 것이 적절하다.

9

14 ① Not to be nervous during the contest, I will practice singing in front of my class first. ③ The player practiced hard to be proud of himself, not to win a gold medal. ④ I was taught from the cradle never to cry. ⑤ For me and my country, it was important not to give up.

15 (1) too ... to부정사 = so ... that+주어+can't[couldn't]+동사원형: 너무 ~해서 …할 수 없다[…하기에는 너무 ~하다] (2) enough to부정사 = so ... that+주어+can[could]+동사원형: ~하기에 충분하다

16 ⓐ with: [관계] ~에 관해서, ~에 대하여, ⓑ All eyes were on ~: 모든 눈이 ~를 주시했다(~에게 머물렀다)

17 Wasiqi가 다리에 이상이 있는데도 계속 결승선을 향해 움직여 결국 테이프를 통과해 달렸다는 것으로 보아, Wasiqi는 '의지가 강한' 성격이라고 하는 것이 적절하다. ① 관대한, ② 외향적인, 사교적인, ③ 수동적인, 소극적인, ⑤ 공격적인

18 Why not?은 '왜 포기할 수 없었죠?'라는 뜻이다.

19 why를 보충하면 된다.

20 '메달을 얻기에 너무도 크게 뒤떨어져 있었다는 것을 알고 있었지만 제가 포기할 수 있는 방법은 없었습니다.'라고 했으므로, 제목으로는 ④번 '내가 포기해야만 하는 것은 포기하는 것이다.'가 적절하다.

21 주어와 목적어가 같으므로 me를 재귀대명사로 고치는 것이 적절하다.

22 Wasiqi와 그의 조국을 위해서는, '포기하지 않는 것'이 중요했다.

23 (A) 단위명사가 형용사처럼 명사를 수식할 때는 단수로 써야 하므로 kilometer가 적절하다. (B) '주어진' 시간이라고 해야 하므로 given이 적절하다. (C) practice는 목적어로 동명사를 취하므로 running이 적절하다.

24 목적을 나타내는 부사적 용법의 to부정사는 in order that ~ may를 사용하여 고치는 것이 적절하다. 부정문의 경우, in order that ~ may not

서술형 실전문제
p.50~51

01 invented **02** Whenever
03 Maybe that's why so many people admire him.
04 (1) We are too busy to go out for a walk.
(2) Jin is so late that he can't take the 9 o'clock train.
(3) The apples are ripe enough to be picked.
(4) This stadium is so large that it can hold 1,000 people.
(5) Ellen exercises every day not to gain weight.
(6) The girl listened carefully in class not to miss a word.

05 (1) Andrew promised me never to be late for the meeting again.
(2) In order not to forget certain events with my dog, I always take pictures with her.
(3) I will practice running every morning so as not to fall behind the other runners.
(4) I was too busy to go to bed before midnight.
(5) No wonder my grade was too low for me to pass the exam.
06 There comes another runner!
07 (A) something wrong (B) closing ceremony
08 run through
09 (A) during (B) behind (C) for
10 reason

01 Thomas Edison이 어떻게 많은 것을 발명할 수 있었는지를 묻는 질문에 대한 대답을 하는 문장이므로 빈칸에는 invented가 적절하다.

02 (B)는 "~할 때 마다"의 뜻으로 부사절을 유도하는 접속사 "whenever"가 적절하다.

03 그것이 ~하는 이유이다 = that's why ~

04 (1), (2) too ... to부정사 = so ... that+주어+can't[couldn't]+동사원형: 너무 ~해서 …할 수 없다[…하기에는 너무 ~하다] (3), (4) enough to부정사 = so ... that+주어+can[could]+동사원형: ~하기에 충분하다 (5), (6) to부정사의 부정은 not이나 never를 to부정사 앞에 붙인다.

05 (1)~(3) 부정사의 부정은 not이나 never를 to부정사 앞에 붙인다. 부사적 용법의 '목적'인 경우 to부정사 대신에 'so as to'나 'in order to'를 쓸 수 있는데 이 경우에도 to부정사의 to 앞에 붙인다. (4), (5) too ... to부정사 = so ... that+주어+can't[couldn't]+동사원형: 너무 ~해서 …할 수 없다[…하기에는 너무 ~하다]

06 부사 'there'를 강조하기 위해 문두로 이동시키면, 주어 'another runner'와 동사 'comes'를 도치시키는 것이 적절하다.

07 그의 다리에 '이상이 있었지만' Wasiqi는 경주를 포기하지 않고 너무나 오래 동안 계속 달려서 그가 경기장에 들어왔을 때 밴드와 자원봉사자들은 '폐막식'을 위한 준비를 하고 있었다.

08 Wasiqi가 그것을 '통과해 달릴 수' 있도록 테이프를 잡고 있기를 원했기 때문이다.

09 (A) 뒤에 기간을 나타내는 명사가 나오므로 during이 적절하다. while+주어+동사, (B) 메달을 타기에 너무도 멀리 '뒤떨어져' 있었다고 해야 하므로 behind가 적절하다. ahead: 앞에, (C) 뒤에 숫자가 나오므로 for가 적절하다. during+기간을 나타내는 명사, for+숫자

10 That's why = For that reason

|모범답안|

01 marathon, finished, closing, ran through,
　　representing

02 (A) dangerous enough　(B) not to be

03 (A) 5 kilometer marathon
　　(B) a lot of time to exercise
　　(C) too slowly
　　(D) within the limited amount of time given
　　(E) running faster every morning

01 finish 끝내다, stadium 운동장, finally 마침내, fall to the ground 땅바닥에 쓰러지다

단원별 모의고사 　　　　　　　　p.53~56

01 transportation　　　　　02 ②
03 (1) war　(2) stadium　(3) celebration　(4) cheered
04 ①　　　05 ②　　　06 before
07 ③　　　08 ⑤　　　09 Not, good at
10 ③　　　11 ②　　　12 ④　　　13 ⑤
14 ③　　　　　15 too difficult for me to solve
16 (1) Sally wore warm clothes not to catch a cold.
　　(2) People should stay quiet in public places not
　　　to disturb others.
　　(3) Amy was too sick to play with her friends.
17 ③　　　　　18 preparations　　　　　19 ②
20 Afghan　　　　　21 ②
22 (A) send athletes　(B) opening
23 running　　　　　24 officials　　25 ⑤

01 두 단어의 관계는 동사-명사의 관계이다. invite 초대하다, invitation 초대, transport 수송하다, transportation 수송

02 영어 설명으로 "강력한 정서나 감정"에 해당하는 단어는 "passion 열정"이다.

03 (1) at war 전쟁 중인 (2) stadium 경기장 (3) celebration 축하 행사 (4) cheer 환호하다

04 사람들 앞에서 노래 부르는 것은 쉬운 일이 아니었다. in public 사람들 앞에서, 공공연하게

05 "어떻게 ~할 수 있었니?"라는 의미로 정보를 묻는 표현은 "How was he/she able to ~?"이다.

06 "여러 해의 훈련 이후에야 그가 그것을 할 수 있었다."는 것은 "그가 그것을 하기 전에 여러 해의 훈련을 했다."는 의미이므로 빈칸에는 before가 적절하다.

07 ③ 주어진 대화에서 Hyeon Chung은 우승자가 아니라 "one of the final four players"(4강전에 출전한 선수)라고 했다.

08 주어진 문장은 사고를 겪은 후에 여러 가지 운동을 시도하고 나서 결국 스키에 관심을 가지게 되었다고 소개하는 문장으로 (E)에 들어가는 것이 자연스럽다.

09 "많은 사람이 ~하는 것은 아니다."는 "Not many people ~."이고 "잘하다, 능숙하다"는 "be good at"이다.

10 ① Eui Hyun Sin이 최초로 금메달을 딴 것인지는 알 수 없다. ② Eui Hyun Sin이 참가한 것은 2018년 Paralympics이다. ④ Eui Hyun Sin 여러 가지 운동을 시도한 후에 스키에 관심을 가지게 되었다. ⑤ Skiing은 쉽지 않기 때문에 많은 사람들이 그를 존경한다.

11 주어진 문장은 화재에서 다친 사람이 있는지 묻는 것으로 그에 대한 대답인 "No, one man saved ten people who were in the building." 앞 (B)가 적절한 위치이다.

12 ① Sora는 화재에 대해 알고 있었다. ② 소년은 아무도 다치지 않은 것을 알고 있었다. ③ 한 사람이 열 명을 구했다. ⑤ 건물에 있는 열 명을 구했다.

13 too ... to부정사 = so ... that+주어+can't[couldn't]+동사원형. 'too ... to부정사'나 'enough to부정사'를 'so ... that'을 이용하여 바꿔 쓸 때 문장의 주어나 목적어이기 때문에 생략되어 있던 to부정사의 목적어를 써 주어야 함에 주의한다.

14 to부정사의 부정은 not이나 never를 to부정사 앞에 붙이므로 I told him never to tell a lie again.이라고 쓰는 것이 적절하다.

15 too ... to부정사: 너무 ~해서 …할 수 없다[…하기에는 너무 ~하다]

16 (1), (2) to부정사의 부정은 not이나 never를 to부정사 앞에 붙인다. (3) too ... to부정사: 너무 ~해서 …할 수 없다[…하기에는 너무 ~하다]

17 ① The song is too difficult to sing. ② The question was easy enough to answer. ④ You must remember not to make a loud noise. ⑤ She is intelligent enough not to miss a trick.

18 소유격 다음에 prepare의 명사형으로 쓰는 것이 적절하고, 폐막식을 위한 준비가 여러 가지일 것이므로 복수형으로 쓰는 것이 적절하다.

19 위 글은 'Wasiqi가 다리에 이상이 있는데도 계속 결승선을 향해 달려 결국 테이프를 통과했다'는 내용의 글이므로, 주제로는 ② 번 '고난에 결코 굴복하지 않는 진정한 스포츠 정신'이 적절하다. give in to: ~에 굴복하다, ⑤ exhausted: 기진맥진한, 진이 다 빠진, 탈진한

20 Afghan: 아프가니스탄(말, 사람)의

21 주어진 문장은 'Why couldn't you give up?'의 뜻으로 ②번 앞 문장의 마지막에서 Wasiqi가 한 말을 되묻는 말이므로 ②번이 적절하다.

22 그 당시 아프가니스탄은 전쟁 중이라서 바르셀로나 올림픽에 '선수들을 보낼 수' 없었고, 그래서 '개회식'에서 아프가니스탄을 대표하는 선수들이 없었기 때문이었다.

23 give up은 목적어로 동명사를 취하므로 running으로 쓰는 것이 적절하다.

24 official: (고위) 공무원[관리], 임원, 조직에서 지휘권을 가진 자리에 있는 사람

25 'Wasiqi가 얼마나 오래 달렸는지'는 알 수 없다. ① When most runners finished racing, and the officials started to prepare for the closing ceremony. ② Yes. ③ No. ④ For his country.

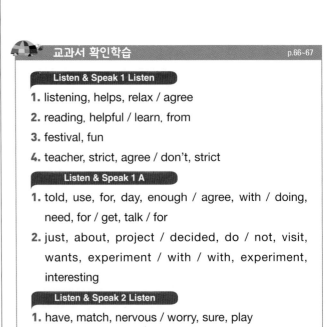

Lesson **2**

Teens' Worries

시험대비 실력평가　　　　　　　　p.60

01 (1) (d)etest　(2) (n)ervous　　02 ④

03 ③　　　04 ⑤　　05 ⑤　　06 ②

01 주어진 보기의 단어는 유의어 관계이다. decide 결정하다, determine 결정하다, hate 몹시 싫어하다, detest 몹시 싫어하다, afraid 걱정하는, 불안한, nervous 불안한

02 주어진 문장의 빈칸에 들어가기에 적절한 것은 "proved"(입증했다)이다. (엘라는 판사에게 그녀가 돈을 훔치지 않았음을 입증했다.) ① 우리 견학에 대한 너의 의견에 동의해. agree ② 클레어가 메이슨에게 데이트를 신청했고, 그들은 영화를 보러 갔다. asked ③ 많은 사람들이 스미스 씨 의견에 동의하지 않았다. disagreed ④ 그는 자신이 실수하지 않았다는 것을 입증했다. (proved) ⑤ 두 아이는 서로 좋아/싫어했다. liked/hated

03 ① 대니얼은 치과에 가는 것을 두려워한다. ② 카운슬러가 나에게 잠을 더 자라고 조언했다. ③ 잭은 최신 모델의 차를 샀다. - latest 최신의 ④ 루카스는 너무 많은 실수를 해서 수학 시험에서 C를 받았다. ⑤ 라이언은 내가 한 말을 오해했다.

04 ① a couple of 두서너 개의, 몇 개의, 몇 사람의 ② end up 결국 ~하게 되다 ③ guy (비격식) 녀석, 남자 (informal) ④ hate 매우 싫어하다 ⑤ in style 유행하는, 유행되는

05 주어진 단어는 "결정하다"라는 뜻으로 "determine"에 해당한다.

06 열 셀 때까지 시작해야 해. get started 시작하다 / 당신이 하루속히 완쾌되기를 바랍니다. get better 회복하다

서술형 시험대비　　　　　　　　p.61

01 management　　　　02 proof

03 for / for　　　　　04 out / out

05 (1) about　(2) end　(3) now　(4) style

06 (1) taking　(2) having　(3) without　(4) together

01 시간 관리를 배우는 것은 그들에게 중요한 기술이다. manage 관리하다 – management 관리

02 주어진 단어는 동사-명사의 관계이다. relax 쉬다, relaxation 휴식, prove 입증하다, proof 증거, 입증

03 • 그 집은 오랫동안 비어 있었다. for a long time 오래 동안 • 그 비행기는 이륙 준비가 되어 있다. be ready for ~할 준비가 되다

04 • 난 저녁 데이트 신청을 받았다. be asked out 데이트 신청을 받다 • 그녀는 방에서 나갔다. go out of ~에서 나가다

05 (1) be worried about ~ = ~에 대하여 걱정하다 (2) end up –ing = 결국 ~하게 되다 (3) for now = 당분간, 지금은 (4) in style = 유행하는

06 (1) 시간이 걸리다 = take time (2) ~하는 데 어려움을 겪다 have a hard time -ing (3) without -ing = ~하지 않고 (4) get together = 모이다

교과서
Conversation

핵심 Check　　　　　　　　p.62~63

1 ⑤　　　　　　　2 ②

01 ⑤는 동의하는지 상대에게 묻는 말이고, 나머지는 모두 동의한다는 표현이다.

02 상대가 불안하다고 했으므로 안심시키는 표현이 적절하다.

교과서 대화문 익히기

Check(√) True or False　　　　　p.64

1 F　2 T　3 T　4 F

교과서 확인학습　　　　　　　p.66~67

Listen & Speak 1 Listen

1. listening, helps, relax / agree
2. reading, helpful / learn, from
3. festival, fun
4. teacher, strict, agree / don't, strict

Listen & Speak 1 A

1. told, use, for, day, enough / agree, with / doing, need, for / get, talk / for
2. just, about, project / decided, do / not, visit, wants, experiment / with / with, experiment, interesting

Listen & Speak 2 Listen

1. have, match, nervous / worry, sure, play
2. nervous, speech / do, worry
3. worried, friends, school / sure, make, friends

1. worried, wrong / upset / Why, do / wore, without / sorry, understand
2. having, learning / had, asked, teacher / What / advised, use, vocabulary, sure

Real-Life Zone

project, taking / agree, One, people, doing / That's, team / know, know, get, to / doesn't, started, like, part / what, do / to, why, doing, Then, you'll, if, wants / try / sure, better, talk, project

Wrap Up

matter, look / ready, finals, desk, study, up, something / management, easy / agree, should / Number, have, Then, down, much, you, finish / try / that, with

시험대비 기본평가 p.68

01 ①　　　02 ④　　　03 ⑤

01 소녀가 엄마의 의견에 대한 반대 의견이 있는 것으로 보아 빈 칸에는 아빠가 앞에 나온 엄마의 의견에 동의하는 의미의 "I agree with her."가 되는 것이 자연스럽다.

02 "Tell her you're sorry."는 소녀의 걱정을 덜어주기 위한 말이 다. 이어서 안심시키는 "I'm sure ~."가 들어가는 것이 적절하 다.

03 앞의 질문에 대하여 (C) 아직 아니라고 대답한 이유로 진호와 미나가 서로 다른 것을 원한다고 말한다. (B) 서로 다른 의견에 대하여 누구에게 동의하는지 묻자 (A) 실험이 재미있을 것이기 때문에 미나에게 동의한다고 대답한다.

시험대비 실력평가 p.69~70

01 ①　　02 ⑤　　03 ②　　04 ②
05 ③　　06 ③　　07 agree　　08 ③
09 ③　　10 ③　　11 ⑤　　12 ⑤

01 역사 만화책을 읽는 것이 유익하다는 말에 동의한다고 하였으므 로 그것에 대한 장점을 언급한 ①이 적절하다.

02 "I had the same problem."이라는 대답이 이어지는 것으로 보아 그 앞에는 문제에 대한 언급이 있었음을 알 수 있다.

03 소녀는 소년과 같은 문제가 있었지만 영어 선생님의 도움으로 어휘 앱을 통해서 문제를 해결하고 있으므로 현재 어려움을 가 지고 있다는 ②는 대화의 내용과 일치하지 않는다.

04 상대에게 무슨 문제가 있는지 묻는 것으로 보아 걱정스러워 보이

거나 불안해 보이는 상황임을 알 수 있다.

05 주어진 문장은 상대의 문제를 해결하기 위한 조언으로 구체적인 방법이 제시되고 있는 문장에 이어서 (C)에 들어가는 것이 가장 적절하다.

06 이 대화에서 동하는 시간 관리를 하지 못해서 기말고사 대비를 제대로 못한 상황이고, Emily가 어떻게 시간 관리를 할지 조언 을 해주고 있다. 시간 관리가 왜 중요한지에 대한 언급은 없다.

07 "어떤 주제에 대하여 다른 사람과 같은 의견을 가지다"는 "agree 동의하다"에 해당한다.

08 (A) ~에게 …하도록 하다 = get 목적어 + to부정사, (B) 시작 하다 = get started

09 ③ 소녀가 문제를 겪고 있는 것은 자기 조별과제에 속한 한 사람 이 맡은 역할을 하지 않는 것이다.

10 (가) "Is something wrong?"이라고 하는 것으로 보아 걱정 스럽거나 불안스러워 보이는 상황이 적절하다. (B) 언니가 화난 이유로 무엇을 했는지 묻는 말로 What이 적절하다.

11 전치사 without의 목적어로 동명사 without이 적절하다.

12 "I'm sure ~"는 자신이 확신한다는 의미로 상대가 잘 거니까 걱정하지 말라는 의미로 안심시키려는 의도라고 할 수 있다.

서술형 시험대비 p.71

01 I'm sure you'll play very well.　　02 agree
03 I'm having a hard time learning new English words.
04 vocabulary　　05 against → for
06 job
07 I'm sure he'll do better after you talk to him.

01 상대가 불안해 할 때 안심을 시키려는 의도로 "~을 확신하다." 라고 할 때는 "I'm sure ~."라고 한다.

02 주어진 대화에서 두 사람은 체육 선생님이 엄격하신지에 대한 서로 다른 의견을 가지고 있기 때문에 서로 동의하는지를 묻고, 대답하는 agree가 적절하다.

03 "~하는 데 어려움을 겪다"는 "have a hard time -ing"이다.

04 "어떤 언어에서 사용되는 단어"는 "vocabulary 어휘"이다.

05 "work against"는 "불리하게 되다"는 뜻으로 도움을 주기위한 앱에 대한 설명으로 적절하지 않다. "work for 효과가 있다"가 되어야 한다.

06 "자신이 맡은 일을 하다"는 의미로 "do one's part = do one's job"이다.

07 "~할 것이라고 확신하다"는 "I'm sure 주어+동사"이다. "그가 더 잘할 것이다 = he'll do better", "네가 그와 이야기한 이후 로 = after you talk to him"

13

p.72~73

핵심 Check

1 (1) watching　(2) Listening
2 (1) if[whether]　(2) if[whether]　(3) whether

시험대비 기본평가

p.74

01 ①

02 (1) walking　(2) Not knowing　(3) if　(4) whether

03 ⑤

04 (1) Looking at me, she smiled brightly.

　(2) While walking home from work, I found this great bakery.

　(3) We need to find out if the rumor is true.

01 접속사 없이 '주어+동사'가 이어지고 있으므로 빈칸에는 '접속사+주어+동사'의 역할을 할 수 있는 현재분사로(그가 나를 보는 능동이므로) 분사구문이 되어야 한다.

02 (1) 접속사가 없으므로 '접속사+주어+동사'의 역할을 할 수 있는 walking이 적절하다. (2) 분사구문의 부정은 분사 앞에 'not'이나 'never'를 쓴다. (3) '내가 그 퍼즐을 풀 수 있다는 것을 물었다'는 말은 어색하다. 사실의 여부를 확인하거나 불확실함을 나타내는 if가 적절하다. (4) 바로 뒤에 'or not'이 이어지고 있으므로 whether가 적절하다.

03 know의 목적어가 나와야 하는데 '~인지 (아닌지)'라는 의미로 명사절을 이끄는 접속사 if가 적절하다.

04 (1) looking을 '접속사+주어+동사'의 역할을 하는 분사로 하여 알맞게 배열한다. (2) 분사구문의 뜻을 명확히 하기 위해 접속사 while을 생략하지 않고 남겨둔 경우이다. (3) '~인지 (아닌지)'라는 의미의 접속사로 어떠한 사실의 여부를 확인하거나 불확실함을 나타낼 때 쓰이는 if를 이용한다.

시험대비 실력평가

p.75~77

01 ③　　　02 ④　　　03 ①

04 (1) if　(2) whether　(3) whether　(4) Neglecting
　(5) talking　(6) Not getting

05 ⑤　　　06 ③　　　07 ①　　　08 ⑤

09 Being　　10 ②　　　11 ②

12 (1) I was　(2) he was　　　　13 ④

14 (1) We don't know if Mark will succeed.

　(2) Whether I believe you or not is not important now.

　(3) Riding a bike, he always wears his helmet.

（4）Not feeling good about it, he wrote a letter to her.

（5）Disappointed with the result, she walked out of her room.

15 ⑤　　　　　　　　　16 ②, ③

17 She advises Sohui to ask Hayeon if[whether] there is something wrong.

---

01 Mike was standing outside the house, waiting for her.

02 '~인지 (아닌지)'라는 의미의 접속사 if[whether]를 쓰는 것이 적절하다. I just wanted to know if[whether] everything was all right.

03 첫 번째 빈칸에는 '~인지 (아닌지)'라는 의미의 접속사 if나 whether가 적절하다. 두 번째 빈칸에는 접속사가 없으므로 '접속사+주어+동사'의 역할을 할 수 있는 Finishing이 적절하다.

04 (1) 내용상 '~인지 (아닌지)'라는 의미의 접속사 if가 적절하다. (2) 내용상 '~인지 (아닌지)'라는 의미의 접속사 whether가 적절하다. (3) 뒤에 or not이 바로 이어서 나오고 있으므로 whether가 적절하다. (4) 접속사가 없으므로 '접속사+주어+동사'의 역할을 할 수 있는 분사구문으로 써야 한다. (5) 분사구문의 뜻을 명확히 하기 위해 접속사 when을 생략하지 않고 남겨둔 경우이다. (6) 분사구문의 부정은 분사 앞에 'not'이나 'never'를 쓴다.

05 '접속사+주어+동사'의 부사절을 분사구문으로 바꾸어 쓸 수 있다. 이때, 분사구문의 뜻을 명확히 하기 위해 접속사를 생략하지 않기도 하지만 주어를 생략하지는 않는다.

06 (A) 내용상 '~인지 (아닌지)'라는 의미가 자연스러우므로 if나 whether가 적절하고, (B) 바로 뒤에 or not이 나오므로 whether가 적절하다.

07 ⓐ 접속사가 없으므로 thinking으로 분사구문을 만들어야 한다. 분사구문이 문장의 중간에 삽입된 형태이다.

08 동사의 목적어로 쓰인 명사절을 이끄는 접속사 if는 whether로 바꿔 쓸 수 있다.

09 'Because I was lonely, I decided to make some friends.'라고 한 문장으로 쓸 수 있고, 이것을 분사구문으로 바꾸면 빈칸에는 'Because I was'를 현재분사 Being으로 고쳐야 한다.

10 '~인지 (아닌지)'라는 의미의 명사절을 이끄는 if나 whether가 적절하며 if는 바로 뒤에 or not을 붙여 쓰지 않는다. Justine이 영어 시험에서 좋은 점수를 받았는지를 묻는 것이므로 asks는 현재로, got은 과거로 나타낸다.

11 주어진 문장과 ②번은 '조건'을 나타낸다. ① 시간 ③ 이유, ④ 동시동작, ⑤ 양보

12 부사절에서 주어가 주절의 주어와 같을 때 '주어+be동사'를 생략할 수 있으며 이것을 분사구문으로 고쳤을 때 being을 생략하고 접속사를 남겨둔 것과 같다.

13 '~인지 (아닌지)'라는 의미의 명사절을 이끄는 if는 바로 뒤에 'or not'을 붙여 쓰지 않는다.

14 (1) if가 know의 목적어로 쓰인 명사절을 이끌고 있는데 명사절에서는 미래시제를 현재시제로 쓸 수 없으므로 succeeds를 'will succeed'로 고치는 것이 적절하다. (2) If가 이끄는 명사절이 주어 역할을 할 수 없으므로 Whether로 고치는 것이 적절하다. (3) 자전거를 타는 '능동'이므로 Ridden을 Riding으로 고치는 것이 적절하다. (4) 분사구문의 부정은 분사 앞에 'not'이나 'never'를 쓴다. (5) Being이 생략된 분사구문으로 '실망시키는' 것이 아니라 '실망한' 것이므로 Disappointing을 Disappointed로 고쳐야 한다. 감정동사의 과거분사임에 유의한다.

15 'As[Because] he wanted to get good grades, he decided to study hard.'를 분사구문으로 바꾼 것이므로 'As[Because] he wanted' 대신에 'Wanting'으로 쓰는 것이 적절하다.

16 ② if는 전치사의 목적어로 쓰인 명사절을 이끌지 못한다. if 대신에 whether로 써야 한다. ③ if는 to부정사와 함께 쓰지 않는다. if 대신에 whether로 써야 한다.

17 if[whether] 뒤에 오는 절은 의문사가 없는 간접의문문으로 'if[whether]+주어+동사'의 어순으로 쓴다.

서술형 시험대비
p.78~79

01 (1) Being so upset, he went out without saying anything.
(2) Cancelling the order, you will lose your money.
(3) Being tired of a lot of homework, I won't give up.
(4) Not feeling good, I stayed in bed all morning.
(5) It being fine, I will start tomorrow.

02 (1) He couldn't tell if she was laughing or crying.
(2) I'm not sure if he explained everything about your compensation.

03 (1) Taking this train, you'll get to Busan at 1 p.m.
(2) Being busy, Amy is always willing to help me.
(3) I wonder if he lives near here.
(4) I am not sure if he still remembers me.

04 (1) Whether he will continue to be successful in future is open to doubt.
(2) Some friends asked me whether or not I had an accident.
(3) I was debating in my mind whether to go or not.

05 (1) if[whether] she can make friends
(2) if[whether] he can play
(3) whether she can do

06 (1) Doing check-in (2) having a talk
(3) Coming out

07 (1) Being sick, he stayed home all day long.
As he was sick, he stayed home all day long.

(2) Don't look at your phone, walking on the street.
Don't look at your phone when[as] you walk on the street.
(3) Can I ask if[whether] you have the ticket?
(4) I wonder if[whether] he can pass the exam.

08 (1) Written in haste, this book has a lot of mistakes.
(2) There being no train left, he had to stay at a hotel.

01 '접속사+주어+동사'로 이루어진 부사절의 주어가 주절의 주어와 일치할 때 접속사와 주어를 생략하고 동사를 분사(동사원형+-ing)로 만든다. (1) '이유', (2) '조건' (3) '양보' (4) 분사구문의 부정은 분사 앞에 'not'이나 'never'를 쓴다. (5) 주절의 주어와 부사절의 주어가 다르므로 주어를 생략하면 안 된다. (독립분사구문)

02 '~인지 (아닌지)'라는 의미의 접속사로 쓰이는 if를 이용한다. if 뒤에 오는 절은 의문사가 없는 간접의문문으로 'if+주어+ 동사'의 어순으로 쓴다.

03 (1), (2) 현재분사가 분사구문을 이끌도록 한다. (3), (4) if가 명사절을 이끌도록 한다.

04 (1) 문두에서 주어절을 이끄는 역할을 하고 있으므로 If를 Whether로 고치는 것이 적절하다. (2) 바로 뒤에 or not이 나오고 있으므로 if를 whether로 고치는 것이 적절하다. (3) whether 다음에는 to부정사를 쓸 수 있지만 if는 쓸 수 없으므로 if를 whether로 고치는 것이 적절하다.

05 (1), (2) 명사절을 이끄는 if나 whether를 이용한다. (3) 전치사 about의 목적어이므로 whether를 이용한다.

06 (1) = When he did '시간' (2) = as she had '동시동작' (3) = when he came '시간'의 분사구문을 이용한다.

07 (1), (2) '접속사+주어+동사'로 이루어진 부사절의 주어가 주절의 주어와 일치할 때 접속사와 주어를 생략하고 동사를 분사(동사원형+-ing)로 만들어서 분사구문으로 바꿔 쓴다. (3), (4) '~인지 (아닌지)'라는 의미의 접속사로 쓰이는 if[whether]를 이용한다. 뒤에 오는 절은 의문사가 없는 간접의문문으로 'if+주어+동사'의 어순으로 쓴다.

08 (1) 책이 '쓰여지는' '수동'의 의미가 되어야 하므로 Writing을 Written으로 고쳐 써야 한다. (2) 부사절과 주절의 주어가 다를 때는 부사절의 주어를 생략하지 않는다. (독립분사구문)

교과서
Reading

확인문제
p.80

1 T 2 F 3 T 4 F 5 T 6 F

1 T 2 F 3 T 4 F 5 T 6 F

교과서 확인학습 A
p.82~83

01 Should
02 has
03 what do you do
04 Here are some things
05 her best friend, has changed, is avoiding
06 don't you
07 What about
08 I feel
09 turns around, walks away from
10 to hear that
11 why she does that
12 I've done anything wrong
13 feels like
14 should, if, something wrong
15 still, with
16 thinking, just because
17 new sneakers
18 What
19 didn't you, couple of
20 in style
21 in these
22 wearing, cooler, more popular
23 because you're you
25 a great guy
26 to prove it
27 was asked out
28 to hurt his feelings
29 advice
30 asked me out
31 for now, go out with
32 focus on
33 should
34 Why don't you
35 I'm afraid
36 If you don't tell, end up hurting
37 you're right
38 Thanks for

교과서 확인학습 B
p.84~85

1 What Should I Do?

2 Everyone has worries.

3 When you have things you worry about, what do you do?

4 Here are some things that three teenagers worry about.

5 Sohui thought Hayeon was her best friend, but now, Sohui feels that Hayeon has changed and she is avoiding her.

6 Sohui: (To her older sister) You know my friend Hayeon, don't you?

7 Sister: Yeah. Why? What about her?

8 Sohui: I feel she's avoiding me.

9 When I see her at school, she turns around and walks away from me.

10 Sister: I'm sorry to hear that.

11 Do you have any idea why she does that?

12 Sohui: No. I don't think I've done anything wrong.

13 It just feels like she doesn't like me anymore.

14 Sister: Maybe you should just ask her if there is something wrong.

15 Sohui: Maybe I should. I still want to be friends with her.

16 Daeho, thinking that new things will make him more popular, often wants new things just because his friends have them.

17 Daeho: Seongjin, look at my new sneakers.

18 What do you think?

19 Seongjin: They're nice, but didn't you just buy new sneakers a couple of months ago?

20 Daeho: Yeah, but they're no longer in style.

21 I look cooler in these, right?

22 Seongjin: Daeho, wearing the latest fashion doesn't make you cooler or more popular.

23 People like you because you're you, not because of your clothes.

24 Daeho: Yeah?

25 Seongjin: Listen, you're a great guy.

26 You don't need new sneakers to prove it.

27 Recently, Minkyeong was asked out by a boy in her class.

28 She wants to say no but does not want to hurt his feelings.

29 Minkyeong: I need your advice.

30 A boy in my class asked me out.

31 I like him, but for now I don't want to go out with him.

32 I need to focus on my studies.

33 What should I do?

34 Counselor: Why don't you tell him why you can't go?

35 Minkyeong: I'm afraid I might hurt his feelings.

36 Counselor: If you don't tell him soon, he will misunderstand your feelings, and you may end up hurting him even more.

37 Minkyeong: Maybe you're right.

38 Thanks for the advice.

시험대비 실력평가
p.86~89

01 in
02 ②, ⑤
03 you're a great guy
04 How[What] about
05 ③
06 about
07 ④
08 ⑤
09 ③
10 ②
11 new sneakers
12 ④
13 ④
14 Recently, a boy in Minkyeong's[her] class asked Minkyeong out.

15 ②　　　　16 new things　　　　17 ③

18 People like you because you're you, not because of your clothes.

19 ④　　　　20 ①, ④　　　　21 ④

01 ⓐ in style 유행하는, 유행되는, ⓑ in: ~을 착용한[입은/쓴]

02 (A)와 ②, ⑤: 현재분사, ①, ③, ④: 동명사

03 '네가 멋진 사람이라는 것'을 가리킨다.

04 Why don't you 동사원형 ~?= How[What] about ~ing?: ~하는 게 어때?

05 이 글은 '민경이가 데이트 신청을 받았지만 당분간은 공부에 집중하기 위해 상대방의 감정을 상하게 하지 않으면서 거절하려고 조언을 구하는' 내용의 글이므로, 제목으로는 ③번 '미안해요! 당분간은 저는 공부에 집중해야 해요!'가 적절하다.

06 worry about: ~에 대해 걱정하다

07 ④ 여기 세 명의 청소년이 걱정하는 것들이 있다고 했으므로, 뒤에 올 내용으로는 '세 명의 청소년의 걱정들'이 가장 적절하다. ⑤ routine: (판에 박힌) 일상

08 ①~④: 소희, ⑤: 하연

09 ⓐ와 ③: 원인, ① 결과, ② 판단의 근거, ④ 형용사 수식 ⑤ 목적

10 ② 학교에서 소희가 하연이를 볼 때, '하연이'가 돌아서서 '소희'로부터 멀리 걸어간다.

11 대호가 몇 달 전에 샀던 '새 운동화'를 가리킨다.

12 ④ trendy: 유행을 따르는(형용사), 유행을 따르는 사람(명사), 대호는 새 물건이 그를 더 인기 있게 만들어 줄 것이라고 생각해서 단지 친구들이 그것을 가지고 있다는 이유로 종종 새 물건을 사기를 원하는 사람이라고 했으므로, '유행을 따르는'이 적절하다. ① 구식의, ② 사람들과 어울리기 좋아하는, ③ 얌전한, 수수한, ⑤ 유행에 뒤떨어진

13 ⓐ for now: 우선은, 현재로는, 당분간은, ⓑ focus on: ~에 주력하다, 초점을 맞추다.

14 ask somebody out: ~에게 데이트를 신청하다

15 (B)와 ②: 훨씬(비교급을 강조) ①, ④: (예상 밖이나 놀라운 일을 나타내어) …도[조차] ③ 평평한, 반반한(형용사) ⑤ 균등한, 동일한(형용사)

16 '새 물건'을 가리킨다.

17 these가 new sneakers를 가리키므로 '신을 신으면'이라는 의미의 착용을 나타내는 전치사 in이 적절하다.

18 'of'를 보충하면 된다.

19 주어진 문장의 that에 주목한다. ④번 앞 문장의 내용을 받고 있으므로 ④번이 적절하다.

20 ⓐ와 ①, ④: 현재완료(결과 용법), 현재완료의 결과 용법은 과거에 행해진 어떤 행동의 결과가 현재까지 영향을 미칠 때 쓴다. ②, ⑤: 계속 용법, ③ 경험 용법

21 이 글은 '친구가 변했다고 느끼는 동생에게, 뭔가 잘못된 것이

있는지 그녀에게 물어보라고 언니가 충고해 주자, 아마 그래야 될 것 같다고 동생이 대답하는' 내용이므로, 제목으로는 ④번 '너는 변했어. 뭔가 잘못된 것이 있는지 궁금해'가 적절하다. ① I mean it.: 진심입니다. ② That's enough.: 이제 됐다!, 그쯤 해둬! ③ Every dog has his day.: 쥐구멍에도 볕들 날 있다. ⑤ ignore: 무시하다

01 hurting　　　　02 Unless you

03 (A) out　(B) hurting his feelings

04 as[because] he thinks that new things will make him more popular

05 because your clothes → because of your clothes

06 (A) his friends　(B) in style

07 (A) What　(B) latest　(C) clothes

08 (my) new sneakers　　　　09 No, he doesn't.

10 why she does that

11 thinks → doesn't think, something → anything

12 (A) has changed　(B) is avoiding　(C) wrong

01 end up ~ing: 결국 ~하게 되다

02 If ~ not = Unless

03 민경이의 반 남자아이가 그녀에게 데이트 신청을 했지만, 그녀는 그의 감정을 상하게 하지 않으면서 거절하기를 원한다. turned ~ down: ~을 거절하다

04 '이유'를 나타내는 분사구문이므로, 접속사 as 또는 because를 사용하여 고치는 것이 적절하다.

05 'because+주어와 동사로 이루어진 절', 'because of+명사(구)'이므로, because of your clothes로 고치는 것이 적절하다.

06 대호는 단지 '친구들'이 그것을 가지고 있다는 이유로 종종 새 물건을 사기를 원하고, 몇 달 전에 산 운동화가 더 이상 '유행이' 아니라는 생각 때문에 다시 새 운동화를 샀다.

07 (A) 'think'의 목적어를 써야 하므로 What이 적절하다. (B) '최신' 유행이라고 해야 하므로 latest가 적절하다. last: 맨 마지막의, latest: 최근의[최신의], (C) 네 '옷'이라고 해야 하므로 clothes가 적절하다. cloths: 옷감들, 직물들, clothes: 옷, 의복

08 '(내) 새 운동화'를 가리킨다.

09 성진이는 '최신 유행하는 것을 입는 것이 대호를 더 멋지고 더 인기 있게 만들어 주지는 않는다.'고 생각한다.

10 간접의문문(의문사+주어+동사)의 순서로 쓰는 것이 적절하다.

11 소희는 자신이 잘못한 것이 있다고 생각하지 않는다. 부정문에서 something을 anything으로 고치는 것이 적절하다.

12 소희의 고민: 나의 가장 친한 친구 하연이가 '변했고' 나를 '피한다'고 느낀다. 조언: 뭔가 '잘못된' 것이 있는지 그녀에게 물어보는 게 어때?

01 ⑤　　02 ①　　03 ③　　04 ②

05 when doing my homework, I need to use it for a long time

06 I'm sure you'll make a lot of friends there.

07 ③　　08 ④　　09 ⑤

10 ⓓ: Ask him why he's not doing his part.

11 (A) for　(B) up　(C) for　12 ⑤　　13 ②

14 ②　　15 ①　　16 ⑤

17 if[whether] she would give up

18 (1) As she listened to music
　　(2) because[as] he was

19 ③　　20 ⓔ, ⑨　　21 ④　　22 ③

23 ②

24 I feel she's avoiding me. When I see her at school, she turns around and walks away from me.

25 ②, ③, ⑤ / ①, ④　　26 ⑤　　27 ③

28 ②　　　　　　　29 ②, ⑤

30 Because for now she needs to focus on her studies.

31 (A) grow taller　(B) shortest

32 as[because] they have lots of protein and calcium

33 (1) 달걀, 우유, 그리고 콩과 같은 음식을 먹어야 한다.
　　(2) 매일 밤 적어도 8시간을 자야 한다.

---

01 친구들이 가지고 있기 때문에 자신도 가지고 싶어 하는 것은 사람들에게 잘 보이기 위한 것으로 popular가 적절하다.

02 "문제가 있는 사람에게 도움이나 조언을 제공하는 직업을 가진 사람"은 "counselor 카운슬러, 상담역"이다.

03 ask A for help = A에게 도움을 요청하다, be ready for ~ = ~에 준비가 되다

04 주어진 문장과 ②의 문장에서 part는 "역할, 배역"이고, 나머지는 문장에서는 "부분"이라는 뜻이다.

05 "숙제할 때"는 "when I do my homework"이지만 "분사구문으로 'when doing my homework"라고 할 수 있다.

06 "나는 확신한다."는 "I'm sure ~"이다.

07 상대의 말에 동의하는 표현은 "I agree.", "Same here.", "You can say that again.", "So do I.", "Me, too." 등이다.

08 "팀의 모든 사람들"은 "Everybody on the team"이고 단수 취급해야 한다.

09 이어서 소년이 어떻게 대응을 해야 할지를 설명하는 것으로 보아 문제를 해결하기 위하여 무엇을 할지 묻는 말이 적절하다.

10 자기 역할을 하지 않는 구성원에게 왜 그 역할을 하지 않는지 물어보고 해결책을 찾는 것으로 "why he's not doing his part."가 적절하다.

11 (A) be ready for ~: ~에 준비가 되다 (B) end up -ing : 결국 ~하게 되다 (C) be helpful for ~: ~에게 도움이 되다

12 each는 단수명사와 함께 사용하므로 "each+단수명사"가 되어야 한다.

13 동하는 시험 공부를 하려고 책상에 앉지만 공부를 하지 않고 결국 다른 일을 하게 된다고 했으므로 책상에 앉지 않는다는 ②는 글의 내용과 일치하지 않는다.

14 주어진 문장은 '시간'을 나타내는 분사구문으로 볼 수 있으며, 시간이나 조건의 부사절에서는 미래시제를 현재시제로 나타내는 것에 주의한다.

15 동사의 목적어로 쓰인 명사절을 이끄는 접속사 if는 whether로 바꿔 쓸 수 있다.

16 출세한 것이 거만해진 것보다 앞서는 시제이므로 'Having made'로 고쳐야 한다. *make a name for oneself: 유명해지다 *arrogant: 거만[오만]한

17 명사절을 이끄는 접속사 if나 whether를 이용하고 주절이 과거 시제이므로 will을 would로 써야 하는 것에 유의한다.

18 (1) '동시동작' (2) '이유'의 분사구문으로 보는 것이 적절하다.

19 ③의 if는 명사절을 이끄는 접속사로 '~인지 아닌지'라는 의미이며, 나머지는 모두 조건의 부사절을 이끄는 접속사 '만약 ~라면'의 의미로 쓰였다.

20 ⓐ ate → eating ⓑ Knowing not → Not knowing ⓒ Seeing → Seen ⓓ Being → It being ⓕ that → if[whether]

21 '접속사+주어+동사'로 이루어진 부사절의 주어가 주절의 주어와 일치할 때 접속사와 주어를 생략하고 동사를 분사(동사원형+-ing)로 만든다.

22 Many people wonder if he will resign before the election. if절이 부사절로 쓰일 때는 미래시제 대신에 현재시제가 쓰이지만 명사절로 쓰였으므로 미래로 나타내야 한다.

23 ② Not having enough money, I cannot buy the smartphone. = Because I don't have enough money, I cannot buy the smartphone.

24 바로 앞 대화에서 소희가 말한 내용들을 가리킨다.

25 ⓑ, ②, ③, ⑤: …하는대로[…하는 것처럼](접속사), ② 어느 누구도 그녀(가 그랬던 것)처럼 블루스를 부르지는 못해. ③ 그것은 내가 의도한 대로 되지 않았다. ⑤ 내가 전에 말한 대로, 네가 와서 지내는 건 언제나 환영이야. ⓒ, ①, ④: ~을 좋아하다 (동사)

26 ⑤ 하연이가 더 이상 자기를 좋아하지 않는다고 소희가 느끼고 있는 것일 뿐이고, 사실 그런지는 아직 모르는 것이므로, 대답할 수 없다. ① Because she feels Hayeon is avoiding her. ② Yes. ③ No. ④ She advises Sohui to ask Hayeon if there is something wrong.

27 주어진 문장의 they에 주목한다. ③번 앞 문장의 new

sneakers를 받고 있으므로 ③번이 적절하다.

28 대호는 새 물건이 그를 더 인기 있게 만들어 줄 것이라고 생각해서 종종 새 물건을 사기를 원하지만, 성진이는 사람들이 대호를 좋아하는 것이 그가 최신 유행하는 것을 입어서가 아니라 그가 그이기 때문이라고 말해준다. 그러므로 제목으로는 ②번 '새 물건들이 정말 너를 더 인기 있게 만들어 줄 수 있을까?'가 적절하다.

29 ②와 ⑤ thoughtful = considerate: 배려심 있는, 사려 깊은, 민경이의 반 남자아이가 그녀에게 데이트 신청을 했지만, 그녀는 그의 감정을 상하게 하지 않으면서 거절하기를 원한다는 것으로 보아, 민경이는 '배려심 있는', '사려 깊은' 성격이라고 하는 것이 적절하다. ① 이기적인, ③ 외향적인, 사교적인, ④ 말하기를 좋아하는, 수다스러운

30 당분간은 공부에 집중해야 하기 때문이다.

31 (A) Hena는 '키가 더 크기를' 원한다. (B) 그녀는 그룹에서 '키가 제일 작아서 기분이 좋지 않다.

32 '이유'를 나타내는 분사구문이므로, 접속사 as 또는 because를 사용하여 고치는 것이 적절하다.

33 (1) I suggest you eat foods like eggs, milk, and beans.
(2) You should sleep at least eight hours every night.

단원별 예상문제
p.99~103

01 (p)roject 02 ⑤ 03 ④ 04 ④
05 ③ 06 ④ 07 ① 08 ④
09 ⑤ 10 ④ 11 ② 12 ③
13 (1) My concern is whether or not they are alive.
(2) I'll check if he will see this painting.
(3) Winning the game, Ben is very happy.
(4) Properly conducted, this business is not a public danger.
14 ①
15 (1) Feeling tired, he took a warm bath.
(2) I make delicious food, dreaming to be a cook.
(3) It being raining, 75 people were waiting for her.
16 if[whether] Minji was[will be] late 17 ④
18 no more[longer] 19 ①, ④, ⑤
20 ③ 21 out of → in 22 ③
23 (A) he's he (B) his clothes
24 Why don't you tell him why you can't go?
25 won't → don't 26 ② 27 ②, ⑤
28 ②, ⑤

01 주어진 단어는 유의어 관계이다. strict 엄격한, rigid 엄격한, project 과제, task 과제

02 그는 너무 소심해서 그녀에게 데이트 신청을 못한다. / ask+사람+out = 데이트 신청을 하다

03 네 치마는 요즘 유행하고 있는 거야. in style 유행하고 있는 / 어젯밤 결국 뭐 했어? end up -ing 결국 ~하다

04 ① 그녀가 지갑을 찰칵 하고 닫았다. snap 찰칵하는 소리를 내며 움직이는 것 ② 그는 낡은 청바지에 운동화를 신고 있었다. sneakers 운동화 ③ 그들은 자녀들에게 항상 아주 엄했다. strict 엄격한 ④ 그의 실수는 경험이 부족해서 발생한 것이었다. mistake 실수 ⑤ 여기 세 명의 청소년이 걱정하는 것들이 있습니다. teenager 청소년

05 상대가 걱정스러워 보인다고 했으므로 안부를 묻거나 걱정을 표현하는 것이 적절하다. ③은 주로 긍정적인 상황에서 "무슨 일이니?"하고 물어보는 표현이다.

06 (A) 화가 났다고 했으므로 그 이유로 "물어보지도 않고 = without asking"이 되어야 한다. (B) 안심시키는 말로 "그녀가 이해할 거라고 확신해. = I'm sure she'll understand."가 적절하다.

07 걱정이 있어서 우울해 보이는 것은 소녀이므로 ①은 대화의 내용과 일치하지 않는다.

08 상대의 말에 동의한다는 의미로 "You can say that again. 네 말이 맞아."가 적절하다. "So do I."는 앞에 말한 내용이 말하는 사람 자신에 관한 것이고 일반동사를 사용할 때 동의의 의미로 쓸 수 있다.

09 시험 준비가 되지 않아서 걱정하는 친구에게 도움이 될 만한 충고를 하고 그것이 유익할 것이라고 말하는 것이 자연스럽다. ⑤ I'm sure that will be helpful for you.

10 동하는 공부하려고 책상에 앉지만 딴 짓을 하게 된다고 해서 그 문제를 해결할 방법을 Emily가 알려주는 대화이다. 이 대화를 읽고 언제 동하가 책상에 앉을지는 알 수 없다.

11 decide의 목적어로 쓰인 명사절은 간접의문문으로 "의문사+주어+동사"의 어순이 되도록 해야 한다.

12 ① 대화에 나오는 소녀는 같은 팀이 아니다. ② 소녀는 대화 속에 나오는 실험과는 관계없다. ④ 진호와 미나가 원하는 것은 다르다. ⑤ 진호가 물어볼지는 알 수 없다.

13 (1) whether 다음에 'or not'을 붙여 쓸 수 있지만 if는 'or not'을 붙여 쓰지 않는다. (2) if가 이끄는 절이 명사절이므로 미래는 미래시제로 나타내야 한다. (3) 접속사가 없으므로 Win을 Winning으로 바꾸어 분사구문으로 만든다. (4) 분사구문이 주어와 수동의 관계이므로 being이 생략된 과거분사 conducted로 시작하는 문장으로 바꾼다.

14 '~인지 (아닌지)'라는 의미의 명사절을 이끄는 if나 whether가 적절하다.

15 (1) '접속사+주어+동사'로 이루어진 부사절의 주어가 주절의 주어와 일치할 때 접속사와 주어를 생략하고 동사를 분사(동사원형+-ing)로 만든다. (2) 의미에 맞게 'with a dream'을 dreaming으로 고쳐 분사구문으로 쓴다. (3) 부사절의 주어가 주절의 주어와 일치하지 않으므로 접속사와 주어를 생략하면 안 된다.

16 명사절을 이끄는 접속사 if나 whether를 이용하여 'if[whether]+주어+동사'의 어순으로 쓴다.

17 ① These foods, having lots of protein and calcium, can help you grow taller. ② Mason listened to the music, taking a shower. ③ When serving in the army, he felt a strong tie with his colleagues. ⑤ Being disappointed, I kept writing and now I'm a writer. colleague: 동료

18 not ~ anymore = no more = no longer

19 ⓑ와 ①, ④, ⑤: 명사절을 이끄는 접속사(…인지 아닌지), ②, ③: (조건을 나타내어) (만약) …이라면

20 ③ 속상한, 마음이 상한, '소희는 가장 친한 친구라고 생각했던 하연이가 변했고 그녀를 피한다고 느끼고 있으므로' '속상한' 심경이라고 하는 것이 적절하다. ① 부끄러운, ② 안도하는, 다행으로 여기는, ④ 겁먹은, 무서워하는, ⑤ 지루한

21 '그건 더 이상 유행이 아니야'라고 해야 하므로, out of style을 in style로 고치는 것이 적절하다. out of style: 유행이 지난, in style 유행하는, 유행되는

22 ⓑ와 ③, ④: 동명사, ①, ②, ⑤: 현재분사

23 성진이는 사람들이 '그가 그이기(대호가 대호이기)' 때문에 대호를 좋아하는 것이지, '그의 옷' 때문이 아니라고 생각한다.

24 Why don't you 동사원형 ~?: ~하는 게 어때?

25 조건절에서는 현재시제가 미래시제를 대신하기 때문에, won't를 don't로 고치는 것이 적절하다.

26 민경이는 그를 '좋아하지만' 당분간은 공부에 집중해야 하기 때문에 그와 데이트하고 싶지 않다고 했다.

27 '~인지 아닌지'라는 뜻을 나타내는 접속사 if나 whether가 적절하다.?

28 swimming, jumping rope, or playing basketball을 예로 들고 있다. ② play tug-of-war: 줄다리기를 하다

서술형 실전문제 p.104~105

01 has 02 get
03 Ask him why he's not doing his part.
04 (1) Because[As, Since] I was interested in soccer, I joined a soccer club.
   (2) Emily opened her birthday present, as she smiled happily.
   (3) Hearing about the accident, she was shocked.
   (4) It being cold tomorrow, I won't go there.
05 (1) He can't decide whether to buy it.
   (2) I don't know if she will come tomorrow.
   (3) Jane watched a baseball game on TV, having dinner.
   (4) Putting eggs on the bread, Yena made the sandwiches more delicious.

06 don't you
07 학교에서 소희가 그녀(하연이)를 볼 때 그녀는 돌아서서 소희로부터 멀리 걸어가는 것
08 (A) worried (B) advises
09 a couple of months ago
10 needs → doesn't need
11 (A) new (B) more popular (C) because of (D) because

01 "~해야 한다"의 의무를 나타내는 표현이 되어야 한다. 주어 Everyone은 단수 취급하기 때문에 "has to"가 되어야 한다.

02 (B)는 "…에게 ~하도록 하다"의 의미로 사역의 의미가 있지만 목적격보어로 to부정사가 쓰였기 때문에 get이 들어가는 것이 적절하다.

03 "왜 ~하는지 물어봐."는 "Ask him why ~."이다.

04 (1) 의미상 '이유'를 나타내는 분사구문이다. (2) 의미상 '동시동작'을 나타내는 분사구문이다. 이때의 접속사는 보통 as를 쓴다. (3) 의미상 '시간'을 나타내는 분사구문으로 바꾼다. (4) 의미상 '조건'을 나타내는 분사구문으로 바꾼다. 이때 주절의 주어와 다르므로 주어를 생략하면 안 된다.

05 (1) whether 다음에는 to부정사를 쓸 수 있지만 if는 to부정사와 함께 쓰이지 않는다. (2) if가 이끄는 절이 명사절이므로 미래는 미래시제로 나타내야 한다. (3) 접속사가 없으므로 had를 having으로 바꾸어 분사구문으로 만든다. (4) 접속사가 없으므로 Put을 Putting으로 바꾸어 분사구문으로 만든다.

06 일반동사가 있는 긍정문이므로, don't를 사용하여 부가의문문을 만드는 것이 적절하다.

07 'When I see her at school, she turns around and walks away from me'를 가리킨다.

08 소희가 그녀의 가장 친한 친구인 하연이가 변해서 그녀를 피한다고 '걱정'하자, 그녀의 언니가 뭔가 잘못된 것이 있는지 하연이에게 물어보라고 '충고한다.'

09 a couple of: 둘의, 두서너 개의, 몇 개의, 몇 사람의

10 성진이는 대호가 멋진 사람이라는 것을 증명하기 위해 새 운동화가 '필요하지 않다'고 말한다.

11 대호의 고민: 나는 '새' 옷이 필요하다. 그것들은 나를 '더 인기 있게' 만들어 줄 것이다. 조언: 사람들은 네 옷 '때문'이 아니라 네가 너이기 '때문에' 너를 좋아하는 것이다.

창의사고력 서술형 문제 p.106

|모범답안|
01 (1) if[whether] listening to music helps you relax
   (2) if[whether] reading history comic books is helpful
   (3) if[whether] our P.E. teacher is too strict

(4) if[whether] our school festival will be a lot of
fun

02 (A) grow taller   (B) being the shortest
(C) eggs, milk, and beans   (D) eight hours

단원별 모의고사

01 (d)isagree   02 ④
03 (1) agree (2) avoid (3) relax (4) worry
04 ①   05 ③   06 ④   07 ②
08 ③   09 ④   10 ③
11 (1) Hearing the news, he dropped down on the
floor from shock.
(2) After talking to my dad, I felt much better.
(3) I am not sure if[whether] you remember me.
(4) Leaving the house, you should check if you
turned off the stove.
12 ③
13 (1) if[whether] he will come to the party tonight
(2) if[whether] he likes playing baseball
(3) if[whether] dinner is ready
14 ①, ③, ④, ⑦   15 ②
16 I don't think I've done anything wrong.
17 that → if 또는 whether   18 ③   19 ②
20 ④   21 ⑤
22 (A) say no   (B) can't go

01 두 단어의 관계는 반의어 관계이다. avoid 피하다, face 마주하다, agree 동의하다, disagree 동의하지 않다

02 영어 설명의 "13세에서 19세 사이에 있는 사람"에 해당하는 단어는 "teenager 십대"이다.

03 (1) 난 전적으로 네 말에 동의해. (agree) (2) 나는 교통 혼잡 시간을 피하기 위해 일찍 출발했다. avoid 피하다 (3) 그냥 느긋하게 영화를 즐겨. relax 느긋하게 쉬다 (4) 시험에 대해서는 걱정하지 말고 그저 최선을 다해. worry 걱정하다

04 너는 그 문제를 풀기 어려울 것이다. "~하는 것이 어렵다, ~하는 데 어려움을 겪다" = have difficulty/a hard time/trouble/a difficult time -ing

05 앞에 나온 문제가 되는 상황에 대한 언급으로 "그것은 좋지 않아."에 해당하는 ③이 적절하다.

06 주어진 문장은 자신의 역할을 하고 있지 않은 구성원의 문제를 해결하기 위한 과정으로 그 방법을 알려주는 내용인 (D)에 들어가는 것이 적절하다.

07 ① 소년은 과제에 시간이 많이 걸린다고 했다. ③ 소녀가 자신의 역할을 좋아하는지에 대해서는 언급하지 않았다. ④ 어떻게 시작할지 모르는 것은 다른 구성원일 것이다. ⑤ 소년의 조언을 듣고

소녀가 물어볼 내용이다.

08 "공부를 하려고 책상에 앉지만 결국 다른 것을 하게 된다."는 의미로 "end up –ing"가 되는 것이 자연스럽다.

09 "write down"에 이어지는 "how much ~"는 간접의문으로 "의문사+주어+동사"의 순서가 되어야 한다. do를 빼고 "how much time you need ~"가 되어야 적절하다.

10 Emily가 동하에게 시간 관리하는 방법을 알려주는 것으로 보아 Emily는 시간 관리하는 방법을 알고 있다고 하는 것이 적절하다.

11 (1) '접속사+주어+동사'로 이루어진 부사절의 주어가 주절의 주어와 일치할 때 접속사와 주어를 생략하고 동사를 분사(동사원형+-ing)로 만든다. (2) 분사구문의 뜻을 명확히 하기 위해 접속사를 생략하지 않기도 한다. (3) '~인지 (아닌지)'라는 의미의 명사절을 이끄는 접속사 if[whether]를 이용한다. (4) 글자 수에 맞추려면 부사절을 분사구문으로 영작해야 한다.

12 ③ if는 'if or not'의 형태로 쓰이지 않으므로 if를 whether로 고쳐야 한다. 또한 if는 보통 주격보어로 쓰이지 않는다.

13 (1)~(3) 의문사가 없는 간접의문문에 쓰인 if[whether]이다. 'if[whether]+주어+동사'의 순서로 쓰는 것이 적절하다.

14 ② comes → will come ⑤ Writing → Written ⑥ Feeling not→ Not feeling

15 이 글은 '소희가 그녀의 가장 친한 친구인 하연이가 변해서 그녀를 피한다고 걱정하자, 그녀의 언니가 뭔가 잘못된 것이 있는지 하연이에게 물어보라고 충고하는 내용'의 글이므로, 주제로는 ②번 '교우 관계에 대한 걱정과 충고'가 적절하다. friendship: 교우 관계

16 'anything'과 같이 '-thing'으로 끝나는 대명사는 형용사가 뒤에서 수식한다.

17 that 뒤에 오는 문장은 확실한 내용을 담고 있는 문장이 와야 하므로 'if 또는 whether(…인지 아닌지)'로 고치는 것이 적절하다.

18 ③: 성진, ①, ②, ④, ⑤: 대호

19 @와 ①, ④: 부사적 용법 ②, ⑤: 명사적 용법 ③: 형용사적 용법

20 ④ 성진이는 최신 유행하는 것을 입는 것이 대호를 더 멋지고 더 인기 있게 만들어 주지는 않는다고 말한다.

21 ⑤번 다음 문장의 충고에 주목한다. 주어진 문장의 질문에 대한 답에 해당하므로 ⑤번이 적절하다.

22 민경이의 고민: 어떻게 그의 감정을 상하게 하지 않으면서 '거절할 수' 있을까요?, 조언: 왜 네가 '데이트를 할 수 없는지' 그에게 말하는 것은 어떨까?

21

Healthy Living, a Happy Life

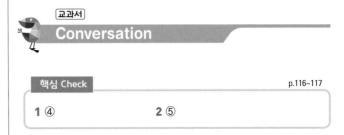

시험대비 실력평가
p.114

01 ⑤	02 ④	03 ③
04 (1) dry (2) irregular	05 ④	06 ⑤

01 주어진 단어는 "이점"이라는 뜻으로 "advantage 이점, 장점"에 해당한다.① 영향 ② 호의 ③ 즐거움 ④ 사건 ⑤ 이점

02 사회 연결망 사이트들의 긍정적 효과와 부정적 효과가 무엇입니까? - effects 효과 / ① 오늘 아침에 네 앞으로 편지가 한 통 왔어. - arrived ② 그는 모든 신체 접촉을 피하는 경향이 있다. - avoid ③ 그는 팔뼈에 금이 갔다. - bone ④ 그 약은 부작용이 좀 있다. - effects ⑤ 뼈를 튼튼하게 하려면 칼슘이 필요하다. - calcium

03 내 얼굴을 봐. 자외선 차단제를 발랐어야 했는데. put on 바르다 / 나는 오늘 아침에 담요를 햇빛에 내놓았다. put ~ out ~을 내놓다

04 주어진 보기의 단어는 반의어 관계이다. avoid 피하다, face 마주하다, wet 젖은, dry 마른, regular 규칙적인, irregular 불규칙적인

05 ④ 이 스테이크는 직화로 요리되었다. direct (열기나 빛이) 직접 닿는

06 ① 다행스럽게도, 그 태풍은 우리 마을에 오기 전에 약해졌다. fortunately 다행스럽게도 ② 추울 때 목도리를 하는 것이 큰 차이를 만들 것이다. make a world of difference 큰 차이를 만들다 ③ 이 책은 나쁜 기분에서 벗어나는 방법에 대해 말한다. mood 기분, 감정 ④ 아이들은 야외에서 노는 것을 즐긴다. outdoors 야외에서 ⑤ 전기 사용이 절정인 시간이 언제인가요? peak 절정의, 최고조의

서술형 시험대비
p.115

01 for / for   02 on / on   03 (p)roperly
04 arrival   05 indirect
06 (1) produces (2) properly (3) role (4) skin
07 (1) sunlight (2) journal (3) grade (4) mind

01 • 햇빛을 쬐며 걷는 것은 여러분의 마음과 몸 모두에 좋습니다. be good for ~에 좋다 • 나는 건강을 위하여 주말에 운동을 하기로 결심했다. for ~을 위하여

02 • 학교에 제시간에 도착하는 것은 중요하다. on time 제시간에
• 세로토닌은 네가 하는 일에 더 잘 집중하도록 도와준다. focus on 집중하다

03 전 사실 파티에 어울리게 옷을 입지 않았어요. – suitably 적절하게 = properly

04 기차가 연착된 것을 사과드립니다. arrive 도착하다 arrival 도착, late arrival 연착

05 주어진 단어는 반의어 관계이다. healthy 건강한, unhealthy 건강하지 못한, direct 직접적인, indirect 간접적인

06 (1) 이 공장은 자동차 부품을 만든다. produce 만들어 내다 (2) 시간 관리를 제대로 하는 것이 성공의 열쇠이다. properly 제대로 (3) Sue는 우리 모둠에서 중요한 역할을 맡고 있다. role 역할 (4) 나는 건조한 피부를 위해 얼굴 크림을 사야 한다. skin 피부

07 (1) 햇살 = sunlight (2) 일기를 쓰다 = keep a journal (3) 학점, 점수, 등급 = grade (4) 명심하다, 유의하다 = keep in mind

Conversation

핵심 Check
p.116~117

1 ④	2 ⑤

01 ④는 "또한, 역시"에 해당하는 표현을 사용한 것으로 보아, 동의하는지를 나타내는 표현이고 나머지는 전달하고자 하는 내용을 강조하는 표현이다.

02 춥지 않느냐고 물어보는 말에 대하여 춥다는 대답을 하는 것으로 보아 재킷을 입지 않은 것에 대한 후회의 의미를 담은 ⑤가 가장 적절하다.

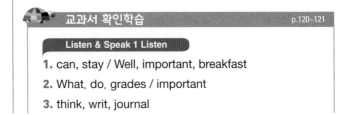

교과서 대화문 익히기

Check(√) True or False
p.118

1 F 2 T 3 F 4 F

교과서 확인학습
p.120~121

Listen & Speak 1 Listen

1. can, stay / Well, important, breakfast
2. What, do, grades / important
3. think, writ, journal

4. write down, spend, on / think

1. What, do, weekend / played, decided, exercise, for / you, important, regularly / Right, about, with

2. late / took, bus / think, leave, earlier / too, won't / arrive, on

1. too / should, brought, one

2. cold / have

3. missed / have, earlier

4. Look, should, put on / right

1. how, movie / enjoy, was / What, about / knew, have, before / sorry, like

2. still, minutes, before, top, down, and, snack / brought, brought / okay, share / keep, mind, some, time

look, energy / because, got, last / usually, enough / know, important, night's, always, up, surfing, playing, phone / sometimes, me / After, regret, morning, have, earlier / different / climbed, dad, tired, home, sleep, after / Outdoor, are, way, get

blanket, wet, checked / rwash / put, sun / Why, wash / blanket, way, keep, clean / know, remember / important, remember, regularly

---

시험대비 기본평가 p.122

01 ① **02** ⑤ **03** ④

01 소년이 규칙적으로 운동하는 것이 중요하다고 한 말과 빈칸 뒤에 이어지는 대답이 "Why not?"이라고 하는 것으로 보아 함께 테니스를 치자는 제안이 있었다고 생각할 수 있다.

02 또 다시 지각했다고 야단치는 것에 대하여 미안하다는 말에 이어서 버스를 잘못 타서 지각하게 되었다는 이유를 덧붙이는 것이 자연스럽다.

03 영화를 즐기지 못했다는 말에 (C) 무엇이 나빠서 영화를 즐기지 못했는지 이유를 묻자 (A) 이미 결말을 알았기 때문이라고 대답하고, 그것에 대해 읽어본 것을 후회한다. (B) 상대의 말에 공감하는 의미로 유감을 표시한다.

시험대비 실력평가 p.123~124

01 ③ **02** ④ **03** ② **04** ③
05 ④ **06** ③ **07** ① **08** ④

---

09 ⑤ **10** I should have brought some snacks.
11 ① **12** ③

01 "too"가 나타내는 것은 앞에 나온 말에 대한 동의의 의미라고 볼 수 있기 때문에, 앞에서 강조하는 의미에 동의하는 말에 해당하는 ③이 적절하다.

02 "It's important to exercise regularly"가 앞의 빈칸에 나온 말에 대한 반응이기 때문에 운동에 대한 언급이 있는 ④가 적절하다.

03 앞에 나온 내용을 보면 소녀가 테니스를 친 것은 주말이기 때문에 "weekday 평일"이라고 할 수는 없다.

04 밤에 늦게 잔 것을 후회한다는 것으로 보아 빈칸에는 밤에 잠을 자지 않고 깨어 있는 것을 나타내는 ③이 적절하다.

05 주어진 문장은 산에 다녀온 이후의 상황을 나타내는 것이기 때문에 (D)가 적절한 곳이다.

06 Ben은 밤늦게 인터넷 서핑을 하면서 보낸 것을 후회하기 때문에 인터넷 서핑을 밤늦게까지 계속하지는 않을 것이다.

07 이어지는 대화를 보았을 때 소녀는 결말을 알고 있어서 영화가 지루했다는 것을 알 수 있으므로 ①이 적절하다.

08 대화의 흐름상 앞에 있었던 일에 대한 유감의 내용이 되어야 하기 때문에 ⓓ"I shouldn't have read about it before seeing it."이 옳다.

09 미나가 본 영화에 대하여 두 사람이 이야기하고 있다. 영화에 대한 미나의 반응은 있지만 소년이 영화를 좋아하는지 싫어하는지는 알 수 없다.

10 간식을 가져오지 않은 것에 대한 후회를 나타내야 하므로 should bring을 should have brought로 고쳐야 한다.

11 (B) 한 사람이 가지고 온 것을 함께 먹는 것은 share에 해당한다. (C) "명심하다, 염두에 두다"는 "keep in mind"이다.

12 두 사람이 등산 중에 휴식을 취하려는 상황에서 소녀가 간식을 가지고 오지 않았다고 하니까 소년이 자기가 많이 가지고 와서 나눠먹을 수 있다고 하는 것으로 보아 간식이 충분하지 않다는 것은 본문의 내용과 일치하지 않는다.

서술형 시험대비 p.125

01 I should have worn a jacket.
02 (B) – (C) – (A) **03** exercise
04 It's important to exercise regularly.
05 playing
06 I shouldn't have read about it before seeing it.
07 I'm sorry **08** good → bad

01 춥지 않은지 묻는 말에 춥다고 하는 것으로 보아 재킷을 입지 않은 것을 후회하는 의미의 "should have+과거분사" 형태가 들어가야 한다.

02 어젯밤 잠을 못 잤다는 말에 (B) 이유를 묻자 (C) TV로 영화를 봤다고 말하고, (A) 그것에 대해 유감을 나타내는 말을 한다.

03 "자신을 더 강하고 건강하게 만들기 위해서 신체 활동을 하다"에 해당하는 단어는 "exercise 운동하다"이다.

04 강조하는 의미의 "~하는 것이 중요하다"는 "It's important to ~"이다.

05 권유나 제안의 표현은 "How about -ing?"이다.

06 유감을 나타내는 의미의 "should have+과거분사"를 써야 한다. before 다음에는 적절한 주어로 쓰일 말이 없으므로 seeing을 쓰도록 한다.

07 내용상 상대의 후회에 대한 유감을 나타내는 "I am sorry"가 적절하다.

08 소녀가 영화를 즐기지 못했다고 했으므로 무엇이 좋지 않는지 묻는 "What was bad about it?"이 적절하다.

Grammar 〔교과서〕

핵심 Check   p.126~127

1 (1) longer (2) less
2 (1) that (2) It (3) whom

시험대비 기본평가   p.128

01 ④   02 ③   03 ②

04 (1) It is you that I love.
  (2) It is calcium that builds strong bones and teeth.
  (3) The more I exercise, the stronger I get.
  (4) The more, the better.

01 'It ~ that 강조 구문'은 'It is/was ~ that ...'의 형태로, 강조하고자 하는 부분을 'It is/was'와 that 사이에 넣고, 나머지 부분을 that 뒤에 써서 주어, 목적어인 명사, 부사(구/절) 등을 강조한다. 공통으로 that이 들어가는 것이 적절하다.

02 the 비교급+주어+동사 ~, the 비교급+주어+동사 …: ~하면 할수록 더 …하다

03 It was John who[that] loved her. 강조되는 어구가 사람일 때는 that 대신에 who를 쓸 수 있다.

04 (1), (2) 'It is/was 강조어(구) that ...'의 형태로 특정 부분을 강조하여 나타낼 때 사용한다. (3), (4) 'the 비교급+주어+동사 ~, the 비교급+주어+동사 …'의 형태로 '~하면 할수록 더 …하다'라는 뜻이며, 점점 더해지거나 덜해지는 것을 표현할 때 사용한다.

시험대비 실력평가   p.129~131

01 ②   02 ①   03 ④   04 ⑤
05 ③, ⑤   06 ③   07 ④   08 ②
09 ①   10 ①, ④

11 (1) The higher I went up, the fresher the air was.
  (2) The more you walk, the more tired you will get.

12 ②

13 (1) This red dress looks the prettier of the two.
  (2) The more water we use, the drier our well will become.
  (3) The more stress I get, the more emotional I become.

14 ⑤   15 ③

16 (1) why → that (2) who → that[which]
  (3) July 26 → on July 26

17 (1) The spicier, the more
  (2) The more, the more (3) when (4) where
  (5) whom

18 ②   19 ①

---

01 the 비교급+주어+동사 ~, the 비교급+주어+동사 …: ~할수록 더 …하다 The hotter it gets, the harder it is to work.

02 ② which → that[who] ③ where → that[when] ④ 두 개의 much → more ⑤ wise → wiser

03 'the 비교급+주어+동사 ~, the 비교급+주어+동사 …: ~할수록 …하다' 구문은 'As+주어+동사+비교급 ~, 주어+동사+비교급 …'으로 바꿔 쓸 수 있다.

04 'It ~ that ...' 강조구문에서 강조하는 대상이 사람일 경우 that 대신에 관계대명사 who로 바꿔 쓸 수 있다.

05 the 비교급+주어+동사 ~, the 비교급+주어+동사 … = As+주어+동사+비교급 ~, 주어+동사+비교급 …: ~할수록 …하다

06 'an apple'을 강조하므로 which나 that을 써야 한다.

07 the 비교급+주어+동사 ~, the 비교급+주어+동사 …: ~할수록 …하다

08 <보기>와 ②번은 강조 용법의 that이다. ① 지시부사 ③ 지시대명사 ④ 접속사 ⑤ 지시형용사

09 the 비교급+주어+동사 ~, the 비교급+주어+동사 …: ~할수록 …하다

10 'It ~ that …' 강조구문에서 강조하는 대상이 사물일 경우 that 대신에 관계대명사 which로 바꿔 쓸 수 있다.

11 the 비교급+주어+동사 ~, the 비교급+주어+동사 … = As+주어+동사+비교급 ~, 주어+동사+비교급 …: ~할수록 …하다
(2) '많이 걸으면 피곤해질 것이다.'라는 의미이므로 비교급을 이용하여 바꿔 쓰면, '더 많이 걸을수록 더 피곤해질 것이다.'라고 쓸 수 있다.

12 ②번은 'It: 가주어, that절: 진주어'이고 나머지는 모두 It ~

that 강조 용법으로 쓰였다.

13 (1) 비교급에는 the를 사용하지 않는 것이 원칙이지만 문장 속에 'of the two'와 같이 비교의 대상이 명확히 둘인 경우 'the+비교급'으로 쓴다. (2), (3) the 비교급+주어+동사 ~, the 비교급+주어+동사 ···: ~할수록 ···하다

14 ① That → It ②, ③ 'It ~ that ...' 강조구문에서 형용사나 동사는 강조할 수 없다. ④ make → makes

15 ① ugly → uglier ② more safe → safer ④ good and good → better and better ⑤ nicer → the nicer

16 (1) why를 that으로 고치는 것이 적절하다. (2) 강조되는 것이 'a good breakfast'이므로 who를 that[which]로 고치는 것이 적절하다. (3) 태어난 날을 강조하는 것이므로 전치사 on을 붙여야 한다.

17 (1), (2) the 비교급+주어+동사 ~, the 비교급+주어+동사 ···: ~할수록 ···하다 (3), (4) 강조하는 대상이 시간 또는 장소의 부사(구/절)일 경우, when(시간) 또는 where(장소)로 바꿔 쓸 수 있다. (5) 강조하는 대상이 사람으로 목적격이므로 that 대신에 whom으로 바꿔 쓸 수 있다.

18 'the movie'를 강조하는 것이므로 'It was the movie that[which] ...'가 적절하다.

19 the gloomier로 쓰는 것이 적절하다.

서술형 시험대비
p.132~133

01 (1) The higher a bird flies, the farther it can see.
(2) The more they have, the more they want.

02 (1) The more stress I get, the more emotional I become.
(2) Ryan thinks the more slowly he eats, the fuller he gets.
(3) The younger you are, the easier it is to learn.
(4) This country is the better of the two.
(5) It was Hamin that[who] played basketball with Eric last Saturday.
(6) It is on Saturdays that[when] there are lots of weddings.
(7) It was in Hangang Park that[where] Ms. Jones was at 2 p.m. last Saturday.
(8) It was Amy's house that[which] James visited last Friday.

03 (1) It was Jenny's family that[who] went to the beach last summer.
(2) It was to the beach that[where] Jenny's family went last summer.
(3) It was last summer that[when] Jenny's family went to the beach.

04 (1) The more I like her, the more I miss her.
(2) The earlier you leave, the earlier you will arrive there.
(3) The harder you study for the exam, the better you will do.
(4) The more careful you are, the fewer mistakes you will make.

05 (1) It was Anna who bought the dress on the Internet last Sunday.
(2) Anna did buy the dress on the Internet last Sunday.
(3) It was the dress which Anna bought on the Internet last Sunday.
(4) It was on the Internet where Anna bought the dress last Sunday.
(5) It was last Sunday when Anna bought the dress on the Internet.

06 (1) the healthier you will feel
(2) the harder doing outdoor activities is
(3) the more dangerous you will be

07 (1) The more you study, the smarter you will become.
(2) The less money you spend, the more money you will have in your account.
(3) It was five years ago that[when] Mr. Smith moved to our apartment.
(4) It was at the Italian restaurant that[where] I learned this recipe.
(5) It was his book that[which] Jack lost at the market.

01 the 비교급+주어+동사 ~, the 비교급+주어+동사 ···: ~할수록 ···하다

02 (1)~(3) the 비교급+주어+동사 ~, the 비교급+주어+동사 ···: ~할수록 ···하다 (4) 비교급에는 the를 사용하지 않는 것이 원칙이지만 문장 속에 'of the two'와 같이 비교의 대상이 명확히 둘인 경우 'the+비교급'으로 쓴다. (5) 강조하는 것이 'Hamin'이므로 that이나 who를 쓰는 것이 적절하다. (6) 강조하는 것이 'on Saturdays'이므로 that이나 when을 쓰는 것이 적절하다. (7) which 다음에 완전한 절이 나오므로 Hangang Park를 강조하는 것으로 볼 수 없다. 'in Hangang Park'를 강조하는 것으로 that이나 where를 쓰는 것이 적절하다. (8) 강조하는 것이 'Amy's house'이므로 that이나 which를 쓰는 것이 적절하다..

03 It was와 that 사이에 강조하고자 하는 부분을 넣고, that 대신에 사람이면 who, 장소일 경우 where, 시간이면 when을 쓸 수도 있다.

04 (1) '많이 좋아하면, 많이 그리워할 것이다.'를 비교급을 이용하

여 '더 많이 좋아할수록 더 그리워할 것이다.'라고 쓸 수 있다.

(2) '일찍 출발하면, 일찍 도착할 것이다.'를 비교급을 이용하여 '더 일찍 출발할수록 더 일찍 도착할 것이다.'라고 쓸 수 있다.

(3), (4) the 비교급+주어+동사 ~, the 비교급+주어+동사 … = As+주어+동사+비교급 ~, 주어+동사+비교급 …: ~할수록 …하다

05 과거시제이므로 강조하고자 하는 부분을 It was와 that 사이에 넣고, 나머지 부분을 that 뒤에 쓴다. 이때 that을 사용하지 말라고 하였으므로 that 대신에 사람이면 who, 사물이면 which, 장소일 경우 where, 시간일 경우 when을 사용한다. 또한 'It is[was] ~ that …' 구문은 동사를 강조할 수 없으므로 동사는 동사 앞에 did를 사용하여 강조한다.

06 the 비교급+주어+동사 ~, the 비교급+주어+동사 …: ~할수록 …하다

07 (1), (2) the 비교급+주어+동사 ~, the 비교급+주어+동사 …: ~할수록 …하다 (3)~(5) 강조하고자 하는 부분을 It was와 that 사이에 넣고, 나머지 부분을 that 뒤에 쓴다. 이때 that 대신에 시간일 경우 when, 장소일 경우 where, 사물이면 which를 사용할 수 있다.

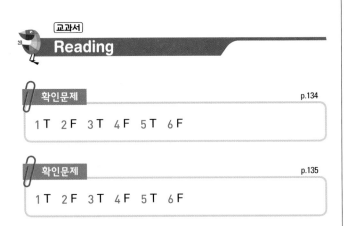

Reading

확인문제   p.134

1 T   2 F   3 T   4 F   5 T   6 F

확인문제   p.135

1 T   2 F   3 T   4 F   5 T   6 F

교과서 확인학습 A p.136~137

01 Sunshine   02 out in the sun

03 Not much

04 too busy, to spend, outdoors

05 plays an important role   06 stay healthy

07 feels happier

08 the body's happy hormone

09 The more sun, the more, happy hormone

10 goes up   11 fight everyday stress

12 calming effect, what you are doing

13 Moreover, a good night's sleep

14 not just

15 also, build strong bones   16 As you all know

17 for the body to use

18 when sunlight shines   19 to go outside

20 As you can see, enjoy its benefits safely

21 getting direct sunlight, to benefit from it

22 Try to go out into, get sunshine on

23 for just a few minutes every day

24 to protect your face and neck

25 a little sunshine, make a world of difference

교과서 확인학습 B p.138~139

1 Enjoy the Sunshine

2 How much time do you spend every day out in the sun?

3 Not much, right?

4 Most people are too busy at school or at work to spend much time outdoors.

5 However, the sun plays an important role in your health.

6 It helps you stay healthy.

7 Everyone feels happier when the sun shines.

8 This is because of serotonin, the body's happy hormone.

9 The more sun you get, the more "happy hormone" the brain produces.

10 When your serotonin level goes up, you feel happier and stronger.

11 This helps you fight everyday stress.

12 Serotonin also has a calming effect, helping you focus better on what you are doing.

13 Moreover, serotonin helps you get a good night's sleep because it helps the brain produce a sleep hormone.

14 Sunshine does not just make you feel and sleep better.

15 It also helps build strong bones.

16 As you all know, it is calcium that builds strong bones and teeth.

17 However, for the body to use calcium properly, it needs vitamin D.

18 Interestingly, the skin creates vitamin D when sunlight shines on it.

19 The easiest way to make strong bones is to go outside and enjoy the sun.

20 As you can see, sunshine has many benefits, but how can you enjoy its benefits safely?

21 Fortunately, getting direct sunlight on your skin for 10 to 20 minutes a day is enough to benefit from it.

22 Try to go out into the sun between classes or during lunch breaks and get sunshine on your arms and hands.

23 A walk in the sun, for just a few minutes every day, is good for both your mind and your body.

24 However, avoid the sun during peak summer hours, between 11 and 3, and use sunscreen to protect your face and neck.

25 Enjoy the sun safely and see how a little sunshine can make a world of difference in your health and your mood.

시험대비 실력평가
p.140~143

01 ⑤　　　　02 (A) Most　(B) outdoors　(C) healthy
03 part　　　04 spend → can't spend　　05 ②
06 sunscreen 또는 sunblock
07 it is calcium that builds strong bones and teeth
08 ③　　　　09 ⑤　　　　10 Vitamin D　11 ③
12 ④　　　　13 ④　　　　14 ①, ④
15 serotonin　　　　　　16 ③
17 (A) serotonin　(B) sleep hormone
18 Sunshine helps build strong bones as well as makes you feel and sleep better.
19 ①, ④　　　　　　20 the body
21 As you can see　　22 ①
23 and it helps you focus better on what you are doing
24 ④

01 앞에 나오는 내용과 상반되는 내용이 뒤에 이어지므로 However가 가장 적절하다. ① 따라서, 그러므로, ② 게다가, 더욱이, ③ 예를 들면, ④ 다시 말해서

02 (A) '대부분의' 사람들이라고 해야 하므로 Most가 적절하다. almost: 거의, most: 대부분(의), (B) outdoor: 옥외[야외]의(형용사) [주로 명사 앞에만 씀], outdoors: 옥외[야외]에서(부사), (C) stay 뒤에 형용사 보어를 써야 하므로, healthy가 적절하다.

03 play a role = play a part: 역할을 맡다, 한몫을 하다

04 대부분의 사람들은 학교와 직장에서 너무 바빠서 많은 시간을 야외에서 '보내지 못한다.' spend를 can't spend로 고치는 것이 적절하다. too ~ to부정사 = so ~ that 주어 cannot ...(너무 ~해서 …할 수 없다), Almost all the people = Most people, outdoors = outside a building or in the open air

05 이 글은 '햇빛의 많은 이점을 안전하게 즐길 수 있는 방법을 소개하고 있는 글'이므로, 제목으로는 ②번 '햇빛의 많은 이점을

안전하게 즐길 수 있는 법'이 적절하다. ④ spare time: 자투리 시간, 여가 시간, ⑤ make a difference: 변화를 가져오다, 차이를 낳다, 영향을 주다, 중요하다

06 sunscreen = sunblock: 자외선 차단제, 특히 더운 날씨에 태양 광선으로부터 당신의 피부를 보호해 주는 크림

07 it ~ that 강조 구문: 강조하고자 하는 부분을 it과 that 사이에 쓰고, it 뒤에 오는 be동사는 문장의 시제에 맞춰 is나 was를 사용한다.

08 ⓑ와 ②, ⑤: 부사적 용법, ①, ④: 명사적 용법, ③: 형 용사적 용법

09 이 글은 '칼슘은 튼튼한 뼈를 만들어 주는데, 그 칼슘을 몸이 적절하게 사용하기 위해서는 비타민 D가 필요하고 햇빛이 피부에 비칠 때 비타민 D를 만들어 내므로 튼튼한 뼈를 만드는 가장 쉬운 방법은 밖으로 나가서 햇빛을 즐기는 것'이라는 내용의 글이므로, 주제로는 ⑤번 '햇빛은 튼튼한 뼈를 만드는 가장 쉬운 방법이다'가 적절하다.

10 '비타민 D'가 필요하다.

11 ⓐ for+숫자: ~ 동안, ⓑ in the sun: 햇빛을 쬐며

12 주어진 문장의 However에 주목한다. ④번 앞 문장의 내용과 상반되는 내용이 뒤에 이어지므로 ④번이 적절하다.

13 ⓐ와 ④: (작업 중의) 휴식 (시간)(명사), lunch breaks: 점심 시간, ① 부수다(동사), ② (~ 사이의) 틈[구멍](명사), ③ (법·약속 등을) 어기다(동사), ⑤ (무엇을 갑자기) 중단시키다 (동사)

14 ⓐ와 ①, ④: 현재분사, ②, ③, ⑤: 동명사

15 '세로토닌'을 가리킨다.

16 여러분의 세로토닌 수치가 '높아지면', 여러분은 더 행복하고 더 건강하게 느낀다.

17 '세로토닌' 덕분에 여러분은 숙면을 취할 수 있는데, 세로토닌이 뇌가 '수면 호르몬'을 생성하도록 도와주기 때문이다. get a good night's sleep = have a good night's sleep: 충분히 숙면을 취하다

18 본문에서는 ⓐ와 ⓑ가 각각의 문장이라서 접속사가 필요하지 않지만, 한 문장일 경우는 접속사를 써야 하므로, not just[only] A but also B = B as well as A(A 뿐만 아니라 B도) 구문을 사용하여 고치는 것이 적절하다.

19 ⓒ와 ②, ③, ⑤: 'It is[was] ~ that ...'의 형태의 강조 구문, ① so ~ that ...: 너무 ~해서 …하다(부사절을 이끄는 접속사), ④ 진주어를 이끄는 접속사

20 '몸'을 가리킨다.

21 as: ~한 것처럼, ~하다시피(접속사)

22 다행히도, 하루에 10분에서 20분 동안 피부에 직사광선을 쬐이는 것은 햇빛으로부터 이점을 얻는 데 충분하다고 했으므로, '햇빛의 이점들을 안전하게 즐길 수 있는 방법은 찾기 어렵다'는 말은 옳지 않다.

23 helping 이하는 분사구문으로 앞 절에 대한 추가 설명을 제공

한다.

24 이 글은 '세로토닌의 이로운 점들'에 관한 글이므로, 제목으로는
④번 '세로토닌의 여러 가지 이로운 점들'이 적절하다. benefit:
이익; 편의, 이로움

서술형 시험대비   p.144~145

01 Most people are so busy at school or at work
that they cannot spend much time outdoors.

02 the sun   03 (A) health   (B) healthy

04 As you get more sun, the brain produces more
"happy hormone".

05 helping you focus better on what you are doing

06 (A) the brain   (B) happy hormone

07 (1) It[Sunshine] makes you feel better.

    (2) It[Sunshine] makes you sleep better.

    (3) It[Sunshine] helps build strong bones.

08 Therefore → However   09 the skin

10 (A) vitamin D   (B) sunlight   (C) enjoy the sun

11 does not make → does not just[only/merely/
simply] make

12 (A) during   (B) protect   (C) a world of

13 10 to 20

01 too ~ to부정사: so ~ that 주어 cannot ...(너무 ~해서 …할
수 없다)

02 '해[햇빛]'를 가리킨다.

03 햇빛은 여러분이 '건강'을 유지하는 데 도움을 주며 여러분의 '건
강'에 중요한 영향을 미친다(역할을 한다). play a role(part)
in = have an effect on

04 the 비교급 ~, the 비교급 …: '~할수록 …하다', As를 이용하
여 고칠 때는 the를 생략하고 비교급을 원래의 자리에 쓰는 것이
적절하다.

05 'on'을 보충하면 된다. focus on: ~에 주력하다, 초점을 맞추다

06 여러분이 햇살을 받을 때 '뇌'는 세로토닌을 만들어 내고, 세로토
닌 수치에 비례하여 여러분은 더 행복하게 느낄 수 있다. 그래서
여러분은 세로토닌을 '행복 호르몬'이라고 부를 수 있다. be in
the sun: 햇살을 받다

07 (1) 햇빛은 여러분이 더 기분 좋게 느끼게 해준다. (2) 햇빛은
여러분이 잠을 더 잘 자게 해 준다. (3) 햇빛은 튼튼한 뼈를 만드
는 것을 돕는다.

08 튼튼한 뼈와 치아를 만드는 것은 칼슘'이지만', 몸이 칼슘을 적절
하게 사용하기 위해서는 비타민 D가 필요하다고 하는 것이 적
절하므로 'However'나 'But' 등으로 고치는 것이 적절하다.

09 '피부'를 가리킨다.

10 몸이 튼튼한 뼈를 만들어 주는 칼슘을 적절하게 사용하기 위해

서는 '비타민 D'가 필요하다. 피부는 '햇빛'이 피부에 비칠 때 비
타민 D를 만들어 내므로, 튼튼한 뼈를 만드는 가장 쉬운 방법은
밖으로 나가서 '햇볕을 즐기는 것'이다.

11 '햇빛은 단지 여러분이 더 기분 좋게 느끼고 잠을 더 잘 자게
하는 것만은 아니다.'라고 해야 하므로 does not just[only/
merely/simply] make로 고치는 것이 적절하다.

12 (A) '여름의 절정 시간 동안'이라고 해야 하므로 during이 적
절하다. during+기간을 나타내는 명사, for+숫자, (B) 얼굴
과 목을 '보호하기 위해'라고 해야 하므로 protect가 적절하다.
prevent: 막다, 예방하다, protect: 보호하다, (C) '큰 차이'라
고 해야 하므로 a world of가 적절하다. a world of: 산더미
같은, 막대한, a number of+복수명사: 많은

13 햇빛으로부터 이점을 얻으려면 하루에 '10분에서 20분' 동안 피
부에 직사광선을 쪼이는 것이 필요하다.

영역별 핵심문제   p.147~151

01 ①   02 ④   03 ⑤   04 ④

05 It's important to arrive at school on time.

06 I shouldn't have read about it

07 ⑤   08 (A) boring   (B) like   09 ⑤

10 ③   11 ②   12 ⑤   13 ①

14 (1) It was Tina that[who] bought a camera at the
shop yesterday.

    (2) Tina did buy a camera at the shop yesterday.

    (3) It was a camera that[which] Tina bought at the
shop yesterday.

    (4) It was at the shop that[where] Tina bought a
camera yesterday.

    (5) It was yesterday that[when] Tina bought a
camera at the shop.

15 ③   16 ④

17 (1) The healthier, the healthier

    (2) the more, the sadder   (3) darker and darker

    (4) where   (5) which

18 It was, that[where]

19 ④   20 ⑤   21 ①, ②   22 ①

23 for 10 to 20 minutes a day

24 between   25 ②

26 As you get more sunlight, you feel happier and
stronger.

27 wash your hands   28 ⑤

29 good breakfast

01 그것은 그녀 평생의 가장 어려운 결정이었다. be동사의 보어로
명사 decision이 적절하다.

02 "사람이나 동물 신체의 표피층"은 "피부 skin"를 가리킨다.

03 버스는 정확히 제시간에 왔다. 제시간에 = on time / 너는 이 추운 날씨에 코트를 입는 것이 낫다. 입다 = put on

04 건강을 유지하기 위해 뭘 하니? stay healthy = 건강을 유지하다, stay = ~한 상태를 유지하다

05 "~하는 것이 중요하다"는 "It's important to ~"이다.

06 "~하지 말았어야 했는데"의 의미로 유감이나 후회를 나타내는 표현은 "shouldn't[should not] have+과거분사"이다.

07 타야 할 비행기를 놓쳤기 때문에 일찍 오지 않은 것에 대한 유감을 나타내는 표현이 적절하다.

08 (A) 영화를 즐기지 못했다는 말에 이어지므로 영화에 대한 부정적인 단어가 적절하다. (B) 상대가 영화를 즐기지 못했다는 말에 대한 유감의 의미가 되는 단어가 적절하다.

09 영화를 보기 전에 읽지 말았어야 했다는 의미이다. 전치사 before 뒤에 오기 때문에 동명사 seeing이 되어야 한다.

10 위 대화에서 미나는 영화를 즐기지 못한 것은 미리 읽은 것 때문이라고 생각하면서 유감스럽게 생각하고 있다.

11 'It is[was] ~ that ...' 강조구문에서 that 대신에 강조하는 것이 사람이면 who, 사물이면 which, 장소일 경우에는 where, 시간일 경우에는 when을 쓸 수 있다.

12 the 비교급+주어+동사 ~, the 비교급+주어+동사 …: ~할수록 …하다

13 ① of the two로 수식을 받는 경우 비교급이라도 the를 붙인다. ② The higher the top of a mountain, the better the view. ③ The more I got to know her, the more I liked her. ④ The angrier she got, the more loudly she yelled. ⑤ The older David gets, the wiser he becomes.

14 강조하고자 하는 부분을 It is[was]와 that 사이에 넣고, 나머지 부분을 that 뒤에 쓴다. that 대신에 강조하는 것이 사람이면 who, 사물이면 which, 장소일 경우에는 where, 시간일 경우에는 when을 쓸 수 있다. 하지만 'It is[was] ~ that ...' 구문은 동사를 강조할 수는 없고 동사는 동사 앞에 do/does/did를 사용하여 강조한다.

15 ① It was my uncle that[who] bought this smartphone for me on my birthday. ② It is Brian that[who] broke the door. ④ It is the new car that my son wants to buy. ⑤ It was on the day that[when] I met her.

16 the 비교급+주어+동사 ~, the 비교급+주어+동사 …: ~할수록 …하다

17 (1), (2) the 비교급+주어+동사 ~, the 비교급+주어+동사 …: ~할수록 …하다 (3) '비교급 and 비교급'은 '점점 더 …하다'의 뜻이다. (4)~(5) 'It is[was] ~ that ...' 구문에서 that 대신에 강조하는 것이 사람이면 who, 사물이나 동물이면 which, 시간이면 when, 장소이면 where를 쓸 수 있다.

18 'It is[was] ~ that ...' 구문은 강조하고자 하는 부분을 It is[was]와 that 사이에 넣고, 나머지 부분을 that 뒤에 쓰며, 강

19 앞에 나오는 내용에 추가하는 내용이 뒤에 이어지므로 Moreover가 가장 적절하다. Moreover 게다가, 더욱이, ② 즉[말하자면], ③ 그러므로

20 세로토닌은 뇌가 수면 호르몬을 생성하도록 도와주기 때문에 여러분이 숙면을 취하도록 해 준다고 했으므로, 세로토닌이 숙면과 아무 관계가 없다는 말은 옳지 않다. have nothing to do with: ~와는 전혀 관계가 없다

21 ⓐ와 ①, ②: 명사적 용법, ③, ⑤: 부사적 용법, ④: 형용사적 용법

22 이 글은 '칼슘은 튼튼한 뼈를 만들어 주는데, 그 칼슘을 몸이 적절하게 사용하기 위해서는 비타민 D가 필요하고, 햇빛이 피부에 비칠 때 비타민 D를 만들어 내므로, 튼튼한 뼈를 만드는 가장 쉬운 방법은 밖으로 나가서 햇빛을 즐기는 것'이라는 내용의 글이므로, 제목으로는 ①번 '햇빛을 즐기기, 튼튼한 뼈를 만드는 가장 쉬운 방법!'이 적절하다.

23 10 to 20 minutes: 10분에서 20분

24 between A and B: A와 B 사이에

25 ② '무슨 근거로 하루에 10분에서 20분 동안 피부에 직사광선을 쪼이는 것이 햇빛으로부터 이점을 얻는 데 충분한 것인지'는 대답할 수 없다. on what ground: 무슨 까닭으로, 무슨 근거로, ① Yes. ③ Between classes or during lunch breaks. ④ During peak summer hours, between 11 and 3. ⑤ By using sunscreen.

26 the 비교급 ~, the 비교급 …: '~할수록 …하다', As를 이용하여 고칠 때는 the를 생략하고 비교급을 원래의 자리에 쓰는 것이 적절하다.

27 외출한 다음에 '손을 잘 씻으면' 감기에 쉽게 걸리지 않을 것이다. catch[take, get, have] a cold: 감기에 걸리다

28 ⑤ 아침 식사를 잘하면 당신의 일에 더 잘 집중할 수 있고 사물들을 더 잘 기억할 수 있다.

29 '좋은 아침 식사'는 당신의 일에 더 잘 집중할 수 있고 사물들을 더 잘 기억할 수 있도록 도와준다.

단원별 예상문제

p.152~155

01 irregularly   02 ③   03 ④

04 ⑤   05 ③   06 ②   07 ①

08 ①   09 ⑤

10 (1) It is the whole thing that[which] we are pretty much unsure about.

(2) It was with her friends that[who, whom] she went to the movies last Sunday.

(3) It was yesterday that[when] a friend of mine bought a luxurious car.

29

11 ④　　　　12 ③, ⑤

13 (1) The more careful we are, the fewer mistakes
we make.

(2) It is sunscreen that you should put on before
you go out.

14 ②

15 Everyone feels happier when the sun shines.

16 ③　　　　17 ③　　　　18 ④

19 safe → safely

20 (A) peak summer hours　　　　21 ⑤

22 ③

23 sunscreen → umbrella　　　24 ④

01 주어진 단어는 반의어 관계이다. wet 젖은, dry 건조한, regularly 규칙적으로, irregularly 불규칙하게

02 태양을 안전하게 즐기고 적은 양의 햇빛이 여러분의 건강과 기분에 얼마나 큰 차이를 만들어 내는지 보세요. / make a world of difference 큰 차이를 만들다

03 나는 여가 시간이 있을 때 보통 인터넷 서핑을 한다. surf the Internet 인터넷 서핑을 하다 / 햇빛은 여러분의 건강에 중요한 역할을 합니다. play an important role 중요한 역할을 하다

04 ① effect 효과 ② flight 항공편 ③ grade 성적 ④ journal 일기, 일지 ⑤ regret 후회하다

05 산꼭대기에 도달하다는 의미의 타동사로 쓰이는 것은 reach이다.

06 "~했어야 했는데"는 "should have+과거분사"의 형태로 과거에 하지 못한 일에 대한 유감이나 후회를 나타낸다.

07 두 사람은 산을 오르는 중이고 꼭대기까지는 30분 정도 남은 지점에 도착했지만 지금까지 얼마나 시간이 걸렸는지는 알 수 없다.

08 stay up late: 늦게까지 자지 않고 있다

09 일찍 잠자리에 들었어야 했다는 의미가 적절하므로 "should have+과거분사"가 와야 한다.

10 강조하고자 하는 부분을 'It is[was]'와 that 사이에 넣고, 나머지 부분을 that 뒤에 쓴다.

11 ④ The redder the apples are, the sweeter they taste.

12 ① The higher I went up, the foggier it became. ② Of the two boys, Simon is the taller. ④ Buying new furniture may prove too costly. 강조되는 부분에 형용사나 동사는 사용할 수 없다. ⑥ He played basketball at the playground. ⑦ last Friday를 강조하는 것이므로 that이나 when을 써야 한다.

13 (1) the 비교급+주어+동사 ~, the 비교급+주어+동사 …: ~할수록 …하다 (2) 강조하고자 하는 부분을 'It is[was]'와 that 사이에 넣고, 나머지 부분을 that 뒤에 쓴다.

14 ②번 다음 문장의 This에 주목한다. 주어진 문장의 내용을 받고 있으므로 ②번이 적절하다.

15 앞 문장 전체를 가리킨다.

16 이 글은 '세로토닌의 이로운 점들'에 관한 글이므로, 주제로는 ③번 '유익한 호르몬인 세로토닌의 역할'이 적절하다. beneficial: 유익한, 이로운

17 ⓐ와 ③: ~한 것처럼, ~하다시피(접속사), 녹이 쇠를 좀먹듯이 근심은 마음을 좀먹는다. ① [보통 'as ~ as …'로 형용사·부사 앞에서] ~와 같은 정도로, ('as ~ as …'에서, 앞의 as가 지시부사, 뒤의 as는 접속사), ② 때(접속사), ④ 이유(접속사), ⑤ [비례] ~함에 따라, ~할수록(접속사)

18 몸이 '칼슘'을 적절하게 사용하기 위해서는 '비타민 D'가 필요하다.

19 동사 enjoy를 수식하는 것이기 때문에, 부사로 고치는 것이 적절하다.

20 '여름의 절정 시간'인 11시에서 3시 사이에는 햇빛을 피하는 것이 좋다.

21 매일 '적은' 양의 햇빛이라도 쬐면 자신의 건강과 기분에 큰 차이를 만들어 낼 수 있다.

22 위 글은 '일기 예보'이다. ① book report: 독후감, ② article: (신문·잡지의) 글, 기사, ④ review: (책·연극·영화 등에 대한) 논평[비평], 감상문, ⑤ travel essay: 기행문

23 서울과 파리는 비가 예보되고 있기 때문에 '우산'을 가지고 가라고 하는 것이 적절하다. sunscreen 자외선 차단제

24 뉴욕은 현재 날씨가 흐리다.

서술형 실전문제
p.156~157

01 ④, How was yesterday different?

02 I finally got a good night's sleep last night

03 Outdoor

04 (1) I think the older Sue gets, the wiser she becomes.

(2) The fewer the words, the better the prayer.

(3) It was in the library that he lent me the book yesterday.

(4) It was last year that[when] my family traveled to Busan.

(5) It was because she lost her mother that the girl was confused.

05 It, she is waiting for in the rain

06 (A) up　(B) calming　(C) helping

07 (A) everyday stress　(B) serotonin level

08 sunlight

02 "하룻밤을 잘 자다"는 "get a good night's sleep"이다.

03 앞에서 언급한 등산을 지칭하는 의미로 "Outdoor activities"가 되도록 해야 한다.

04 (1), (2) the 비교급+주어+동사 ~, the 비교급+주어+동사 …: ~할수록 …하다 (3) that 다음에 이어지는 절이 완전하므로 'the library'를 'in the library'로 고쳐야 한다. (4) last year를 강조하고 있으므로 that[when]을 써야 한다. (5) who 다음에 나오는 절이 완전하므로 who를 that으로 고쳐 'because she lost her mother'라는 부사절을 강조하는 문장으로 만들어야 한다.

05 빗속에서 버스를 기다리고 있는 그림이므로 'It is'와 that 사이에 the bus를 넣어 강조한다. be동사가 주어졌으므로 'is waiting for'로 현재진행형으로 쓴다.

06 (A) 세로토닌 수치가 '높아지면' 더 행복하고 더 건강하게 느끼는 것이므로 up이 적절하다. (B) '진정시키는' 효과라고 해야 하므로 calming이 적절하다. (C) and it helps나 분사구문으로 써야 하므로 helping이 적절하다.

07 여러분이 '매일의 스트레스'를 이겨낼 필요가 있다면 여러분의 '세로토닌 수치'를 높이는 편이 낫겠다. 왜냐하면 그것이 여러분을 더 행복하고 더 건강하게 느끼도록 도와줄 수 있기 때문이다. may as well ~: ~하는 편이 낫다

08 '햇빛'을 가리킨다.

09 see의 목적어로 간접의문문(의문사+주어+동사) 순서로 쓰는 것이 적절하다.

10 여러분은 여름의 절정 시간인 11시에서 3시 사이에는 햇빛을 피하고 얼굴과 목을 보호하기 위해 '자외선 차단제'를 사용하면서, 하루에 10분에서 20분 동안 피부에 직사광선을 쪼임으로써 그것의 '많은 이점'을 '안전하게' 즐길 수 있다.

창의사고력 서술형 문제   p.158

|모범답안|

01 1. stress, happier   2. focus   3. sleep
   4. vitamin D, bones

02 (1) It is Paul that[who] is having breakfast.
   (2) It was Susan that[who] prepared breakfast.
   (3) It is ham and egg that[which] Paul is having.
   (4) It is in the kitchen that[where] they are.

03 (A) after going out   (B) wash your hands
   (C) direct sunlight   (D) 10 to 20 minutes
   (E) a good breakfast

01 deal with 처리하다, 해결하다 focus on 집중하다

02 강조하고자 하는 부분을 'It is[was]'와 that 사이에 넣고, 나머지 부분을 that 뒤에 쓴다.

단원별 모의고사   p.159~162

01 unhealthy   02 ③   03 ⑤
04 (1) mood   (2) outdoors   (3) peak   (4) properly
05 ②   06 ④   07 ③   08 ①
09 ②   10 ⑤

11 (1) I become richer, I am happier
   (2) the magnet is bigger, it is stronger
   (3) you practice more, your English speaking skills are better

12 (1) It is your smartphone that[which] you should put away.
   (2) It was not until I came to Korea that[when] I learned Hangeul.
   (3) It was for dessert that Jina had a chocolate cake.
   (4) It is Minji and Jian that[who] want to join the art club.

13 ④   14 ②, ④, ⑥, ⑦

15 (1) The longer I boil the soup, the better it tastes.
   (2) The better the weather is, the better I feel.
   (3) It was at school that[where] Layla met Jinho.
   (4) It is her father that[who/whom] Ella respects the most.

16 ②

17 The more sun you get, the more "happy hormone" the brain produces.

18 (When your serotonin level goes up,) you feel happier and stronger.

19 ①, ②, ④   20 ③   21 ②
22 Benefits   23 ③

01 두 단어의 관계는 반의어 관계이다. wide 넓은, narrow 좁은, healthy 건강한, unhealthy 건강하지 못한

02 "자신들에게 일어난 일을 규칙적으로 기록하는 책"은 "journal 일지, 일기"이다.

03 라일라는 외출 전에 항상 자외선 차단제를 바른다. / sunscreen 자외선 차단제 apply 바르다

04 (1) 그는 늘 기분이 안 좋다. (mood 기분) (2) 비 때문에 그들은 야외에서 식사를 하지 못했다. (outdoors 야외에서) (3) 호텔들이 성수기에는 항상 만원이 된다. (peak 최고조의) (4) 텔

레비전이 제대로 작동이 안 된다. (properly 제대로, 적절하게)

05 앞에서 담요가 비에 젖었다는 것으로 볼 때 날씨에 관해서 주의를 기울이지 않은 것에 대한 유감의 의미가 적절하다.

06 주어진 문장은 상대가 알려주는 새로운 사실에 대한 응답이므로 자연친화적인 방법에 대한 설명 다음인 (D)에 들어가는 것이 적절하다.

07 "Did you wash it?"라는 질문에 No라고 대답하는 것으로 보아 여자는 담요를 빨지 않았다.

08 "you look full of energy today"에 대한 대답이기 때문에 잠을 잘 잤다는 내용이 적절하다. 밤에 잠을 잘 자는 것을 나타내는 표현이 "get a good night's sleep"이다.

09 ② 접속사 or로 이어지는 동사 "play"는 surfing과 병렬 관계에 있기 때문에 playing이 되어야 한다.

10 Ben이 등산을 다녀온 뒤에 잠을 잘 잤다는 말은 있지만, 어떤 야외 활동을 좋아하는지에 대한 언급은 없다.

11 'the 비교급, the 비교급' 구문은 'As+주어+동사+비교급 ~, 주어+동사+비교급 …'으로 바꿔 쓸 수 있다.

12 강조하고자 하는 부분을 시제에 맞춰 'It is[was]'와 that 사이에 넣고, 나머지 부분을 that 뒤에 쓴다. 이때 that 대신에 사람이면 who, 사물이면 which, 장소일 경우 where, 시간일 경우 when을 쓸 수 있다.

13 the 비교급+주어+동사 ~, the 비교급+주어+동사 …: ~할수록 …하다 bitter는 형용사로 '맛이 쓴, 격렬한'의 뜻이며 비교급은 'more bitter'이다.

14 ② The faster you go, the earlier you will reach your grandma's house. ④ It was the window that John broke. ⑥, ⑦ 'It ~ that …' 강조 구문은 동사나 양태부사를 강조하는 데 쓰이지 않는다.

15 (1), (2) the 비교급+주어+동사 ~, the 비교급+주어+동사 …: ~할수록 …하다 (3), (4) 강조하고자 하는 부분을 시제에 맞춰 'It is[was]'와 that 사이에 넣고, 나머지 부분을 that 뒤에 쓴다. 이때 that 대신에 사람이면 who, 사물이면 which, 장소일 경우 where, 시간일 경우 when을 쓸 수 있다.

16 선행사를 포함하는 관계대명사 'what'을 쓰는 것이 적절하다.

17 the 비교급 ~, the 비교급 …: ~할수록 …하다

18 '(여러분의 세로토닌 수치가 높아지면,) 여러분은 더 행복하고 더 건강하게 느끼는 것'을 가리킨다.

19 ⓐ와 ①, ②, ④: 동명사, ① get ahead of: [경쟁자 따위]를 앞지르다, 능가하다, ③, ⑤: 현재분사

20 이 글은 '햇빛의 많은 이점을 안전하게 즐길 수 있는 방법을 소개하고 있는 글'이므로, 주제로는 ③번 '햇빛의 많은 이점을 안전하게 즐길 수 있는 방법'이 적절하다.

21 하루에 10분에서 20분 동안 피부에 직사광선을 쪼이는 것은 햇빛으로부터 이점을 얻는 데 '충분하다.'

22 benefits: 혜택들, 이득들, 좋은 점들, 여러분이 어떤 것으로부터 얻는 도움이 되는 것들 또는 어떤 것의 결과로 나오는 이점들, helps: 도움이 되는[요긴한] 것들

23 햇빛을 충분히 쬐면 밤에 잠을 '더 잘 잘 것이다.'

교과서 파헤치기

Lesson 1

단어 TEST Step 1 — p.02

01 운동선수	02 축하하다, 기념하다	
03 ~할 때마다	04 시합	05 존경하다
06 결정하다	07 유명한	08 일어나다
09 열정	10 부상을 입다	11 사고
12 대표하다	13 대중	14 깨닫다
15 존중하다	16 부상	17 받다
18 다치다	19 거짓말	20 연습
21 갑자기	22 부근의; 부근에	
23 관료, 공무원, 경기 임원		24 식, 의식
25 개발자	26 특별히	27 훈련
28 실험하다	29 준비	30 작가
31 환호성을 지르다, 환호하다		32 제거하다
33 외치다	34 ~쪽으로, ~을 향하여	
35 ~에 관심이 많다	36 포기하다	37 독학하다
38 ~을 자랑스러워하다		39 결과적으로
40 ~을 끝내다	41 나타내다, 상징하다	
42 ~에 다가가다	43 멀리 뒤쳐진	

단어 TEST Step 2 — p.03

01 realize	02 competition	03 decide
04 practice	05 developer	06 remove
07 hurt	08 accident	09 ceremony
10 represent	11 cheer	12 finish line
13 admire/respect	14 injury	
15 athlete	16 author	17 injure
18 celebration	19 experiment	20 public
21 happen	22 nearby	23 knock
24 suddenly	25 toward	26 official
27 passion	28 accept	29 preparation
30 whenever	31 prepare	32 especially
33 winner	34 training	35 stand for
36 give up	37 far behind	38 be into
39 be done with	40 come up to	41 teach oneself
42 as a result	43 be proud of	

단어 TEST Step 3 — p.04

1 author, 작가 2 far, 멀리 3 accept, 받다
4 athlete, 운동선수 5 passion, 열정 6 realize, 깨닫다
7 remove, 없애다 8 toward, ~을 향해서
9 give up, 포기하다 10 injury, 부상 11 training, 훈련
12 marathon, 마라톤 13 represent, 대표하다
14 stadium, 경기장 15 reporter, 리포트, 기자
16 congratulate, 축하하다

대화문 TEST Step 1 — p.05~06

Listen & Speak 1 Listen

1. How, able to, runner / ran, every day
2. abie, basketball / short, practiced shooting three-point
3. How, able, speak, well / learned, watching
4. How, become, reporter / practiced speaking, public

Listen & Speak 1-A

1. How, able / think, invented, first try, true / really / Whenever, experimented / why, admire
2. How, final, players, competition / could, only after, training / playing tennis / started to play, seven

Listen & Speak 2 Listen

1. Have, heard, winner, contest / haven't, won / winner, own
2. Have, heard, guitar player / taught herself
3. heard, world famous dance / watched, many times
4. heard, photographer / haven't, kind of pictures, take / takes, of street

Listen & Speak 2-A

1. Have, heard, cartoon / interested in drawing cartoons / want to be, join / know, interested, drawing
2. Have, heard / what / stands, into, making, pencil case / What, after, finish / done, pencil, planning to make, desk

Real-Life Zone

Have, heard of, skier / Who, he / skier, won, medal / great / was, accident, early twenties, hurt / able to become / accident, several, get, especially, in skiing / Skiing, are good / why, respected

Wrap Up

heard, fire / heard, was, nearby, hurt / one, saved, were / How, able to save / knocked, every door, tell, leave / amazing

Listen & Speak 1 Listen

1. B: How was she able to become a great runner?

G: She ran 3 kilometers every day.

2. G: How was he able to become a basketball player?

B: He was short, but he practiced shooting three-point shots a lot.

3. B: How was she able to speak English so well?

G: She learned English by watching many Hollywood movies.

4. G: How was he able to become a famous reporter?

B: He practiced speaking with people in public.

Listen & Speak 1-A

1. B: How was Thomas Edison able to invent so many things?

G: Many people think that he invented things on his first try, but that's not true.

B: Oh, really?

G: Yes. Whenever he invented something, he experimented many times.

B: Maybe that's why so many people admire him.

2. G: How was Hyeon Chung able to be one of the final four players in the tennis competition?

B: He could do it only after years of hard training.

G: I see. When did he start playing tennis?

B: He started to play tennis when he was seven.

Listen & Speak 2 Listen

1. B: Have you heard of the winner of the singing contest?

G: No, I haven't. Who won?

B: The winner is Vintop, who wrote all of his own songs.

2. G: Have you heard of Mia, the guitar player?

B: Yes, I have. I heard that she taught herself to play.

3. B: Have you heard about BTG, the world famous dance group?

G: Yes, I have. I have watched their video many times on the Internet.

4. G: Have you heard of Jiho, the photographer?

B: No, I haven't. What kind of pictures does he take?

G: He usually takes pictures of street artists.

Listen & Speak 2-A

1. B: Have you heard about the cartoon club, Edutoon?

G: Yes, I have. Are you interested in drawing cartoons?

B: Yes, I want to be a famous cartoon writer, so I want to join that club.

G: Oh, I didn't know that you're interested in drawing cartoons.

2. G: Have you heard of D.I.Y.?

B: No, what is D.I.Y.?

G: D.I.Y. stands for 'do-it-yourself.' I'm really into it. Right now, I'm making a pencil case.

B: What are you going to make after you finish that?

G: When I'm done with the pencil case, I'm planning to make my own desk.

Real-Life Zone

G: Have you heard of Eui Hyun Sin, the skier?

B: No. Who is he?

G: He's a Paralympian skier. He won the first gold medal for Korea in the 2018 Winter Paralympics.

B: Wow! That's great.

G: He was in a car accident in his early twenties and hurt his legs.

B: How was he able to become a skier?

G: After his accident, he tried several different sports to get better. Then he became especially interested in skiing.

B: Skiing is not easy. Not many people are good at skiing.

G: That's why he's so respected.

Wrap Up

B: Sora, have you heard about the fire last night?

G: Yes, I heard that there was a big fire in a building nearby. Was anybody hurt?

B: No, one man saved ten people who were in the building.

G: Oh, really? How was he able to save so many people?

B: He knocked on every door to tell people to leave the building.

G: Wow, that's amazing!

01 Last Runner

02 finished, more than, before

03 no more, coming, officials

04 removed, prepare, closing ceremony

05 shouted, There, another runner

06 entering, something wrong with

07 kept going toward

08 volunteers stopped, preparations, ceremony

09 All eyes, on, runner

10 Suddenly, celebration music, cheered

11 Go for it　　　12 ran, finish line with

13 Finally, ran through, fell　　14 His name was

15 was from

16 came up to, asking　　17 happened to

18 injured, during, practice run

19 got worse, give up　　20 Why not

21 that, far behind, win

22 only athlete, representing Afghanistan

23 no way, give up

24 at war, isn't it　　25 have been, for

26 That's why, able, athletes

27 sad for, back then

28 Were, running, then

29 started running after　　30 lots of races

31 won a marathon　　32 As, result, able to

33 How, feel

34 proud of myself, from

35 not to give up

36 didn't come, to win

37 enough to, finish, race

01 Last Runner

02 finished, more than

03 no more, coming, officials

04 removed, finish line, prepare for, closing ceremony

05 shouted, There comes another

06 something wrong with

07 Still, kept going toward

08 stopped their preparations, closing ceremony

09 All eyes were on

10 Suddenly, celebration music, volunteers cheered

11 Go for it　　　12 with a tape

13 Finally, ran through, fell to　　14 His name

15 was from

16 came up to, started asking　17 happened to

18 injured, during a practice run

19 got worse during, give up　　20 Why not

21 far behind

22 only athlete, representing Afghanistan

23 no way, give up

24 at war, isn't it　　25 have been, for

26 That's why, able to

27 was sad for, back then, opening ceremony

28 Were, running　　29 started running

30 lots of races　　31 won a marathon

32 As a result　　33 How, feel

34 proud of myself, to be from

35 not to give up　　36 to win

37 it was enough, to finish

1 마지막 주자

2 마지막 주자가 한 시간도 더 전에 경주를 끝냈다.

3 "더 들어오는 선수는 없을 겁니다."라고 경기 임원들은 결론을 내렸다.

4 그들은 결승선에서 테이프를 걷어내고 1996년 미국 애틀랜타 하계 올림픽의 폐막식을 준비하기 시작했다.

5 누군가가 외쳤다. "봐! 저기 또 다른 선수가 온다!"

6 한 선수가 경기장으로 막 들어오고 있었는데, 그의 다리에 이상이 있었다.

7 그러나 그는 계속 결승선을 향해 움직였다.

8 밴드와 자원봉사자들이 폐막식을 위한 준비를 멈추었다.

9 모든 눈들이 그 선수에게 머물렀다.

10 갑자기 밴드가 축하 음악을 연주하기 시작했고, 자원봉사자들이 환호했다.

11 "달려! 달려! 잘해라!"

12 두 명의 자원봉사자가 테이프를 가지고 결승선으로 달려갔다.

13 결국, 그 주자는 테이프를 통과해 달렸고, 바닥에 쓰러졌다.

14 그의 이름은 압둘 베사르 와시키였다.

15 그는 아프가니스탄 출신이었다.

16 기자들은 와시키에게 가서 그에게 질문을 하기 시작했다.

17 리포터: 당신에게 무슨 일이 있었나요?

18 와시키: 저는 연습 경기를 하던 중 다리를 다쳤습니다.

19 경기 중에 제 상처는 점점 더 심각해졌지만, 저는 포기할 수 없었습니다.

20 리포터: 왜 포기할 수 없었죠?

21 당신은 메달을 얻기에 너무도 크게 뒤떨어져 있었다는 것을 알고 있었잖아요.

22 와시키: 저는 아프가니스탄을 대표하는 유일한 선수입니다.

23 제가 포기할 수 있는 방법은 없었습니다.

24 리포터: 아프가니스탄은 여전히 전쟁 중입니다, 맞아요?

25 와시키: 네, 우리나라는 16년째 전쟁 중입니다.

26 그것이 우리가 4년 전 바르셀로나 올림픽에 선수들을 보낼 수 없었던 이유입니다.

27 저는 개회식에서 아프가니스탄 선수를 볼 수 없었던 그 당시, 제 나라에 대해 매우 슬펐습니다.

28 리포터: 그 당시 마라톤을 뛰고 있었나요?

29 와시키: 아니요. 저는 바르셀로나 올림픽 이후에 달리기를 시작했습니다.

30 저는 많은 경주에서 뛰었어요.

31 마침내 독일 마라톤에서 우승했지요.

32 그 결과 애틀랜타에 올 수 있었어요.

33 리포터: 지금은 기분이 어떠신가요?

34 와시키: 저는 제 자신이, 그리고 제가 아프가니스탄 출신인 것이 자랑스러워요.

35 저와 제 조국을 위해서는, 포기하지 않는 것이 중요했어요.

36 저는 이곳에 이기러 온 것이 아닙니다.

37 제가 여기에 있고 경주를 끝마친 것으로 충분합니다.

본문 TEST Step 4 · Step 5   p.15~18

1 The Last Runner

2 The last runner finished the race more than an hour before.

3 "There will be no more runners coming," the officials decided.

4 They removed the tape at the finish line and started to prepare for the closing ceremony for the 1996 Atlanta Summer Olympics in the United States.

5 Someone shouted, "Look! There comes another runner!"

6 A runner was just entering the stadium, but there was something wrong with his legs.

7 Still, he kept going toward the finish line.

8 The band and the volunteers stopped their preparations for the closing ceremony.

9 All eyes were on the runner.

10 Suddenly, the band started playing celebration music, and the volunteers cheered.

11 "Go! Go! Go for it!"

12 Two volunteers ran to the finish line with a tape.

13 Finally, the runner ran through the tape and then fell to the ground.

14 His name was Abdul Baser Wasiqi.

15 He was from Afghanistan.

16 Reporters came up to Wasiqi and started asking him questions.

17 Reporter: What happened to you?

18 Wasiqi: I injured my leg during a practice run.

19 The injury got worse during the race, but I couldn't give up.

20 Reporter: Why not?

21 You knew that you were too far behind to win a medal.

22 Wasiqi: I am the onlya athlete here representing Afghanistan.

23 There was no way I could give up.

24 Reporter: Afghanistan is still at war, isn't it?

25 Wasiqi: Yes, we have been at war for 16 years.

26 That's why we were not able to send athletes to the Barcelona Olympics four years ago.

27 I was sad for my country back then when I could see no Afghan athletes in the opening ceremony.

28 Reporter: Were you running marathons then?

29 Wasiqi: No. I started running after Barcelona.

30 I ran in lots of races.

31 Finally I won a marathon in Germany.

32 As a result, I was able to come to Atlanta.

33 Reporter: How do you feel now?

34 Wasiqi: I am proud of myself and proud to be from Afghanistan.

35 For me and my country, it was important not to give up.

36 I didn't come here to win.

37 For me, it was enough to be here and to finish the race.

구석구석지문 TEST Step 1   p.19

Communication Task

1. Have, heard of
2. a famous rock climber
3. was, able to become
4. for five hours every day

Language in Use B

1. set my clock, not to be late for
2. Because, a long way to, it, not to miss
3. Without having breakfast, left, went to
4. Surprisingly, was nobody
5. Then, remembered that
6. From now on, let, happen, what day it is

Writing Workshop Step 3

1. Have a Goal to Win
2. want to win, singing contest
3. I think, have a good voice
4. However, too shy to sing in front of
5. Not to be nervous, practice singing in front of

Communication Task

1. A: Have you heard of Jain Kim?
2. B: Yes, I have. She's a famous rock climber.
3. A: How was she able to become a famous rock climber?
4. B: She trained hard for five hours every day.

Language in Use B

1. Last night, I set my clock for 8 o'lock not to be late for school today.
2. Because it is a long way to my school, it is important not to miss the bus.
3. Without having breakfast, I quickly left the house and went to the bus stop.
4. Surprisingly, there was nobody.
5. Then, I remembered that today was Saturday.
6. From now on, not to let it happen again, I will always check what day it is.

Writing Workshop Step 3

1. I Have a Goal to Win the Singing Contest
2. I want to win the school singing contest.
3. I love singing, and I think I have a good voice.
4. However, I am too shy to sing in front of many people.
5. Not to be nervous during the contest, I will practice singing in front of my class first.

Lesson 2

01 피하다	02 카운슬러, 상담역	03 최근에
04 증명하다, 입증하다		05 쉬다
06 실험	07 아직도	08 인기 있는
09 어휘	10 최신의	11 관리
12 걱정하는, 불안한	13 결승, 기말고사; 마지막의	
14 문제	15 다치다	16 시합
17 기분이 상한	18 부분, 배역, 역할	19 단백질
20 도움이 되는	21 동의하지 않다	22 운동화
23 오해하다	24 엄격한	25 청소년
26 결정하다	27 매우 싫어하다	28 걱정; 걱정하다
29 실수	30 번호를 매기다	31 웅변대회
32 체육 교사	33 충고하다	34 과제
35 유행하는, 유행되는		
36 당분간은, 현재로는		
37 ~에게 데이트를 신청하다		
38 ~하지 않고, ~ 없이		39 집중하다
40 결국 ~하게 되다	41 오랫동안	
42 ~하는 데 어려움이 있다		43 더 이상 ~가 아닌

01 upset	02 counselor	03 decide
04 match	05 experiment	06 strict
07 avoid	08 matter	09 popular
10 prove	11 hate	
12 speech contest		13 misunderstand
14 still	15 disagree	16 protein
17 helpful	18 sneakers	19 final
20 vocabulary	21 latest	22 management
23 part	24 hurt	25 project
26 advise	27 P.E. teacher	28 number
29 relax	30 mistake	31 teenager
32 worry	33 recently	34 try
35 not ~ anymore	36 in style	37 focus on
38 for now	39 end up -ing	40 for a long time
41 do one's part		
42 have a hard time -ing		43 be ready for

1 recently, 최근에   2 latest, 최신의   3 sneakers, 운동화

4 avoid, 피하다   5 hate, 매우 싫어하다

6 vocabulary, 어휘   7 disagree, 동의하지 않다

8 worry, 걱정   9 popular, 인기 있는   10 mistake, 실수

11 prove, 증명하다, 입증하다   12 teenager, 청소년

13 agree, 동의하다   14 counselor, 카운슬러, 상담역

15 experiment, 실험   16 relax, 쉬다

Listen & Speak 1 Listen

1. listening to, helps, relax / agree
2. reading, comic books, helpful / learn, from
3. festival, lot, fun
4. teacher, strict, Don't, agree / don't, strict

Listen & Speak 1 A

1. told, use, for only one hour, day, enough / agree with / doing, need, for a long time / get together, talk / for, understanding
2. just, about, project / decided what, do / not, visit, wants to, experiment / agree with / with, because, experiment, interesting

Listen & Speak 2 Listen

1. have, match, nervous / Don't worry, sure, play
2. nervous, speech contest / sure, do, worry
3. worried, friends, school / Don't, sure, make, friends

Listen & Speak 2 A

1. worried, something wrong / upset with / Why, do / wore one of, without / sorry, understand
2. having, learning / had, asked, teacher for advice / What / advised, use, vocabulary, sure, work for

Real-Life Zone

project, taking / agree, One of, people, doing, part / That's, team / know, know how to get, to / doesn't, get started, like, part / what, do / to, why, doing, Then, you'll, if, wants / try / sure, better after, talk, with, project

Wrap Up

matter, look worried / ready, finals, desk, study, up, something else / management, easy / agree, should / Number, have, Then, down, much, you need to finish / try / that, helpful, luck with

Listen & Speak 1 Listen

1. B: I think listening to music helps you relax.
   G: I agree.
2. G: I think reading history comic books is helpful.
   B: I agree. I learn a lot from them.
3. G: Our school festival is going to be a lot of fun.
   B: I agree.
4. B: Our P.E. teacher is too strict. Don't you agree?
   G: No, I don't agree. I don't think he's too strict.

Listen & Speak 1 A

1. G: Mom told me I could use the computer for only one hour a day. She thinks that's enough time.
   M: I agree with her.
   G: Sometimes, when doing my homework, I need to use it for a long time.
   M: Hmm. Then maybe we should all get together and talk about it.
   G: Thanks for your understanding, Dad.
2. B: I just talked about the science project with Jinho and Mina.
   G: Has your team decided what you will do?
   B: No, not yet. Jinho wants to visit a science museum, but Mina wants to do an experiment.
   G: Who do you agree with, Jinho or Mina?
   B: I agree with Mina because I think the experiment would be more interesting.

Listen & Speak 2 Listen

1. B: I have a big soccer match tomorrow. I'm nervous.
   G: Don't worry. I'm sure you'll play very well.
2. G: I'm nervous about tomorrow's speech contest.
   B: I'm sure you'll do fine. Don't worry.
3. G: I'm worried about making friends at my new school.
   M: Don't worry. I'm sure you'll make a lot of friends there.

Listen & Speak 2 A

1. B: You look worried. Is something wrong?
   G: Yes, my sister is upset with me.
   B: Why? What did you do?
   G: I wore one of her shirts without asking.
   B: Tell her you're sorry. I'm sure she'll understand.
2. B: I'm having a hard time learning new English words.
   G: I had the same problem, so I asked my English teacher for advice.
   B: What did he say?
   G: He advised me to use an English vocabulary

app. It has helped me a lot. I'm sure it would work for you, too.

Real-Life Zone

B: The team project for English class is taking a lot of time.

G: I agree. I have a problem. One of the people on our team isn't doing his part.

B: That's not good. Everybody on the team has to do their job.

G: I know, but I don't know how to get him to do his part.

B: Maybe he doesn't know how to get started or doesn't like his part.

G: Then what should I do?

B: Talk to him. Ask him why he's not doing his part. Then tell him you'll help him if he wants.

G: Okay. I'll try that.

B: I'm sure he'll do better after you talk to him. Good luck with your project.

G: Thanks.

Wrap Up

G: What's the matter, Dongha? You look worried.

B: I'm not ready for the finals. I sit at my desk to study but end up doing something else.

G: Well, time management is not easy.

B: I agree. What should I do?

G: Number the things you have to do. Then write down how much time you need to finish each one.

B: Thank you, Emily. I'll try your idea.

G: I'm sure that will be helpful for you. Good luck with your finals.

본문 TEST Step 1   p.28~29

01 Should, Do   02 Everyone, worries

03 When, things, worry

04 Here, things, teenagers. about

05 has changed, is avoiding   06 older, don't you

07 What about   08 feel, avoiding

09 turns around, walks away

10 sorry to hear   11 why she does that

12 done anything wrong

13 feels like, doesn't, anymore

14 should, if, something wrong

15 Maybe, should, still, with

16 thinking, popular, just because

17 at, new sneakers   18 What, think

19 didn't you, couple of   20 no longer in style

21 look cooler, right

22 wearing, latest, cooler, popular

23 because you're you, clothes

25 a great guy   26 need, to prove

27 Recently, asked out, class

28 say, but, hurt, feelings   29 need, advice

30 asked me out   31 for now, go out

32 need to focus on   33 should, do

34 Why don't you, can't   35 afraid, hurt, feelings

36 misunderstand, end up hurting

37 Maybe, right   38 Thanks for, advice

본문 TEST Step 2   p.30~31

01 What Should   02 has worries

03 worry, what do you do

04 Here are some things, worry about

05 her best friend, has changed, is avoiding

06 older, don't you   07 What about

08 I feel, avoiding

09 turns around, walks away from

10 to hear that   11 why she does that

12 I've done anything wrong

13 feels like, doesn't, anymore

14 Maybe, should, if, something wrong

15 still, with

16 thinking, make, popular, just because

17 look at, new sneakers   18 What, think

19 didn't you, couple of months ago

20 no longer in style   21 cooler in these

22 wearing, latest fashion, cooler, more popular

23 because you're you, because of

25 a great guy   26 to prove it

27 was asked out   28 to hurt his feelings

29 need, advice   30 asked me out

31 for now, go out with   32 focus on, studies

33 should

34 Why don't you, can't go   35 I'm afraid, might hurt

36 If you don't tell, misunderstand, end up hurting

37 you're right   38 Thanks for, advice

본문 TEST Step 3   p.32~33

1 제가 어떻게 해야 할까요?

2 누구나 고민은 있습니다.

3 여러분은 걱정되는 것이 있을 때 무엇을 하나요?

4 여기 세 명의 청소년이 걱정하는 것들이 있습니다.

5 소희는 하연이가 그녀의 가장 친한 친구라고 생각했지만,

지금은 하연이가 변했고 그녀를 피한다고 느낍니다.

6 소희: (그녀의 언니에게) 내 친구 하연이 알지, 그렇지?

7 언니: 응. 왜? 그녀가 어떤데?

8 소희: 나는 그녀가 나를 피하고 있다고 느껴.

9 학교에서 내가 그녀를 볼 때 그녀는 돌아서서 나로부터 멀리 걸어가.

10 언니: 그거 참 안타깝구나.

11 너는 그녀가 왜 그렇게 하는지 아니?

12 소희: 아니. 나는 내가 잘못한 것이 있다고 생각하지 않아.

13 단지 그녀가 더 이상 나를 좋아하지 않는다고 느껴져.

14 언니: 혹시 모르니 뭔가 잘못된 것이 있는지 그녀에게 물어봐.

15 소희: 아마 그래야겠어. 나는 여전히 그녀와 친구로 지내고 싶거든.

16 대호는 새 물건이 그를 더 인기 있게 만들어 줄 것이라고 생각해서 단지 친구들이 그것을 가지고 있다는 이유로 종종 새 물건을 사기를 원합니다.

17 대호: 성진아, 내 새 운동화 봐.

18 어때니?

19 성진: 멋지다. 그런데 너 겨우 몇 달 전에 새 운동화 사지 않았니?

20 대호: 응, 하지만 그건 더 이상 유행이 아니야.

21 이걸 신으니까 더 멋져 보이지, 그렇지?

22 성진: 대호야, 최신 유행하는 것을 입는 것이 너를 더 멋지고 더 인기 있게 만들어 주지는 않아.

23 사람들은 네가 너이기 때문에 너를 좋아하는 것이지, 네 옷 때문이 아니야.

24 대호: 그래?

25 성진: 들어봐. 너는 멋진 사람이야.

26 그것을 증명하기 위해 새 운동화가 필요하지 않아.

27 최근에 민경이는 그녀의 반 남자아이에게 데이트 신청을 받았습니다.

28 그녀는 거절하고 싶지만 그의 감정을 상하게 하고 싶지는 않습니다.

29 민경: 저는 선생님의 조언이 필요해요.

30 같은 반 남자아이가 저에게 데이트 신청을 했어요.

31 저는 그를 좋아하지만 당분간은 그와 데이트하고 싶지 않아요.

32 저는 공부에 집중해야 해요.

33 제가 어떻게 해야 할까요?

34 상담 선생님: 왜 네가 데이트를 할 수 없는지 그에게 말하는 것은 어떨까?

35 민경: 제가 그의 감정을 상하게 할까 봐 걱정돼요.

36 상담 선생님: 네가 그에게 빨리 말하지 않으면, 그는 네 감정을 오해할 것이고, 너는 그를 더 아프게 할 수도 있단다.

37 민경: 선생님 말씀이 맞는 것 같아요.

38 조언 감사합니다.

1 What Should I Do?

2 Everyone has worries.

3 When you have things you worry about, what do you do?

4 Here are some things that three teenagers worry about.

5 Sohui thought Hayeon was her best friend, but now, Sohui feels that Hayeon has changed and she is avoiding her.

6 Sohui: (To her older sister) You know my friend Hayeon, don't you?

7 Sister: Yeah. Why? What about her?

8 Sohui: I feel she's avoiding me.

9 When I see her at school, she turns around and walks away from me.

10 Sister: I'm sorry to hear that.

11 Do you have any idea why she does that?

12 Sohui: No. I don't think I've done anything wrong.

13 It just feels like she doesn't like me anymore.

14 Sister: Maybe you should just ask her if there is something wrong.

15 Sohui: Maybe I should. I still want to be friends with her.

16 Daeho, thinking that new things will make him more popular, often wants new things just because his friends have them.

17 Daeho: Seongjin, look at my new sneakers.

18 What do you think?

19 Seongjin: They're nice, but didn't you just buy new sneakers a couple of months ago?

20 Daeho: Yeah, but they're no longer in style.

21 I look cooler in these, right?

22 Seongjin: Daeho, wearing the latest fashion doesn't make you cooler or more popular.

23 People like you because you're you, not because of your clothes.

24 Daeho: Yeah?

25 Seongjin: Listen, you're a great guy.

26 You don't need new sneakers to prove it.

27 Recently, Minkyeong was asked out by a boy in her class.

28 She wants to say no but does not want to hurt his feelings.

29 Minkyeong: I need your advice.

30 A boy in my class asked me out.

31 I like him, but for now I don't want to go out with him.

32 I need to focus on my studies.

33 What should I do?

34 Counselor: Why don't you tell him why you can't go?

35 Minkyeong: I'm afraid I might hurt his feelings.

36 Counselor: If you don't tell him soon, he will misunderstand your feelings, and you may end up hurting him even more.

37 Minkyeong: Maybe you're right.

38 Thanks for the advice.

4. I suggest you eat foods like eggs, milk, and beans.

5. These foods, having lots of protein and calcium, can help you grow taller.

6. Also, you should sleep at least eight hours every night.

7. I hope these tips will be helpful to you.

After You Read B

1. I fell like my best friend avoids me.

2. Why don't you ask her if there is anything wrong?

3. I need new clothes. They'll make me more popular.

4. People like you because you're you, not because of your clothes.

5. How can I say no without hurting his feelings?

6. Why don't you tell him why you can't go?

구석구석지문 TEST Step 1
p.39

Communication Task

1. I think, should start later

2. agree with, get more sleep, if, later

3. should start later

4. don't agree with, will finish later

Writing Workshop

1. grow taller, being the shortest

2. like to know how, get taller

3. are wondering, can get taller

4. suggest, foods like eggs

5. having lots of protein, calcium, help, grow taller

6. Also, at least eight hours

7. will be helpful to

After You Read B

1. fell like, avoids me

2. Why don't you, anything wrong

3. new clothes, make, more popular

4. because you're you, because of your clothes

5. no without hurting his feelings

6. Why don't, why you can't go

구석구석지문 TEST Step 2
p.40

Communication Task

1. A: I think school should start later in the morning.

2. B: I agree with you. We can get more sleep if school starts later.

3. A: I think school should start later in the morning.

4. B: I don't agree with you. School will finish later if it starts later.

Writing Workshop

1. I want to grow taller. I do not feel good being the shortest in the group.

2. I'd like to know how I can get taller.

3. I heard you are wondering if you can get taller.

16 protect, 보호하다

단어 TEST Step 1 — p.41

01 이득; 이득을 보다	02 게다가	03 진정시키는
04 자연친화적인	05 후회하다	06 만들어 내다
07 피하다	08 마침내	09 이불, 담요
10 항공편, 비행	11 성적	12 규칙적으로
13 뇌	14 다행스럽게도	15 칼슘
16 일지, 일기	17 세로토닌	18 젖은
19 자외선 차단제	20 기분, 감정	21 제대로
22 빛나다	23 보호하다	24 이미
25 피부	26 날씨	27 야외에서
28 절정의, 최고조의; 절정, 최고조		29 복습하다
30 안전하게	31 직접적인, (열기나 빛이) 직접 닿는	
32 효과	33 뼈	34 건강한
35 착용하다, 바르다		
36 ~을 명심하다	37 A와 B 둘 다	38 ~로 가득 찬
39 깨어 있다	40 ~했어야 했는데	41 내놓다
42 너무 ~해서 …할 수 없다		43 ~에 유익하다

단어 TEST Step 2 — p.42

01 already	02 interestingly	03 benefit
04 moreover	05 healthy	06 calming
07 sunlight	08 nature-friendly	09 outdoors
10 skin	11 avoid	12 flight
13 blanket	14 fortunately	15 check
16 hang	17 review	18 brain
19 finally	20 sunshine	21 effect
22 weather	23 journal	24 bone
25 mood	26 peak	27 produce
28 regret	29 regularly	30 role
31 wet	32 properly	33 protect
34 safely	35 full of	36 put on
37 be good for	38 on time	39 both A and B
40 put out	41 stay up	42 keep ~ in mind
43 surf the Internet		

단어 TEST Step 3 — p.43

1 peak, 절정, 최고조   2 mood, 기분, 감정
3 sunshine, 햇빛   4 benefit, 이득을 보다
5 go up, 올라가다   6 review, 복습하다   7 role, 역할
8 skin, 피부   9 wet, 젖은   10 blanket, 이불, 담요
11 shine, 빛나다   12 regularly, 규칙적으로
13 brain, 뇌   14 bone, 뼈   15 journal, 일지, 일기

대화문 TEST Step 1 — p.44~45

Listen & Speak 1 Listen

1. can, stay healthy / Well, important to eat, breakfast
2. What, do to get, grades / important, review
3. think, write, journal
4. to write down, spend, on / think, too

Listen & Speak 1 A

1. What, do, weekend / played, decided to exercise, for / you, important, exercise regularly / Right, about playing, with / not
2. late / took, wrong bus / think, leave, earlier / too, won't be late / arrive, on time

Listen & Speak 2

1. too / should have brought, one
2. cold / should have worn
3. missed, flight / have, earlier
4. Look at, should have put on / right

Listen & Speak 2 A

1. how, movie / enjoy, was boring / What, about / knew, ending, have, before seeing / sorry, like
2. still, minutes, before, top, sit down, and, snack / brought, brought, okay, brought, share / keep, mind, some, time

Real-Life Zone

look, energy / because, got, last / usually, enough sleep / know, important, night's, always stay up, surfing, playing, with, phone / sometimes happens, me / After, regret, morning, have, earlier / different / climbed, dad, tired, home, sleep, after, went to bed / Outdoor, are, way to help, get

Wrap Up 1

blanket, wet, should have checked / wash / put, out, sun / Why, wash / blanket, way, keep, clean / know, remember / important, remember, regularly

대화문 TEST Step 2 — p.46~47

Listen & Speak 1 Listen

1. G: How can we stay healthy?
   B: Well, it's important to eat a good breakfast.
2. B: What can we do to get good grades?
   G: It's important to review every day.
3. B: I think it's important to write a journal after reading.
   G: I agree.

4. B: It's important to write down what you spend your money on.

G: I think so, too.

1. B: What did you do on the weekend?

G: I played tennis. I have decided to exercise on the weekend for my health.

B: Good for you. It's important to exercise regularly.

G: Right. How about playing tennis with me?

B: Why not?

2. M: John, you are late again.

B: I'm sorry. I took the wrong bus.

M: I think you need to leave home a little earlier.

B: I think so, too. Next time I won't be late.

M: It's important to arrive at school on time.

1. G: Your bag is too small.

B: Yes. I should have brought a bigger one.

2. G: Aren't you cold?

B: Yes. I should have worn a jacket.

3. B: We missed our flight.

G: Oh, no. We should have come earlier.

4. G: Look at my face. I should have put on some sunscreen.

B: Yes. You're right.

1. B: Mina, how was the movie?

G: I didn't enjoy it. It was boring.

B: What was bad about it?

G: I already knew the ending. I shouldn't have read about it before seeing it.

B: Oh, I'm sorry you didn't like it.

2. B: We still have 30 minutes to go before we reach the top of the mountain. Let's sit down over there and have a snack.

G: Oh, I brought only water. I should have brought some snacks.

B: That's okay. I brought a lot. We can share.

G: I'll keep it in mind to bring some snacks next time.

G: Ben, you look full of energy today!

B: Do I? Maybe that's because I finally got a good night's sleep last night.

G: Why? Don't you usually get enough sleep?

B: No, I know it's really important to get a good night's sleep, but I always stay up late surfing the

Internet or playing with my phone.

G: That sometimes happens to me too.

B: After I do that, I regret it the next morning and say, "I should have gone to bed earlier last night."

G: How was yesterday different?

B: Well, yesterday afternoon I climbed the mountain with my dad. I was really tired when I got home. I went to sleep right after I went to bed.

G: Outdoor activities are a great way to help you get a good night's sleep.

W: Oh, your blanket is wet from the rain! I should have checked the weather.

B: Did you wash it?

W: No. I just put it out in the sun this morning.

B: Why didn't you wash it?

W: Hanging a blanket in the sun is a nature-friendly way to keep the blanket clean.

B: Oh, I didn't know that. I'll remember that.

W: And it's also important to remember to do it regularly.

01 Enjoy, Sunshine

02 much, spend, out in

03 Not much

04 too busy, spend, outdoors

05 However, plays, role, health

06 helps, stay healthy

07 feels happier, shines

08 because, body's happy hormone

09 more, hormone, brain produces

10 When, goes up, stronger

11 fight everyday stress

12 calming effect, what, doing

13 Moreover, night's sleep, produce

14 not just, feel, better

15 also, build strong bones

16 As, builds, bones, teeth

17 for, body, use, properly

18 creates, when sunlight shines

19 easiest, bones, go outside

20 As, see, benefits safely

21 direct sunlight, skin, benefit

22 classes, breaks, sunshine, arms

23 walk, few minutes, mind

24 peak, protect, face, neck

25 safely, little, difference, mood

43

01 Enjoy, Sunshine

02 spend, out in the sun

03 Not much

04 too busy, at work to spend, outdoors

05 However, plays an important role

06 helps, stay healthy   07 feels happier, shines

08 because of, the body's happy hormone

09 The more sun, the more, happy hormone, produces

10 goes up, feel happier, stronger

11 helps, fight everyday stress

12 calming effect, focus, what you are doing

13 Moreover, a good night's sleep, helps, produce

14 not just, sleep better

15 also, build strong bones

16 As you all know, bones, teeth

17 for the body to use, properly

18 Interestingly, creates, when sunlight shines

19 The easiest way, to go outside

20 As you can see, enjoy its benefits safely

21 getting direct sunlight, to benefit from it

22 Try to go out into, between, during, get sunshine on

23 for just a few minutes every day, both, and

24 avoid, peak, to protect your face and neck

25 a little sunshine, make a world of difference, health, mood

1 햇빛을 즐기세요

2 여러분은 매일 햇빛 속에서 얼마나 많은 시간을 보내나요?

3 많지 않죠, 그렇죠?

4 대부분의 사람들은 학교와 직장에서 너무 바빠서 많은 시간을 야외에서 보내지 못합니다.

5 그러나 햇빛은 여러분의 건강에 중요한 역할을 합니다.

6 그것은 여러분이 건강을 유지하는 데 도움을 줍니다.

7 모든 사람들은 해가 비칠 때 더 행복하게 느낍니다.

8 이것은 몸의 행복 호르몬인 세로토닌 때문입니다.

9 여러분이 햇빛을 쬘수록 뇌는 행복 호르몬을 더 만들어 냅니다.

10 여러분의 세로토닌 수치가 높아지면, 여러분은 더 행복하고 더 건강하게 느낍니다.

11 이것은 여러분이 매일의 스트레스를 이겨 내는 데 도움을 줍니다.

12 세로토닌은 또한 진정 효과가 있고, 여러분이 하는 일에 더 잘 집중할 수 있도록 도와줍니다.

13 게다가, 세로토닌은 뇌가 수면 호르몬을 생성하도록 도와주기 때문에 여러분이 숙면을 취하도록 해 줍니다.

14 햇빛은 단지 여러분이 더 기분 좋게 느끼고 잠을 더 잘 자게 하는 것만은 아닙니다.

15 그것은 또한 튼튼한 뼈를 만드는 것을 돕습니다.

16 여러분 모두가 알다시피, 튼튼한 뼈와 치아를 만드는 것은 칼슘입니다.

17 그러나 몸이 칼슘을 적절하게 사용하기 위해서는 비타민 D가 필요합니다.

18 흥미롭게도, 피부는 햇빛이 피부에 비칠 때 비타민 D를 만들어 냅니다.

19 튼튼한 뼈를 만드는 가장 쉬운 방법은 밖으로 나가서 햇빛을 즐기는 겁니다.

20 보시다시피, 햇빛은 많은 이점이 있지만, 어떻게 그것의 이점을 안전하게 즐길 수 있을까요?

21 다행히도, 하루에 10분에서 20분 동안 피부에 직사광선을 쪼이는 것은 햇빛으로부터 이점을 얻는 데 충분합니다.

22 수업 시간 사이나 점심시간에 햇빛을 쬐러 밖으로 나가서 팔과 손에 햇빛을 쬐어 보세요.

23 매일 단 몇 분 동안 햇살을 쬐며 걷는 것은 여러분의 마음과 몸 모두에 좋습니다.

24 그러나 여름 절정 시간인 11시에서 3시 사이에는 햇빛을 피하고, 얼굴과 목을 보호하기 위해 자외선 차단제를 사용하세요.

25 태양을 안전하게 즐기고 적은 양의 햇빛이 여러분의 건강과 기분에 얼마나 큰 차이를 만들어 내는지 보세요.

1 Enjoy the Sunshine

2 How much time do you spend every day out in the sun?

3 Not much, right?

4 Most people are too busy at school or at work to spend much time outdoors.

5 However, the sun plays an important role in your health.

6 It helps you stay healthy.

7 Everyone feels happier when the sun shines.

8 This is because of serotonin, the body's happy hormone.

9 The more sun you get, the more "happy hormone" the brain produces.

10 When your serotonin level goes up, you feel happier and stronger.

11 This helps you fight everyday stress.

12 Serotonin also has a calming effect, helping you focus better on what you are doing.

13 Moreover, serotonin helps you get a good night's sleep because it helps the brain produce a sleep

hormone.

14 Sunshine does not just make you feel and sleep better.

15 It also helps build strong bones.

16 As you all know, it is calcium that builds strong bones and teeth.

17 However, for the body to use calcium properly, it needs vitamin D.

18 Interestingly, the skin creates vitamin D when sunlight shines on it.

19 The easiest way to make strong bones is to go outside and enjoy the sun.

20 As you can see, sunshine has many benefits, but how can you enjoy its benefits safely?

21 Fortunately, getting direct sunlight on your skin for 10 to 20 minutes a day is enough to benefit from it.

22 Try to go out into the sun between classes or during lunch breaks and get sunshine on your arms and hands.

23 A walk in the sun, for just a few minutes every day, is good for both your mind and your body.

24 However, avoid the sun during peak summer hours, between 11 and 3, and use sunscreen to protect your face and neck.

25 Enjoy the sun safely and see how a little sunshine can make a world of difference in your health and your mood.

Communication Task

1. A: I think it's important to exercise every day. Do you exercise every day?

2. B: No, I don't. But I'll try.

3. A: Okay.

After You Read A

1. The Benefits of Sunshine

2. Sunshine helps you deal with stress and feel happier.

3. Sunshine helps you focus better on what you are doing.

4. If you get enough sunshine, you will sleep better at night.

5. When the sun shines on your skin, your skin produces vitamin D, which is needed for strong bones.

Writing Workshop

1. Health Comes First!

2. Wash your hands after going out. You will not catch a cold easily if you wash your hands well.

3. Get direct sunlight for 10 to 20 minutes every day.

4. The more sunlight you get, the happier and stonger you feel.

5. It is a good breakfast that helps the brain work properly.

6. When you eat a good breakfast, you can focus more clearly on your work and remember things better.

Communication Task

1. it's important to exercise, exercise every day

2. No, don't, try

3. Okay

After You Read A

1. Benefits, Sunshine

2. helps, deal with, feel happier

3. helps you focus better on what

4. get enough sunshine, will sleep better

5. When, sun shines on your skin, which is needed

Writing Workshop

1. Health, First

2. Wash, after going out, will not catch a cold, if

3. direct sunlight, every day

4. The more, that, happier, stonger you feel

5. It, that, brain work properly

6. When, focus more clearly on your work, remember, better

MEMO

MEMO

MEMO